# आत्मा

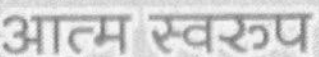


## आत्म दर्शन

अग्नी चक्र

विशुध्द चक्र

अनुहत चक्र

मणीपूर चक्र

स्वाधिष्टान चक्र

आधार चक्र

### उर्ध्वभाग

नाभीपासोनवर सप्तस्वर्ग
नाभी स्थानी भूलोक
हृदयस्थानी भुवलोक
कंठस्थानी स्वर्लोक
मुखस्थानी जनलोक
ललाट स्थानी तपोलोक
मूर्ध्नी स्थानी सत्यलोक

### अधोभाग

नाभी पासोनखाली सप्तपाताळे
कटी स्थानी अतळ,
जंघा स्थानी वितळ,
जानु स्थानी सुतळ,
पोटऱ्या स्थानी रसातळ,
घोटे स्थानी तळातळ,
पाऊले स्थानी महातळ,
तळवे स्थानी पाताळ

# बाबा आत्मा

# आत्मा गुरुदेव

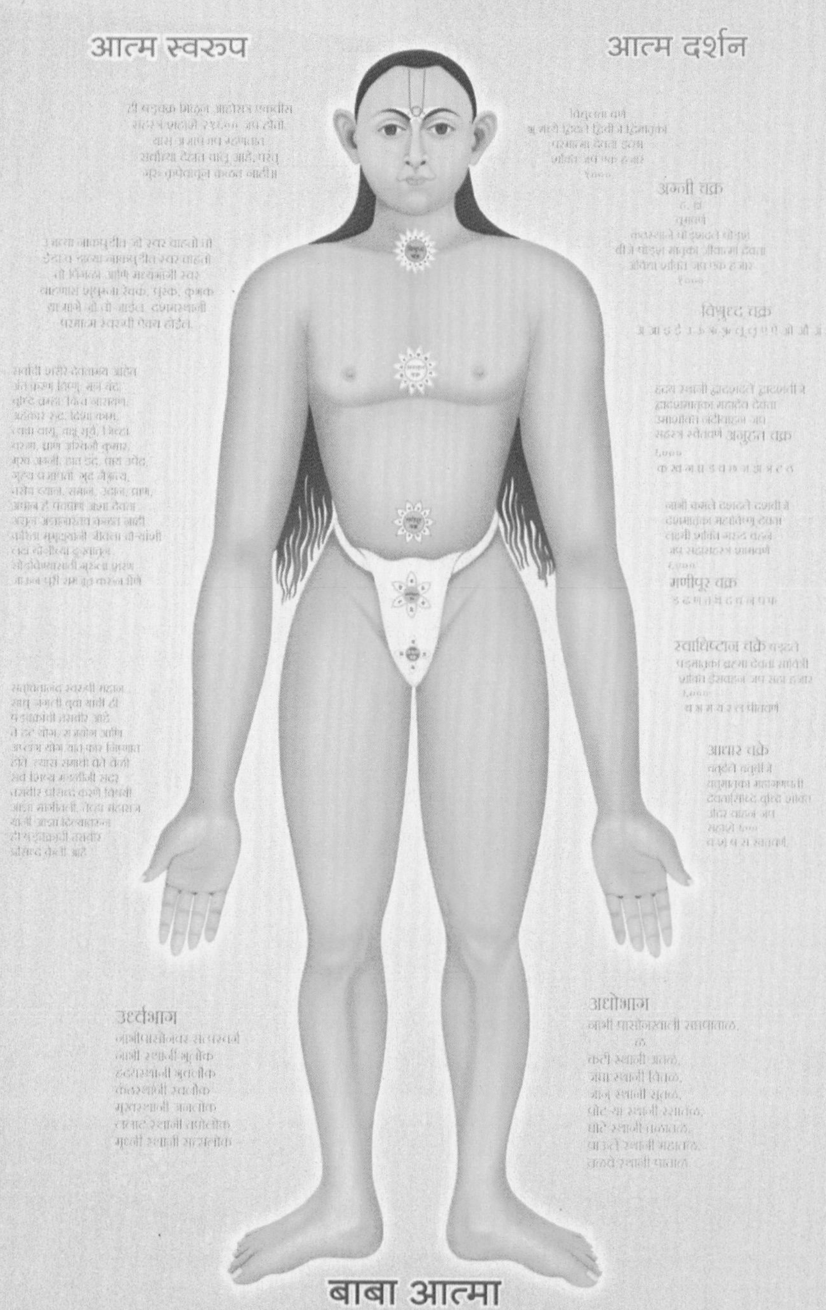
आत्म स्वरुप
आत्म दर्शन
अग्नी चक्र
विशुध्द चक्र
अनुहत चक्र
मणीपूर चक्र
स्वाधिष्टान चक्र
आधार चक्र
उर्ध्वभाग
नाभीपासोनवर सप्तस्वर्गे
नाभी स्थानी भूर्लोक
हृदयस्थानी भुवर्लोक
कंठस्थानी स्वर्लोक
मुखस्थानी जनलोक
ललाट स्थानी तपोलोक
मूर्ध्नी स्थानी सत्यलोक
अधोभाग
नाभी पासोनखाली सप्तपाताळ.
कटी स्थानी अतळे,
जंघा स्थानी वितळ,
जानु स्थानी सुतळ,
पोटऱ्या स्थानी रसातळ,
घोटे स्थानी तळातळ,
पाऊले स्थानी महातळ,
तळवे स्थानी पाताळ.
बाबा आत्मा

# Suryanamaskar
## Sun Salutations

I have now received a copy of [this book] and I am most impressed by how you have merged the modern science in the tradition. I hope to introduce the book to our teachers. I am looking forward to seeing you in a few months. With prayers and blessings.

Mahamandaleshwar **Swami Veda Bharati**
Spiritual director of Sadhana Mandir (Swami Rama's Ashram), Rishikesh
Spiritual director of Swami Rama Sadhaka Grama, Rishikesh
Spiritual guide of the Himalayan Institute Hospital Trust, Dehradun, Uttarakhand
Founder and spiritual guide of the Association of the Himalayan Yoga Meditation Societies International (AHYMSIN)
August 22, 2014

# In praise of SURYANAMASKAR : Sun Salutations

This unique and extraordinary book is aimed at those who kindle to the sadhana of Surya Namaskar. For them, it will become a bible. Krzysztof Stec writes with attractive enthusiasm about the wonderful benefits of this simple practice, which contains all the elements of hatha yoga. He mentions that Swami Muktananda endorsed the rapid-fire method. In my days at Muktananda's ashram in the early 1970s, Muktananda encouraged some of the more vital young men in this practice. They would do as many as 200 Surya Namaskar in rapid succession, in just a few minutes. He explained that they were burning up their tamas. There is no greater enterprise than sadhana for God-realization. In this book, Krzysztof demonstrates that Surya Namaskar is a complete method.

**Mahamandaleshwar Swami Shankarananda**
Shiva Ashram, Melbourne, Australia
(www.shivayoga.org)
January 26, 2013

In this book, Krzysztof brings out the holistic details of Suryanamaskar, using a modern scientific methodology. Krzysztof has brought out the fine details using the exposure he has gained and using his wide-ranging experience. In his usual meticulous style, he has researched the origin of Sun Salutation in the Four Vedas and Puranas and brought forward a simple understanding of the most significant and effective set of practices in one's practice. He has also dwelled at length into the modern scientific reasoning behind the effectiveness of the Suryanamaskar. Suryanamaskar is practised usually as a set of 10 or 12 postures. ... Krzysztof has proposed a four-level Suryanamaskar using a scientific paradigm.

**H.R. Nagendra,** PhD
President, Swami Vivekananda Yoga Prakashana, Bangalore
Vice-Chancellor, S-VYASA Yoga University
May 26, 2012

*More reviews on pp. 336-342*

# SURYANAMASKAR

## Sun Salutations

Krzysztof Stec

MOTILAL BANARSIDASS PUBLISHERS
PRIVATE LIMITED • DELHI

**First MLBD Edition: Delhi, 2017**
First edition 2012, Second edition 2013
Third edition 2015 printed as *Dynamic Suryanamaskar: Sun Salutations*



ISBN: 978-81-208-4092-8

Also available at
**MOTILAL BANARSIDASS**
41 U.A., Bungalow Road, Jawahar Nagar, Delhi 110 007
8 Mahalaxmi Chamber, 22 B. D. Road, Mumbai 400 026
203 Royapettah High Road, Mylapore, Chennai 600 004
236, 9th Main III Block, Jayanagar, Bangalore 560 011
8 Camac Street, Kolkata 700 017
Ashok Rajpath, Patna 800 004
Chowk, Varanasi 221 001

Please send your comments to: Krzysztof Stec
E-mail: krzysztof.z.stec@gmail.com

*Image of* Atma Yogi *prepared according to original displayed at Jangli Mandir on Jangli Road in Pune (MH), India*
Asanas *by Karthik S., S-VYASA, Bengaluru*
*Book layout by Bharatheesha P., S-VYASA, Bengaluru*

*Published by*
MOTILAL BANARSIDASS PUBLISHERS PRIVATE LIMITED
*www.mlbd.com • mlbd@mlbd.com*
*Printed by* Replika Press Pvt. Ltd.

*With Great Veneration and Love*

*To my Sat-Guru*

*Shree Samarth Janglidas Maharaj*

*and*

*Other Enlightened Masters*

# FOREWORD

Surya Namaskar is a magical name in Indian history and now becoming popular all over the world, it has become a global household name. Surya Namaskar has many references in the *Vedas* and *Puranas*. Since that time this yoga has been practiced by many people all over the world. To begin one's day with the Surya Namaskar is very beneficial as it connects the individual with the cosmos.

Out of so many people interested in yoga and spirituality some persons have taken Suryanamaskar as their life style. One such person is Krzysztof Stec from Poland who loves this practice. I remember that as soon as he arrived at Vishwatmak Jangli Maharaj Ashram almost 10 years ago he was talking about and encouraging everyone to start practicing Suryanamaskar. He has been practicing it every day for many years, and in a little more than two hours he performs in excess of 1008 rounds of Suryanamaskar. Such feat is astonishing and worth praising. He has built tremendous stamina and extraordinary endurance over the years with such regular and disciplined practice. The medical practitioners in the nearby town of Kopargaon have examined him and came to conclusion that he has the physiological parameters of 25 year old youngster (as of today he is running 59 years old). Only two years ago he completed a demanding two years' master degree program at the department of physical education at one of the primary universities of India, at Banaras Hindu University, Varanasi. There he had to compete and work-out with colleagues who were one third his age! Last year when he undertook 42 days' complete fast for the Gurupurnima (*anusthan*), he began without water (or any food) and continued for full 23 days and later, to complete the fast, he drank only water. In spite of such severe *tapasya* (discipline and austerity), when most other people usually stay in bed and barely move or to help themselves get several I.V., he was so energetic and full of vitality that he was swimming daily the distance of 5 to 8 kilometers.

His continuous study, love, affinity and full involvement with Suryanamaskar led him to deeper research of the subject. In his research he invented and discovered a new style of doing Suryanamaskar, for which he has coined the name *Dynamic Suryanamaskar*. Recently he has conducted three month long Suryanamaskar experiment with Vishwatmak Jangli Ashram Gurukula students. He has involved 100 students from the upper division of our schools, grades eleven and twelve, as well as some adults. He has tested them thoroughly from many different angles applying various psychological, physiological, anthropological and physical fitness tests. As we still have to wait for the official results of his testing the preliminary scores have shown almost 'miraculous' results and conclusions. The practice as taught in the style of *Dynamic Suryanamaskar* is now widely accepted by our youngsters and is very popular. Many of our own students taught it to their parents and continue practicing it on their own. A few representative reports from our students participating in the Suryanamaskar project you will find in this book. The writer himself being very dynamic and enthusiastic has become popular among our gurukula students. But above all the practice of *Dynamic Suryanamaskar* has proven its immense usefulness for our students and for meditation practitioners, since meditation is the main activity of our spiritual center. After closer observation of the beneficial results it had during the pilot study at our school, the management of the trust is committed to implement the practice for everyone in the ashram and the gurukula in the near future. We hope that all our staff of about 100 teachers and 3000 gurukula students will start practicing it. Therefore this timely book, which is a very practical manual, will have immense value for all of them since it appears that this style has not been handled yet by any author before.

Krzysztof Stec is a long time follower of Shree Samarth Janglidas Maharaj, a Satguru who is always in meditation and has given the divine message that 'God lives in our heart and it is attained through meditation'. Om Gurudev, Samarth Janglidas Mauli or simply Babaji has blessed Krzysztof Stec immensely. As long as I have known Babaji he has always been in favour of physical exercises and in particular of practicing yogic asanas, so he was extremely pleased to learn that Krzysztof had such strong daily discipline of Hatha Yoga. He went to stay at his house for a month in Poland twice, in 2003 and 2004. And on the other hand Krzysztof has stayed many times at our ashram for prolonged retreats meditating and practicing various Hatha Yogic techniques along with *Dynamic Suryanamaskar*.

Everybody has heard the phrase 'sound mind in sound body', but it is quite different when after the regular practice of *Dynamic Suryanamaskar* one can experience the above phrase. I trust and pray that this small but great 'packaged' set of asanas all our students will learn and take it with them home for life.

My feeling is that this particular form of Suryanamaskar called *Dynamic Suryanamaskar* will be revolutionary in the coming future and wish him all the best for the advancements of his studies in the subject.

*Kokamthan, July 15, 2011*
*Gurupurnima Day*

**Dnyandeo Namdeo Sangle**
Principal
OmGurudev Secondary and
Higher Secondary Gurukul
Kokamthan, Tal. Kopargaon
Dist. Ahmednagar, Maharashtra

# PREFATORY ESSAY ON THE DEVELOPMENT OF MODERN YOGA

Yoga is one of the six orthodox systems of Indian philosophy. In that Indian philosophical tradition, yoga is mainly a metaphysical system, one which describes reality in terms of universal spirituality. However, during the 20th century yoga underwent a dramatic process of secularization as it gradually became detached from traditional rituals and religious systems.

A number of studies have described and classified the phenomenon of the penetration of oriental practices into Western culture. For sociologists and anthropologists it has been seen as a natural process of ‚taming the other'. Following Elizabeth De Michelis, formerly of the University of Cambridge, yoga's adaptation to Western countries can be considered to fall into three phases: popularization (1950 - 1975), consolidation (1975 - 1990) and acculturation (1990 - to date). In her book *A History of Modern Yoga: Patanjali and Western Esotericism*, she states that there were distinctive features, which characterized each of the three stages. The popularization phase was the period when the first public yoga classes were given and the first yoga textbooks were published. In the consolidation phase, which is still on-going in some European countries, including Poland, soundly based yoga centers became established, standardization of yoga teacher training was introduced, journals on yoga began to be published on a regular basis, and yoga was introduced into therapeutic, educational and sports programs. In the acculturation phase yoga is fully accepted in appropriate contexts, yoga schools and centers are formally recognized by state institutions, such as ministries of education, standards of knowledge and skills are officially set, and the term 'yoga instructor' is recognized professionally. In this phase yoga becomes an integral part of the therapeutic or rehabilitation system of a given country. As a result, medical doctors, especially general practitioners, increasingly recommend the practice of physical yoga for therapeutic purposes. For example, according to one of the most influential yoga periodicals, *Yoga Journal,* in 2008 over 14 million Americans did yoga exercises as a result of a recommendation from their therapists or doctors. However, in some European countries such recommendations are still made only rather sporadically. Nevertheless, the awareness of health professionals in those countries is gradually changing, mainly as a result of the publication of research reports on the benefits of practicing some forms of yoga. Most probably, with time, research grants will become available and national organizations, similar to *Yoga Alliance USA* or *The British Wheel of Yoga,* will be founded, and yoga schools will be registered.

For the Western materialist approach to the body, yoga deprived of its spirituality constitutes an interesting addition to the wide variety of other exercises of a therapeutic nature already available. However, the debate on the value of yoga practices detached from their cultural environment is not yet over. The texts on this issue, written by eminent humanists from the beginning of the 20th century, and continuing to be written by contemporary researchers, confirm that an interest in yoga was for a long time perceived in terms of eccentricity or of some sort of 'pseudo-spiritual gymnastics' rather than as a serious proposal for a new philosophy of life. Mircea Eliade, one of the 20th century's most prominent experts on India's esoteric practices, maintained that yoga transplanted to another culture was deprived of its spirituality, and thus had very little to offer to the West. C. G. Jung expressed more than once his opinion on the possibility of adapting yoga to the conditions of Western culture. He differentiated the theoreticalphilosophical aspects, particularly those regarding the processes of consciousness, which he favored, from the practical issues, about which he was skeptical. However, Oskar Schmitz, in his book *Psychoanalyse und Yoga,* clearly indicated his opinion that, of all the psychoanalytic schools, the direction chosen by Jung was the closest to the methods and practices of yoga. Max Müller, an outstanding scholar and one of the founders in the 19th century of the Western academic field of Indian studies, at one time expressed opposition to *hatha* yoga practices. In his work on Vedanta philosophy he wrote that, in the beginning, yoga was a truly deep philosophical system, but over time it had degenerated and had become transformed into *hatha* yoga, whose physical exercises had become a 'specific torture'. However, on another occasion Müller mentioned that, taking into account its limitations, yoga was an excellent discipline, and in some sense everybody should be a yogi. Georg Feuerstein, one of the most famous of contemporary yoga researchers, had no doubt about the present general understanding of yoga in the West. Soon after yoga had reached Western countries at the end of the 19th century, it had lost its spiritual orientation in favor of being seen as a means to physical fitness. On the other hand, according to Sarah Strauss, author of the analytical work *Positioning Yoga: Balancing Acts across Cultures,* in the past few years there has been a clear growth in the perception of yoga as a coherent system useful for self-development. Strauss thinks that the modern understanding of yoga has ceased to limit itself to the strictly physical benefits and has become more aware of yoga as providing a potential strategy for coping with life. The latter involves mainly searching for unlimited self-development as a form of self-realization. This is understood as developing a certain freedom of mind so as to enhance the health potential of the body. Admittedly, in practice much of Western yoga was for decades limited to the mere assuming of 'acrobatic' body positions, but gradually yoga practices became more comprehensive and increasingly able to meet needs other than the physical.

However, the main interest in yoga in Western countries continues to be in its effects on the body, which are, of course, concrete and measurable. It is easier to explain and justify an interest in yoga on that basis. People participating in yoga sessions often concentrate on precision, gracefulness and mindfulness in their bodywork. The body is not only the most significant concrete value for the modern Western understanding, but it also, in some sense, becomes an ersatz or substitute for the lost dimension of spirituality. In classical yoga the human organism is presented as possessing a divine body without which it is impossible to achieve understanding and liberation. It functions as the most potentially effective vehicle for overcoming the temporal world. According to Gorakhnath (Gorakshanath), the author of various yogic treatises, including the *Goraksha Samhita* and *Goraksha Shataka,* the power of corporeal yoga (*hatha* yoga) does not lie in taking control over muscles and viscera but in combining and balancing two opposing subtle forces, internal energies. Their combining and balancing bring a sense of harmony and completeness and prepare the way for spiritual freedom.

Thus yoga does not treat the physical body as a separate entity. It has a holistic vision of body, mind and soul. The text of *The Yoga Sutras* of Patanjali is a good example of this approach. It devotes only a few lines to strictly physical practices. The practice of Suryanamaskar falls into a slightly different category, in that it seems not to have been mentioned specifically in texts before the 19th century. However, in a number of ancient Indian texts there are references to dynamic practices involving the body during sunrelated ceremonies or rituals. It is commonly thought that the natha yogis, who are considered to have used precursors of *hatha* yoga practices, also used such sun-related practices. Joseph Alter in *Yoga in Modern India* and David Gordon White in *The Alchemical Body: Siddha Traditions in Medieval India* make it clear from their analysis of the texts and documents of the 14th and 15th centuries that this was the period when the philosophical and physiological aspects of yoga became combined into a coherent whole.

The response to yoga in Western countries has been changing and will, no doubt, continue to change. One significant development occurred when it was discovered that a lot of yoga techniques and exercises had a prophylactic anti-stressing effect. A further subsequent development occurred as the result of the discovery of yoga's potential for giving positive experiences of physical and psychological well-being. However, as is widely known, the idea of seeking improved well-being through physical exercise is not new in Western culture. It should also be noted that the modern form of physical yoga, itself founded in India at the beginning of the 20th century, was partly inspired by the numerous Western systems of bodywork then under development. For example, more than 140 years ago Gustav Zander, a Swedish physician, developed several kinds of special apparatus to help the less able undertake physical exercise as a way of improving their health. The parallel to dynamic Suryanamaskar movements is very clear. One of his machines was the famous F2, a kind of horse-riding simulator making 180 movements per minute. Before World War I, when his organization was at its peak, there were several dozen Zander Institutes in Germany alone, and one each in London and New York. The number of patients in Germany alone reached 100 thousand annually, a high figure for that period. It is also worth mentioning the activity of Friedrich Müller, born in Königsberg, Prussia, and known as Eugen Sandow. Researchers of physical exercise regard him as the father of modern fitness methods. His book *Body Building or Man in the Making* was the inspiration for a series of innovations in the field. He started with a London club called *Physical Culture Studio* and became the personal coach of King George V. He was the inventor for use in gyms of numerous machines, which were quite similar to those used later by Iyengar. The Müller/Sandow methods are also considered to have been a precursor of modern motor rehabilitation treatments. Still today, numerous therapeutic schools are inspired by his ideas. According to Joseph S. Alter from the University of Pittsburgh, Müller/Sandow, the creator of the idea of bodybuilding, had the most significant impact on the founding of 'new forms' of yoga. In his research work *Yoga in Modern India: The Body between Science and Philosophy,* Alter, from an anthropological and historical perspective, describes successive phases in the relationship between yoga and, in a broad sense, physical culture. According to Alter, it was Müller/Sandow who introduced physical culture, understood in this new way, to the YMCA (Young Men's Christian Association), which was then a renowned organization in India, and elsewhere. Elmer L. Johnson, in his work *The History of YMCA Physical Education,* writes more about the influences of Western forms of physical activity on classical yoga. It is also reasonable to wonder about the possible influence of both Ling's system of gymnastics and Niels Bukh's 'primary gymnastics' on the sets of exercises proposed by the unquestioned fathers of modern physical yoga, Shri Tirumalai Krishnamacharya and Swami Kuvalayananda, and through them on the choices of series of *asanas* made by B.K.S. Iyengar and K. Pattabhi Jois. Another reason why this question should be asked is that this kind of exchange of ideas within physical culture was intensified by the participation of India in the Olympic Games for the first time, in Paris in 1924. More or less at this time, one of the ideas of both Krishnamacharya and Swami Kuvalayananda was to propagate yoga through its introduction into physical education.

Numerous studies have shown that in countries of Western culture yoga is practiced mainly by women. It is an interesting trend that dates back to the 1920s and 1930s. It is possible to follow a series of links between those Western forms of physical exercise typically used by women, and Indian yoga. Referring to *hatha* yoga, American women Genevieve Stebbins and Cajzoran Ali used the term 'harmonial gymnastics' or 'spiritual stretching'. Stebbins was inspired by François Delsarte, a French teacher of movement and voice who was well known in the second half of the 19th century in Europe. Delsarte's method became popular, which resulted in the founding of numerous 'Delsarte Clubs' and the consequent influencing of the clothing industry and that of other everyday objects. The movement of 'oriental dancing' originated from this atmosphere of interest in the body. It was an initiative of Ted Shawn and dancers Ruth St. Denis and Maud Allen. The method was a compilation of transcendentalism, theosophy, Vedanta and yoga. Stebbins tried to link yoga positions in a sequence of movements, and probably this form of exercises can be defined as a prototype of 'flow yoga'. Annie Payson Calls adopted a similar approach, using a system of gentle gymnastics, which she called either 'relaxationism' or 'mystical breath-work'. Cajzoran Ali suggested a training called 'breath culture', thus introducing a system for working with energy which flows through the psycho-somatic centers (*chakras*). In 1929, in London, Mollie Bagot Stack began giving her training in harmonial gymnastics. It was an attempt to feminize the domain of the body, which hitherto had been dominated by a masculine emphasis on strength and power. She based her teaching on relaxation techniques and yoga *asanas*, which she had learned during a stay in India. In her concept she focused on the health and cosmetic goals of the exercises for women, but she also indicated the potentiality of the system for achieving a balance between body, mind and universe. Completely different was the German Hede Kallmeyer's approach to the exercises inspired by Delsarte. She suggested a form of gymnastics designed to improve body awareness. She was one of the first in Europe to approach the human organism from a holistic point of view, which could be defined as 'the spiritualization of the flesh'. Kallmeyer's proposal was based on the concept of life energy that penetrates the body. Somatic integration of 'energetic' experiences was later continued by certain well known therapists inspired by psychoanalytical trends, such as Wilhelm Reich and Alexander Lowen. Both of them were also inspired by yoga. In his work *Yoga and Relaxation,* Tony Crisp underlines Reich's special relationship with yoga. In the 1930s, the exercise philosophy of 'health and strength' (which is also the title of a journal) was gradually replaced by that of 'stretch-and-relax'. In the same period the *Health and Strength* journal published numerous photographs of Indian physical culture yogis. Beside these pictures of muscular male yogis, there were sets of exercises for women, which were based on gentle stretching poses similar to classical yoga positions. It is interesting to note that there was already a clear distinction between yoga for men and yoga for women. Whereas the version for men was based on balance, acrobatic and strength exercises, the version for women consisted of sets of *asanas,* with a preference for gentle sitting meditation positions. At the same time in Great Britain the photographs of Aldona Wallach, whose approach was considered the forerunner of the modern postural yoga method, were widely known. In Poland a similar role was assumed much later, in the 1960s, by the dancer Malina Michalska.

In India also, the start of the 20th century was significant for the development of physical yoga. Nearly all the texts of that time referred directly or indirectly to numerous practices at different levels, which included gymnastic exercises or physical training, hygienic practices, *kriya* (cleansing) techniques, and breathing exercises. In a very interesting book, *Yogic Physical Culture or the Secret of Happiness,* published in Bangalore, Yogacharya Sundaram and K.V. Iyer introduced for the first time in 1928 something like spiritual yoga, endeavoring to reach religious fullness through an ascetic perfection of the body; it was called a "Physical Culture Religion". Two great progenitors of yoga popularization, Sri Yogendra and the aforementioned Swami Kuvalayananda, declared that their science came from Paramahamsa Madhavdas Maharaj. He was a Bengali man about whom little is known beyond the fact that he was supposed to have learnt the secrets of yoga during an excursion to the Himalayas in the second half of the 19th century. Swami Kuvalayananda was under the influence of Sri Aurobindo, but was even more influenced by the suggestions of Rajratna Manikrao, a great supporter of physical fitness, simple exercises and physical training on a large scale for the masses. Not coincidentally, we owe our scientific knowledge about physical yoga mostly to Swami Kuvalayananda's Kaivalyadhama Institute, where yoga became the unique method of physical development and therapy. The other of the great teachers of therapeutic yoga, Shri Yogendra, was first a wrestler and supporter of gymnastics, and then became a yogin. Kuvalayananda and Yogendra knew each other very well, and worked in relatively close proximity to one another in creating their separate centers in Maharashtra for research on yoga. The influence of both of them on the reception of yoga in India and the West cannot be overestimated. Yogendra founded the first institute of yoga in the world, whereas Kuvalayananda managed to convince the great authorities of his day that his research studies based on Western scientific methods were worthwhile. Among those who went to see Kuvalayananda were Mahatma Gandhi, Pandit Jawaharlal Nehru, and Indira Gandhi. Thanks to these visits, they learned at first hand about the scientifically demonstrated therapeutic values of yoga. Undoubtedly, this period of radical change combining the methods of East and West had a major impact on the development of a number of extant widely known and popular schools of yoga.

Nowadays, physical fitness has become an enormous market. Managers of this business, therefore, are constantly trying to develop new forms of packaging for their 'old-new' exercises. Comparing the docudrama *Pumping Iron,* which recorded the preparations of bodybuilders for a competition some time in the 1970s, with the 'menu' offered today by, for example, a German chain of fitness clubs, which offers over 120 different courses every week, makes clear the scale and pace of change. More than that, sophisticated systems of individual coaching or of monitoring by transponders enable clients to have personalized courses, where their preferences and potentialities are taken into account, with regard, for example, to recommended load and intensity, preferred day and time of classes, and even place in the gym. Of course, a fit body looks good, brings a sense of well-being, and attracts prestige in modern society. The German market, for example, comprises six thousand fitness clubs, which can count on seven million regular attendees paying their monthly membership fees. A vast percentage of the members are looking for forms of physical exercise that can also be useful in coping with psychological tensions. As a result, the range of services offered by fitness clubs is constantly being updated and adapted. In addition, the number of venues and centers offering a wide range of bodywork is itself increasing. On the one hand, there are chains of clubs that have hundreds of thousands of members, and, on the other, there are refined and exclusive hotels offering luxury spa services. The chains of centers and clubs that dominate the market offer a vast range of exercises adapted to the latest trends. For example, one offers 'the world's fastest ever workout'. The client performs exercises in purposefully crowded small gyms and additionally wears a special low-voltage jacket meant to accelerate adipose tissue burning. Others offer forms of exercise that are inspired by dynamic yoga, including: Woyo - a kind of combination of simple physical yoga and muscle strengthening exercises; Jukari - close to circus art, acrobatic exercises on the trapeze; Body Art - defined as methodological work on groups of muscles with the use of physical yoga exercises; Pilardio – a sort of a marriage of Pilates exercises and Cardio workout; Body Combat - defined as a real martial art for men, the purpose of which is to combat body weaknesses; it rather resembles a drill which uses exercises taken from martial art sports, mainly oriental; Core - a workout designed to strengthen trunk muscles, mainly of the abdomen and back; in addition there are also various devices called 'vibrating platforms', on which it is sufficient simply to stand and allow the entire body to be shaken.

Different kinds of yoga practices have in recent times become widely available in the West. On the one hand, body-focused yogis are trying to concretize yoga by reducing it to physical exercises. On the other hand, those of a philosophical or spiritual disposition can look to yoga practices to help with calming and stilling the mind. However, concepts such as *atman*, *prana* and *samadhi* are far from being accepted by Western rationalism and contemporary science. For the time being at least, only a very few yoga practitioners in the West are likely to be looking for a method of transcendence through yogic metaphysics. It is far more likely that yoga will remain as a form of exercise oriented on physical health. Mark Singleton, in his work *The Origins of Modern Posture Practice*, confirms this observation. He shows that yoga is considered increasingly useful from the points of view of medicine and aesthetics. Suryanamaskar exercises have become an integral part of yoga practices for many and can be of particular interest to researchers. On the one hand, the practices are concrete, as they have a structure of movement and effort, which is measurable by physiologists and physicians, and on the other hand, they reflect a wider, existential context. The exercises in 'Sun Salutation' symbolize the rhythm and transitoriness of nature and life. The sequence of body positions and the movement that unites them reflect the rhythm of the seasons and the activity of the whole universe. They also reflect the rhythms and cycles of the physical body: sleeping/waking, activity/non-activity, relaxation/tension. Doing Suryanamaskar exercises allows the practitioner to feel the discomfort of the body's stiffness followed by the pleasure of its elasticity and the lightness of its movements. Even during a short sequence of repetitions one can observe the changes in heart rhythm, deepness of breathing, activity of the brain and ability to maintain concentration. Sometimes during practice people have the perception that in actuality they themselves are the rhythm and their lives are the rhythm. In the Katha Upanishad there appears the parable of the chariot whose different parts represent each of the human elements indispensable for doing the practice, i.e. body, senses, mind, reason and soul. In the Shvetashvatara Upanishad there is an indication of where to find a place suitable for practice: "Let yoga be practiced within a cave protected from the high wind, in a place which is level, pure and free from pebbles, gravel and fire, undisturbed by the noise of water or of market-booth and which is delightful to the mind and not offensive to the eye" (chapter 2.10).

In Poland, it is thought that the vast majority of Suryanamaskar exercises are practiced as a form of recreation and anti-stress training. Such were the hopes and intentions of the progenitors of yoga popularization, when they began their research into the scope of yoga therapy, carried out at the University of Physical Education in Warsaw all those years ago. The first studies were carried out by Wieslaw Romanowski, a physician and physiologist, and Tadeusz Pasek, a tireless popularizer of Indian culture. Thanks to their initiative the first academic textbook on yoga, *The Theory and Methodology of Relaxation and Concentration Exercises*, was published in 1975. Pasek was the man whose enthusiasm and organizational effort led to the first attempts to provide courses for yoga instructors. Despite such a promising start, which dates back to the 1960s, still today in Poland yoga is only in the consolidation phase, although there are perhaps some weak signs characteristic of the acculturation phase. Nevertheless, despite the growing interest in yoga exercise - it is estimated that in Poland about forty thousand people practice yoga on a regular basis - much basic information, on the nature of the exercises themselves and which tradition or yoga school is being followed, is not available. Not only may some people be practicing newly developed types of yoga-inspired exercises, e.g. dynamic yoga, postural yoga, psychosomatic yoga, and holistic yoga, but the motivation to undertake any kind of yoga practice is also very variable. Some people may want muscle relaxation, others mental well-being, some stillness of the mind, and yet others the final liberation understood in terms of spirituality.

The book you are holding in your hands, dear reader, touches the essence of dynamic yoga practices. The book is addressed not to yoga theoreticians but to yoga practitioners. Without personal practice it is hardly possible to gain more than a faint appreciation of the value of this innovative work by Krzysztof Stec. Its heart is practice, which can be applied in recreation and sport as well as in therapy and rehabilitation, and in great or small degree. One of the greatest Hindu sages, Shankaracharya, underlined the difference between *jnana* and *vijnana*. Whereas the former refers to 'second-hand' knowledge acquired from literature and authorities, the latter refers to true knowledge derived from personal experience. I do hope that you, dear reader, while learning a lot from the information in this book, will learn even more from the personal experience that comes from putting at least some of its recommendations into practice.

**Prof. dr hab. Leslaw Kulmatycki**
Department Head, Humanities Sciences and Health Promotion,
University of Physical Education in Wroclaw, Poland
August 2012

# CONTENTS

# LIST OF TABLES

# AUTHOR'S NOTE

Suryanamaskar, when followed with sincerity, brings the practitioner many benefits at every level of existence. In my first fifteen years of yogic practice it was slow and with a very low number of rounds and level of intensity. In fact I was paying very little attention to Suryanamaskar considering it a rather strange adaptation of an ancient Vedic ritual. My style of hatha yoga practice was that of Swami Kuvalayananda, Swami Shivananda of Rishikesh or the Bihar School of Yoga. I had my share of interesting yogic experiences, but my progress intensified tremendously once one of Swami Muktananda's devotees persuaded me to try it a different way. That was in 1981. Before that time I was hardly doing any Suryanamaskar rounds, so naturally I was very proud when, after some six months of practice, I reached the level of 216 rounds (108 cycles). At that time I was unaware that a human being could do over a thousand rounds. I already felt the wonderful benefits of having amazing vigour and stamina, which I could test to my heart's content in the hills of the San Francisco Bay Area. This kind of vigour and enthusiasm I found very useful for meditation.

Meeting, in late 2002, Janglidas Maharaj rekindled my interest in performing large numbers of Suryanamaskars in addition to my other classical hatha yogic routine. Thus, slowly, I started increasing my practice until I reached that amazing number of more than 1008 rounds. Accounts of some of my experiences the reader will find in this book, but, to describe most of them, a separate book would have to be written. Over the thirty years of practice and after many millions of Suryanamaskars performed, I hope that I can have in the reader's eyes some credibility when I speak on the subject. Since inner experiences are by their very nature subjective, I felt that it would make sense to try to verify them by some objective and scientific methods. After all, the truth is one but it has many faces, which should not contradict one another.

In this book I have tried to project these two dimensions, the objective one as well as the subjective. The reader will be the judge of whether such exposition of the subject has been successful. The techniques described are strongly based on my own practice, with which I always try to verify 'dry' techniques and methods taken from the written or spoken word. I believe that information should be transformed into knowledge by the fire of practice, otherwise it is just ideas in our heads and, instead of being yogis, we become preachers.

Finally, it is essential to understand the concept that physical intensity in yoga eventually becomes transmuted into spiritual zeal and intensity, both of which are needed in order to bring about some real spiritual progress. You might remember the old *Swami Ramakrishna* story, in which a *Shishya* was constantly pestering his *guru* for an experience of God. After this had been going on for a while, the master became a little impatient with the student, and during the usual morning bath in the river

Ganges he grabbed his student by the neck and pushed him forcefully under the water, holding him down strongly. Of course, the student was desperate for air and struggling like anything to come up, but the master would not relent. Only when the student started to lose his strength did the master allow him up to get some air, but as soon as the student had recovered a little the master pushed him under again. After several repetitions of this process the master released his grip and the student came up, gasping for breath. Then, coming to his senses, the student started shouting at the master 'You tried to drown me, how could you do such a thing? I trusted you completely!' The master responded, 'Just tell me, what were you thinking when you were under water?' The student thought for a moment and then replied 'I wanted air, and nothing but air'. The master said 'That is the point. If your desire to know God had the same intensity as your desire at that moment for air, you would meet God in an instant'. This teaching on the importance of intensity should be well understood by all yogis. In our practice we should constantly bear in mind the need to go from what is known (the physical) to what is unknown and subtle (the mental and the spiritual).

I truly wish and hope that this book will inspire readers into undertaking the practice of Suryanamaskar, this ancient health system aimed at optimal peak performance. Take it into your homes and houses, and realize the riches it has to offer. I promise that you will not be disappointed.

**Krzysztof Stec**

# ACKNOWLEDGEMENTS

The author would like to express his appreciation and gratitude to Mr. N. Suryavanshi, the President of Vishwatmak Jangli Maharaj Ashram Trust and Mr. D.N. Sangle, the Principal of the Om Gurudev Secondary & Higher Secondary Gurukul for providing him with an opportunity to work both on this book and on his three months long Suryanamaskar doctoral experiment.

Much credit in my yoga education and yoga research should be given to the Kaivalyadhama Yoga institute, of Lonavla, Maharashtra. It is the Kaivalyadhama staff, whose work was guided by the standards set by Swami Kuvalayananda, who molded my understanding of how scientific research should be undertaken in yoga. Not only did I benefit from obtaining Kaivalyadhama's Diploma in Yoga Education, but, over the years, various staff members have always been helpful and have supported my further growth and interest in yoga. Most recently the Institute graciously allowed me to use its testing equipment to run and complete my doctoral tests.

The author also conveys his sincere gratitude to Dr. Mukund V. Bhole, a former Joint Director of Research, Kaivalyadhama, for his ongoing guidance in understanding yogic anatomy and physiology.

Special thanks are also due to Dr. Manmath M. Gharote of the Lonavla Yoga Institute, Maharashtra for his help in locating the ancient text of Asanayoga-Hathabhasya-paddhati by Kapalakurantaka, and help with understanding Hindu scriptures.

My sincere thanks to Dr. S.H. Deshpande, the director of S.H.V.P. Mandal, Amravati, Maharashtra for his timely help with preparation of this book preface. His deep knowledge of the indigenous physical activities in India was invaluable.

Heartfelt thanks to my daughter, Kashmiri Kristina Mukti, a Ph.D. candidate in cognitive linguistics, and Kevin Greene of England, who painstakingly and with great patience corrected this draft.

My compliments are due to Dr. Roxanne Gupta of the United States for sharing her amazing knowledge on the Suryanamaskar tradition and for making many invaluable suggestions for this book.

Thanks are due to the group of students of the OmGurudev Secondary and Higher Secondary Gurukul, Kokamthan for their cooperation and sincere practice as the subjects of my doctoral study.

The author would like to express his sincere gratitude and appreciation to Dr. Rajeev Choudhary, Lecturer at the Department of Physical Education, Banaras Hindu University, Varanasi, for his training in the science of experimental design and statistics.

Lastly, my warm appreciation to all those who have been a constant source of inspiration ever since I first learnt about yoga, including my maternal uncle, a Benedictine monk, Ludwik Mycielski O.S.B., and my first yoga teacher, the late Professor Tadeusz Pasek.

# PREFACE

Solar system is known reality of this Universe. Sun is center point of system and various planets in the system orbit round this point with their own inertia. Earth is no exception. It follows its own path to move round the Sun, in addition, it also revolves around its own axis creating the phenomena of day, night and seasons. Earth is the only living planet of the system where vegetative life exists. Sun provides light to the earth.

Photosynthesis process in the plants starts in the presence of sunlight. The day and night cycle creates circadian rhythm in living creatures that governs their biochemical, physiological and behavioral processes. Heat generated from the rays of Sun is mainly responsible on large-scale evaporation of water from ocean, rivers, lakes and such other open storages. It returns back to earth in a purified form as rainwater, which gives life to plants, animals and all living creatures including man. Sun is the perennial source of energy to keep going life on earth. Therapeutic use of solar rays is also prescribed in some of the texts. Realizing significance of the Sun and its utility in preservation of life, man from pre-historic times started worshipping this Sun God.

Ancient Indian scriptures like *Vedas, Upanishads, Puranas,* Epics and other classical literature contain praise and prayers offered to the Sun God. Lucid description about rising sun and its glow, movements and various sounds of birds at the dawn, attractive colours that spread on the horizon and in the sky, etc. are found in these scriptures. Indian people with twelve different names know the Sun God. Huge temples are still found in India built in ancient period to worship Sun God. World famous Konark *Surya Mandir* of Orissa is in the list of world heritage monuments.

It is no wonder, therefore, that the physical culturists and protagonists of yogic culture of ancient times had considered Sun God as symbol of strength and energy and designed the system of bodily exercises where while praying to the God Sun physical movements were performed in a rhythmic and repetitive way to exercise the whole body. They selected the early morning time to perform these exercises called "Suryanamaskar". Yogic *asanas* are also performed during the same time. According to them, early morning time is the most suitable for performing physical exercises. Cosmic energy is released prior to the rising of the Sun, purity of atmospheric air remains at its optimum level and temperature congenial. This practice of performing early morning exercises is observed most beneficial for the development of our physique and it is continued even today in traditional schools of *Akharas* and *Vyayamshalas. Ayurvedic* Texts (on ancient system of medicine) also prescribe performing of '*Vyayam*' (exercise) early morning. Such a system of physical culture seems suitable for the people of tropical countries.

Suryanamaskar is a type of exercise that combines asanas with *bandhas* and *mudras* in a sequential way. It has also a typical rhythm of '*puraka*', '*kumbhaka*' and '*rechaka*' - the three phases of yogic respiratory movements - that has to be synchronized with the bending and stretching movements for obtaining optimum benefit of exercise.

Traditional system of exercise developed in India centuries past and yet found practiced today needs scientific investigation to find out its relevance in present period. This system has special characteristics of its own. It is claimed that it promotes health and fitness. It is suitable to all individuals irrespective of gender and age. It requires small space to perform. It is mostly equipment-free and inexpensive. It creates similar physiological effects on various systems of the body as are seen with the practice of other forms of exercise. There are several items of exercise in this system. Suryanamaskar is one such item of exercise towards which the author of this book, Mr. Krzysztof Stec of Poland is attracted for scientific study. He is presently in India for carrying out his research on the unique style of Dynamic Suryanamaskar. Based on his investigation, he has brought forward his observations in this informative book. His work seems to be pioneer in this field and more so, when considered written by a foreign scholar on traditional Indian form of exercise called Suryanamaskar.

The author has taken review of ancient and modern literature on sun worshipping in Indian culture and elsewhere. He has also produced relevant scientific information on the power of its rays plus various therapies developed out of the investigations made by earlier researchers. The author has further explained various techniques and ways of performing sun worship described in *Rishikesh Series*.

The third part of the book contains psycho-physiological research carried out over the years in many different laboratories and the results obtained there from this type of exercise. This review of scientific investigation shows: 1. Researches being carried out world-over on India's traditional system of exercise, of which people have little knowledge. By presenting this information in the book, the author has rendered useful service to the inquisitive readers. 2. The extensive collection, reading and analysis of scientific data made by the present author reflect upon his analytical mind and his devotion to the subject. Towards end of the book the author has given substantial evidences in the form of references and appendices.

The book is beautifully decorated with colorful and attractive cover. Mr. Krzysztof Stec deserves every praise for bringing out such an informative book on scientific lines. I am confident that the book will capture international market.

**Dr. S.H. Deshpande**

Director

S.H.V.P. Mandal

Amravati, Maharashtra

# SURYANAMASKAR

## Sun Salutations

## Standard International Transliteration Code
(Used to transliterate Sanskrit words in the text)

| | | |
|---|---|---|
| अ | = | a |
| आ | = | ā |
| इ | = | i |
| ई | = | ī |
| उ | = | u |
| ऊ | = | ū |
| ऋ | = | ṛ |
| ए | = | e |
| ऐ | = | ai |
| ओ | = | o |
| औ | = | au, ou |
| अं | = | ṁ |
| अः | = | ḥ |
| क | = | ka |
| ख | = | kha |
| ग | = | ga |
| घ | = | gha |
| ङ | = | ṅa |
| च | = | ca |
| छ | = | cha |
| ज | = | ja |
| झ | = | jha |
| ञ | = | ña |
| ट | = | ṭa |
| ठ | = | ṭha |
| ड | = | ḍa |
| ढ | = | ḍha |
| ण | = | ṇa |
| त | = | ta |
| थ | = | tha |
| द | = | da |
| ध | = | dha |
| न | = | na |
| प | = | pa |
| फ | = | pha |
| ब | = | ba |
| भ | = | bha |
| म | = | ma |
| य | = | ya |
| र | = | ra |
| ल | = | la |
| व | = | va |
| श | = | śa |
| ष | = | ṣa |
| स | = | sa |
| ह | = | ha |
| क्ष | = | kṣa |
| त्र | = | tra |
| ज्ञ | = | jña |

# 1

# INTRODUCTION

"Yoga has a complete message for humanity.
It has a message for the human body.
It has a message for the human mind,
and it also has a message for the human soul."

Swami Kuvalayananda (1883 – 1966)

Physical activity is one of the most basic aspects of human life. Its essential value has been emphasized in a variety of ways throughout the ages. One distinct type of physical activity is physical education, where sports and games play a vital role. Worldwide, the past few decades have seen sporting activities become increasingly sophisticated technically, with growing popularity as a separate profession, which has resulted in an enormous expansion of related educational and training facilities. As far as life in general is concerned, participation in sports and physical fitness increases productivity and promotes social harmony and discipline.

An extension of this approach to life is also espoused by national health care systems, which address the physical, psychiatric, psychological and social aspects of life. At the same time, the World Health Organization (WHO) has added the component of spiritual health to its definition of health and in its guidelines for health workers. Spiritual health is indeed an aspect of human well-being that requires our full attention.

In this regard, the millennia-old system of Yoga gives a positive and convincing answer. It is not a religious system, nor a cult, nor a system of dogmas. It is a practical and experiential system based upon long-standing human existential experiences, which are above and beyond any religion, nationality, culture, profession or gender, etc. It is secular and universal, as are physical education and the medical sciences.

Recent scientific research carried out in the field of Yoga has helped Yoga relaxation techniques be recognized, and used, by top sportsmen and businessmen alike. These techniques also have found a place in physiology and medical books. The work of neuroscientists and neuro-cardio-scientists working in collaboration with eminent Buddhist teachers and yogis has shed some light on the mechanisms involved in meditation techniques and on the subject of human consciousness.

For example, in 2004 in The Wall Street Journal Sharon Begley described an experiment performed on a group of advanced Tibetan Buddhist monks. By using functional magnetic resonance imagining (fMRI) during deep meditation it was observed that the activity in the prefrontal cortex was much, much greater than when the same experiment was done on novices, and the frontal lobes of the advanced meditators were almost twice as thick. One of the hottest topics in brain science is neuroplasticity, or the brain's ability to modify its structure and function, depending on the stimuli, which may be either internal or external. Also other research shows that it is an open possibility for the brain, just as in the case of other organs or the rest of the body, to alter and sculpt itself by intention and practice, just as muscles can be sculpted by body-building or many other sports.

Another important discovery was made about the interrelation of the five neural structures in the human body. This is well described by Joseph Chilton Pearce in his book entitled *The Biology of Transcendence*. The book is a fascinating compilation of research from many different laboratories off the main-stream. Let him speak in his own words about these discoveries, which seem to support the ancient intuitions of Indian rishis, saints and sages:

> "A new breed of biologists and neuroscientists has revealed why we behave in so paradoxical a manner that we continually say one thing, feel something else, and act from an impulse different from either of these. After centuries of bad remedies prescribed for a disease that has been wrongly diagnosed, this new research gives us the chance to remove the blocks to the transcendent within us and allows us to develop a nature that lies beyond rage and violence.
>
> A major clue to our conflict is the discovery by these new scientists that we have five different neural

structures, or brains, within us. These five systems, four of them housed in our head, represent the whole evolution of life preceding us: reptilian, old mammalian, and human. Nature never abandons a good idea but instead builds new structures upon it; apparently each new neural structure we have inherited evolved to correct the shortcomings in or problems brought about by nature's former achievements. Each new creation opened life to vast new realms of possibility and, at the same time, brought new problems, thus calling once again for 'rising and going beyond' through the creation of yet another neural structure. Thus, while we refer to transcendence in rather mystical, ethereal terms, to the intelligence of life, transcendence may be simply the next intelligent move to make.

As long intuited by poet and saint, the fifth brain in our system lies not in our head, but in our heart, a hard biological fact (to give the devil of science his due) that was unavailable to the prescientific world. Neuro-cardiology, a new field of medical research, has discovered in our heart a major brain center that functions in dynamic with the fourfold brain in our head. Outside our conscious awareness, this heart-head dynamic reflects, determines, and affects the very nature of our resulting awareness even as it is, in turn, profoundly affected."

(The Biology of Transcendence, 2002)

Neuroscience has been making startling discoveries about the human heart, where work in a number of fields, particularly those associated with molecular biology, neuro-cardiology, and biophysics, has demonstrated that the heart has a number of similarities, in its cellular structure, functioning, and links with the rest of the body, to the brain proper, indeed to such an extent that it has itself been termed a 'little brain'. The following excerpt from an interview with the educator and author Joseph Chilton Pearce helps to explain this development:

> "Molecular biologists have discovered that the heart is the body's most important endocrine gland. In response to our experience of the world, it produces and releases a major hormone, ANF - which stands for Atriol Neuriatic [Atrial Natriuretic] Factor - that profoundly affects every operation in the limbic structure, or what we refer to as the 'emotional brain'. This includes the hippocampal area where memory and learning take place, and also the control centers for the entire hormonal system. And neurocardiologists have found that 60 to 65% of the cells of the heart are actually neural cells, not muscle cells as was previously believed. They are identical to the neural cells in the brain, operating through the same connecting links called ganglia, with the same axonal and dendritic connections that take place in the brain, as well as through the very same kinds of neurotransmitters found in the brain.

> Quite literally, in other words, there is a 'brain' in the heart, whose ganglia are linked to every major organ in the body, to the entire muscle spindle system that uniquely enables humans to express their emotions. About half of the heart's neural cells are involved in translating information sent to it from all over the body so that it can keep the body working as one harmonious whole. And the other half makes up a very large, unmediated neural connection with the emotional brain in our head and carries on a twenty-four-hour-a-day dialogue between the heart and the brain that we are not even aware of."
>
> (*Journal of Family Life* magazine, Vol. 5 #1 1999)

The concept of the functional 'heart brain' was first discussed in 1991 by one of neurocardiology's pioneers, Dr. J. Andrew Armour. His extensive research had revealed that the complexity of the heart's nervous system easily qualified it as a 'little brain' and that its elaborate circuitry made it possible for it to act independently from and in parallel with the cranial brain. It could sense, feel, learn and remember just as the central nervous system could. The book entitled *Neurocardiology* by Dr. Armour and Dr. Jeffrey Ardell gives a comprehensive overview of the function of the heart's intrinsic nervous system and of the role of central and peripheral autonomic nervous system neurons in the regulation of cardiac function. The heart's nervous system consists of approximately 40,000 neurons which monitor chemical, hormonal, rate and pressure information that is sent by afferent pathways to the brain.

These signals have a regulatory function over many autonomic system processes, affect organs, other glands, blood vessels and the heart itself, and may also influence the higher parts of the brain. Perception and cognition are also affected, and, in consequence, so is decision making.

The work of Dr. Jon Kabat-Zinn has been responsible for the recognition of the role played by Yoga techniques and Yoga approaches in pain and stress management, while the work of Dr. Dean Ornish has provided a way to treat coronary blocks through life-style changes in which Yoga plays a crucial part. His Yoga staff running the Program for Reversing Heart Disease credited Suryanamaskar as "the most beneficial yogic practice" for their heart patients.

Other interesting and ground-breaking experiments were conducted by Bruce Lipton Ph.D. at Stanford University Medical Center. He gave an account of them in his book *The Biology of Belief*. In it this former researcher and medical school professor describes the way single cells receive information. His research shows that genes and DNA do not control life, but that in fact it is the other way around. This means that signals from the environment control DNA and the genes, by selecting a blueprint from the total pool of genes. These signals include even the energy of messages carried by positive or negative thoughts. The implication of his research is such as to change completely our view of life. He proposes a new synthesis of quantum mechanics and the latest biological research, which boils down to the idea that we can change our bodies as we retrain our minds. These discoveries have given momentum to the new science known as epigenetics.

Russian researchers report similar observations. They have discovered that the human body can be programmed by language, i.e. by words both spoken and thought. Russian research has provided evidence that it is possible to influence DNA and the genes through words and the sounds of various frequencies, without cutting or replacing the genes, as is done in the West. Only 10% of human DNA is used to build proteins and it is this small part that is being intensively researched in the West, while the other 90% is considered "DNA junk". Russian scientists began to investigate the "DNA junk" or unused part of DNA. They have combined the resources of genetic experts and linguists and found that the "unused" 90% part of DNA obeys the same laws as all human languages, and that DNA structure is based on regular rules of grammar. Thus, according to this research, languages have not appeared accidentally but are a reflection of our DNA.

The team of a Russian biophysicist and an expert in molecular biology, Dr. Pjotr Garjajev researched the vibrational behavior of DNA. In short, they found that chromosomes function as holographic computers, using their inborn DNA as small lasers. This means that by providing certain vibrations, just like a mini laser ray, the investigators were able to influence the DNA frequency and in the end influence genetic information. The basic structure and language pairs in the DNA (as explained above) are effectively the same. Therefore there is no need for any decoding of DNA. We can simply accomplish that by using words and sentences of human language!

Living substance DNA (live tissue and not in a test tube) will always respond to the 'laser rays' that can be modulated by language, or even radio waves, provided that the appropriate frequency is used (e.g. sound). This discovery finally and scientifically explains why affirmations, hypnosis, etc. may have such a strong effect on humans and their bodies. This is because it is quite normal and natural behavior that our DNA reacts to language. Russian scientists have built devices that influence cellular metabolism by modulating sound and light frequencies, and in that way are able to promote calm and healing in living tissue.

The Russian researchers were even able to discover informational patterns of particular DNA and transmit them to the DNA of another cell, and by that means were able to reprogram the recipient cell to become a different gene. As a result they were able to transform a frog embryo into a salamander embryo. In that way all the genetic information was transmitted without any side effects or disharmony, consequences which are very common when using the different technology of cutting and joining of selected DNA genes. Such discoveries strongly suggest that simply using vibrations and proper frequencies is sufficient to influence our genes. Could it be that the ancient "intuitional scientists" called *rishis*, Indian sages and saints, who were using mantras, were right all along?

Of course, the frequency of the sound used must be properly selected and applied, and that is the reason why not all attempts of this kind are successful. It was found by Russian researchers that an individual must do inner work and develop internally before it is possible to develop and stabilize such conscious communication with DNA. Furthermore, it was found that stress, worries, or an over-active intellect either completely prevent effective 'hyper-communication' of this kind, or the information will be completely distorted and thus ineffective. In nature, 'hyper-communication' was used successfully by evolution over millions of years. Organized movement in living insects proves that in a dramatic way. Contemporary man knows it only at a more subtle level, as through the experience of intuition or of being inspired. It is worth noting that this recent interpretation of reality is nothing new to yogis, sages and *rishis*. They have been saying something similar for millennia, and they developed the whole integrated system of yogic science.

"*Our body is essential for every achievement*" said an ancient seer. That body should not be diseased but rather strong and healthy, with perfect harmony between the physical, mental, and spiritual aspects. One's natural state should include an all-encompassing feeling of unusual lightness, a fullness of health, and an experience of overall contentment. Bliss and perfection, overflowing vitality and energy, are the human birthright.

Who would not like to be strong, beautiful and healthy? Yet such characteristics do not manifest themselves merely by desire, nor are they commodities that can be purchased on world markets. They are something that only self-effort or tapasya can create. Furthermore, the Hindu four-fold goal of human life (*dharma, artha, kama* and *moksha* - duty, wealth, pleasure, and emancipation) is most easily obtained in a strong and healthy body. As the sage Charaka says in the *Charaka Samhita*, freedom from disease is health. While Indian medicine provides many effective remedies for illness, it acknowledges that prevention is much more effective than cure. In addition, statistics show that the cost of prevention is less than one tenth that of fighting a manifested given illness. One of the best prophylactic measures against disease is regular physical exercise. The centuries-old system of Yoga with its distinct practice of Suryanamaskar remains the perfect all-inclusive health practice, even in today's busy world.

There are many types of sport and physical culture in the world. India itself has developed a large number (more than 30) of its own indigenous systems, such as *malkhamb, kushti* (Indian wrestling), wrestling clubs, *lathi, barchi*, clubs, *baithak, kathi, patta, talwar, bhala*, dumb bells, spring dumb bells, *kho-kho, kabaddhi*, etc, etc. In addition, there are many Western systems of exercise and sports to choose from, such as football, volleyball, handball, basketball, gymnastics, tennis, hockey, swimming, athletics, bicycling, mountaineering, cricket, etc., etc. Unfortunately these sports cannot ensure equal exercise to all parts of the body and, in addition, participation in many of them depends on the individual's age, gender, or economic status. Although participation in them may offer some contribution to mental well-being, only rarely will there be an effect on spiritual well-being. Neither of these effects can match the contribution of Yoga to well-being in these two areas.

Why is that so? It is because a strong body needs to be reigned by a strong mind and a strong spirit. The former without the latter two is incomplete. The development of body power should go hand in hand with the development of mental and spiritual power. The integrated development of all facets of personality is the essential tool for reaching the four human goals of life mentioned earlier. That is why Shri Krishna states in the *Bhagavad Gita* (B.G.) *"I am the power, untainted by desire or attachment, in the powerful"* (VII, 7), emphasizing mental and spiritual power over physical. A weak person has no chance for *Atma Jnana* (Self-realization); as the *Kathopanishad* declares *"Atma is never accessible to the powerless"*.

To become so powerful in these three aspects, the usual recommendation is to adopt the habits and mindset of a *brahmacharya*. Through *brahmacharya* there is conservation and control of subtle *ojas* which enhances and speeds up the spiritual progress. Of course, this does not exclude married people; as an ancient sage and great expert on Yoga Yajnavalkya explains in conversation with his wife Gargi in the *Yajnavalkya Samhita* (I.55) *"A householder who copulates only with his own wife at the appropriate periods of her menstrual cycle in the prescribed manner is said to be a brahmacharin"*.

Sages and yogis of various traditions around the world discovered ways to worldly and spiritual progress in a very practical way, by living their teaching in their everyday lives. In India they created the system known as Yoga. The classical Yoga compiled by the sage Patanjali consists of eight *angas* (steps or parts) and is called *Ashtanga Yoga*. These steps are: *yama* (*restrictions*), *niyama* (observances), *asana* (postural patterns), *pranayama* (regulation of breath), pratyahara (withholding of senses), *dharana* (fixation of the mind), *dhyana* (meditation) and *samadhi* (perfect concentration).

Yoga developed into a great variety of traditions, procedures and techniques which at times are quite complicated and difficult to master. Many of these techniques are still known only through oral tradition and are taught only to initiates. Even well-known practices often vary greatly from school to school. There is an obvious need for a proper, unified description and classification of them.

Suryanamaskar, or sun-salutation, is of ancient origin and serves as the cornerstone upon which the science of Yoga rests according to a well known teacher of yoga, Shri K. Pattabhi Jois. Through the unique combination of *asana, pranayama* and meditation, Suryanamaskar can be considered to be the ideal way to practice yoga, as it helps to develop the strength of the body and mind on the one hand and to aid in the attainment of spiritual focus on the other. Without bringing the mind to a state in which it can push the body through the various stages of yoga practice, say the texts, students cannot be certain of avoiding injury and of making due progress.

Even in some Western countries, as, for example, Poland, the benefits of Suryanamaskar have been recognized at governmental level. In 2001 the Polish Ministry of National Education issued an official recommendation number 1173/2001, where it states that this practice should be used by Polish schools as a form of corrective (therapeutic) exercises.

A similar governmental recommendation exists in various Indian states, as, for example, the State of Maharashtra or the State of Rajasthan.

# PART - I

- Origin
- History
- Solar Science

# 2

# THE SUN IN WORLD TRADITIONS

The act of worship is a basic human instinct. Whether people are civilized or barbarians, they worship some kind of God or deity. Historical data tell us that sun worship predates the Christ by at least four or five millennia.

People of many traditions and cultures have prayed to the Sun as the giver of life, light and heat; they treated the Sun as a benefactor of mankind. Its glory, power and splendor, its primary role in the creation and maintenance of life, its regularity in lighting the earth had secured for the Sun a pre-eminent and important place from the beginning of the human race. The Sun was considered a visible embodiment of natural and supernatural powers, the dispeller of darkness, the giver of warmth, and the bestower of life.

A quick look around different cultures of the world gives an idea of how special and unique a place the Sun holds in the minds of men. For example, the ancient Persian god Mithra was connected with the Sun while, in ancient Mesopotamia, the Assyrian and Babylonian civilizations worshipped the Sun-God. Traveling to America, one finds that, in order to worship the Sun, the Aztecs and Mayans built enormous pyramids, which survive to this day.

Mayans were expert mathematicians and astrologers, who could keep time and the calculations of the solar year with high accuracy. Mayan cosmology honored the Sun-God Itzamna, also called Kinich Ahau, as the only supreme god of the sky. The Pyramid of the Sun in Chichen-Itza is one of the largest Mexican pyramids. It is so precisely aligned with the Sun's rays that, in the spring, the shadow of the pyramid steps appears as a snake entering the Earth, while in the fall, the same shadow appears as a snake leaving the Earth. Another very large Mexican Pyramid of the Sun at Teotihuacan is so precisely aligned with the Sun that the Sun is directly overhead at noon time on two dates in the year, May 19th and July 25th. The heart of the city is the cave of the Pyramid's inner sanctuary, to which the whole city is aligned.

Sun worship was also well developed in Peru, where the Sun was believed to be the ancestor and founder of the powerful Incas. The Inca rulers made Sun worship their state religion and they reigned as representatives of the Sun God. Similarly, Sun adoration was the main worship of the Caucasian tribes in Asia. And in Beijing, China there is a Ri-Tan temple dedicated to the Sun. There, Chinese emperors conducted their rituals every year.

The three religions of Judaism, Islam and Christianity also use light as a form of god, virtue, and deep spirituality. For centuries, the Jewish menorah (seven branch candelabra), has been keeping alive the flame of hope during periods of darkness since the destruction of Jerusalem by the Romans. The Qu'ran, Islam's holy book, says in the 24th chapter that "God is the Light of the Heavens and the Earth". In the Christian world-view Christ is the true Light, and Christians are children of Light at perpetual war with the powers of darkness. Many of the world's god men to whom sacrifices are or were made have their traditional birthday on December 25th (Christmas Day). This represents the ancient recognition that (from the perspective of the northern hemisphere) the Sun makes a yearly descent southward until December 21st or 22nd, the winter solstice, when it stops moving southerly for three days and then starts to move northward again. During this time, people back long ago believed that 'God Sun' had 'died' for three days and was 'born again' on December 25th. After December 25th, the Sun moves one degree, this time north, foreshadowing longer days. And thus it was said that the Sun died on the cross, was dead for 3 days, only to be resurrected or born again. Consider the following statements: The Sun is the "*Light of the World*" (John 8:12). The Sun rising in the morning is the "*Savior of mankind*", as well as the "healer" or "savior" during the day, the sun wears a corona, "crown of thorns" or halo, "*The Lord God is a sun...*" (Psalms 84:11). "*The Sun of Righteousness [Jesus] will rise with healing in his wings for you people who fear my name*" (Malachi 4:2). "*And he was transfigured before them, and his face shone like the sun, and his garments became white as light*" (Matthew 17:2). "*I am the light of the world; he who follows me will not walk in darkness, but will have the light of life"* (John 8:12).

Egypt was another country that developed a great "civilization of consciousness", where the Sun was worshiped as "Ra" from the fifth dynasty that is from about 2500 B.C.E. Ancient Egyptian mythology is full of references to the God "Ra", the creator, the inventor of kinship and the very first king. The Sun-King would sail each day across the sky in his boat of a million years. All Egyptian kings were embodiments of the Sun-God, and, as such, were considered divine and sacred to Egyptians. After their death, they were accepted by the gods into the afterlife and triumphed over death, in the same way that the Sun triumphs daily over the darkness of the night.

From Egypt, Sun worship moved to Greece and on to Western Europe. In fact, the word "radiation" comes from the name of the Sun-God "Ra". In those days, both Greeks and barbarians would prostrate to the Sun at dawn and at dusk, paying respect to the god Helios. The Greek Sun-God Apollo, "the Shining One" is often portrayed on his chariot racing towards the Sun. Romans also worshipped this great luminary under the name Mithras, and built many temples to worship him across their Empire. The Mithras worship tradition originally came from Persia and this god was frequently identified with the Greek Sun-God Helios.

3

# THE SUN IN HINDU SCRIPTURES

In India the Sun worship dates to prehistoric times. The Hindu scriptures are full of hymns praising the Sun-God, extolling his qualities as protector and life-giver and destroyer of darkness and evil. The *Vedas* and *Puranas* give to the Sun a very distinguished place:

आप्रा दयावापृथिवी अन्तरिक्षं सूर्य आत्मा जगतस्तस्थुषश्च ॥

*āprą dayāvāpṛthivī antarikṣaṁ sūrya ātmā jagatastasthuṣaśca* | |

*Rig Veda 1,115-2*

*Sun is the sustainer of the Universe comprised of movable and immovable.*

The Sun is considered to be the "Lord of all creation", which every morning wakes up the universe and men. It is the guardian and preserver of cattle and a companion of travelers. Therefore the Sun is one of the important deities of the *Vedas* and is personified as *Surya*. In the morning He is adored by *Rig Veda*, at mid-day by *Yajur Veda*, and in the evening by

*Sama Veda*. He is *Ravi, Brahma, Vishnu, Rudra* and *Bhaskara,* in fact he is the trinity (*Trimurti*).

In the *Vedic* hymns the Sun of inner self awareness or the "spiritual sun" forms their central theme. The Sun, being at the core of all live existence, is viewed as the meeting point between the relative manifestation on Earth and the transcendental reality. The early *Vedic* rishis had a deep mystic realization of the unity of the whole creation, with a heliocentric view of life, where the divine light and the Sun's light were in fact not different.

Many *Vedic* sacrifices were developed and co-ordinated throughout the year and seasons where *Surya* was proclaimed as a dominant god of the year or season. In the early part of the *Vedic* age many different functions were attributed to the Sun and He was invoked and worshipped accordingly. He was worshipped under different names corresponding to the function performed, for example as *Pushan* He was the guardian of cattle and crops, as *Vishnu* He was the creator and was worshipped as god of fertility, as *Surya* as giver of light and warmth, etc. In such manner the Sun-God was the one who controlled all inanimate and animate objects and therefore was considered the Supreme Being. In the later *Vedic* period the Sun continued to be invoked in all His various aspects and was given names accordingly.

*Surya,* the *Vedic* God of Light, was always shown as riding a golden chariot pulled by seven horses across the sky and with His attentive eyes watching all the good and bad deeds done by mortals and immortals. The stars "creep off like thieves" as He "the maker of light" appears with His "hair of flame", where the wheel is the wheel of time and the seven horses are the days of the week. *Surya* is the Lord of Time. The people of *Vedic* times believed that when a man dies he joins the Sun's disc (Roger Coghill, 2000).

Perhaps the best known and the most holy solar mantra from *Rig Veda* is the *Gayatri Mantra,* which is dedicated to the Sun-God *Savita*:

ॐ भूर्भुवः स्वः ।
तत्सवितुर्वरेण्यं भर्गो देवस्य धीमहि ।
धियो यो नः प्रचोदयात् ।

*om bhūrbhuvaḥ svaḥ* ।
*tatsaviturvareṇyaṁ bhargo devasya dhīmahi* ।
*dhiyo yo naḥ pracodayāt* ।

*Rig Veda III.62.10*

*Let us meditate upon*
*The glorious effulgent light of the Cosmic Sun*
*May it illuminate our minds and protect our actions*

Likewise, in all other periods as for example *Upanishadic* or *Puranic,* the Sun is also elaborately worshipped. During the *Upanishadic* period the Sun was worshipped as god of fertility and vegetation, creator of day and night, and as a giver of light and warmth. In the *Suryopanishad* it is stated that a person who worships the Sun becomes all powerful, active and intelligent, and will enjoy a long life. In the *Akshyupanishad Purusha* is considered to be the Sun-God *Surya* which with His thousands of Sun rays shines for the good of humanity. The

*Brahma Sutras* state that "*The word light (Sun) to be understood as Brahman (I.1.24)*".

A more formal invocation, which is frequently used to begin the Sun worship and Surya Namaskar practice, is a hymn from the *Upanishads*:

असतो मा सद्गमय । तमसो मा ज्योतिर्गमय ।
मृत्योर्मा अमृतं गमय । ॐ शान्तिः शान्तिः शान्तिः ।

*asato mā sadgamaya | tamaso mā jyotirgamaya |*
*mṛtyormā amṛtaṁ gamaya | om śāntiḥ śāntiḥ śāntiḥ |*

*Brihadaranyaka Upanishad I, iii, 28*

*O Lord, the essence of Light*
*Lead me from the unreal to Real*
*From darkness to light*
*From death to Immortality*
*Om, Peace, Peace, Peace*

In the *Ramayana* there are many references to the Sun, for example *Surya* is described as a father of the monkey king Sugriva, and he also trains Hanuman by being his guru. The Lord Rama has learned the Sun mantra called *Aditya Hridaya* (Sun's heart) directly from the sage Agastya and by so doing has ensured his success in his battle against the demon king Ravana (*Valmiki Ramayana*).

In the epic the *Mahabharata* the great hero Karna is said to be born of *Surya*. There is another well-known story with Shri Krishna's son Samba who was very proud of his beauty. He was so proud that once he made a mistake of ridiculing the celebrated sage Narada, who being ever mischievous, decided to take his revenge on the arrogant Samba. Samba was tricked by Narada into going to a pool where his stepmothers, the beautiful consorts of Shri Krishna, were bathing, unaware of being watched. Shri Krishna became furious when he learned about his son's peeping and, as a result, he placed a curse of leprosy on Samba. Only later did Shri Krishna learn that the canny Narada had tricked the boy, but by then he could not revoke his curse. Krishna advised his son to seek the Sun-God's help. Heeding this advice, Samba went to Prabhasa Kshetra, where he performed twelve years of long and arduous penance to the Sun, the healer of all diseases, and as a result he received the Sun's *darshan,* during which he was instructed to bathe in the sea. The bathing in the sea finally cured Samba of leprosy *(Skandapurana, Ch. 128).*

Samba was so delighted with the cure that he decided to erect a *Surya Mandir* on that very spot. It was called Konark or "Place of the Sun". The temple devoted to the Sun at Konark on the coast of Orissa, also known as "Black Pagoda", can be viewed even today, though the extant building was constructed by the medieval king Narasingha Deva. The Konark temple chariot, in which *Surya* is being pulled across the sky, has been built along the east-west axis of the temple. This sky procession was a continuous rejoicing each day as the *Surya's* journey brought light, warmth, and life to Earth. The Konark's chariot with its twenty-four wheels is being pulled by seven horses, which represent the seven days of the week and the seven *rishis* who govern our constellation.

In yet another sun story the sage Dhaumya taught the *Surya* mantra to Yudhisthira, who worshipped the Sun and received a boon of *akshayapatra*. Also, the sage Narada reached the fulfillment of his desires by means of adoration of the Sun. In the tantric period starting in about the eighth century C.E. there are also many references to practices of Sun worship.

The *Vedas* give beautiful descriptions of the Sun's qualities, where He is described as fortune and knowledge giver, and one who cures disease. The following descriptions show the Sun's qualities: "The rising Sun destroys germs" (*Atharva Veda*), "Health must be obtained from the Sun" (*Rig Veda*), "The Sun is the soul of all the universe", "O Sun God, thou hast the rays which benefit the whole Universe; thou inspirest all. Rise thou high in the sky and cure me of my jaundice and leprosy", "Transfer my discomforting yellow color to the parrot or turmeric, which love this color", "This Sun before me is rising with all this force destroying this enemy which is my disease. I have no power to destroy this enemy. Let the Sun himself do so" (*Rig Veda*). "Sunrise is the life force of the people" (*Prashna Upanishad*), "I sip this water which has washed the feet of the Sun-God (meaning it was exposed to sunlight), which removes all disease and untimely death", "By reciting the *Surya* mantra with faith, boils, itches, and other skin disease, leprosy, *Visarpa*, cholera and other ailments, fevers, and demonic afflictions are cured" (*Bhavishyottara Purana*). In the yogic tradition Surya Namaskar awakens the individual's true nature and releases vital energy for the development of higher awareness.

The Sun has five important qualities: *Ananta Pavitrata* (absolute purity), *Prana* (vital life force), *Niyama* (daily rises and sets), *Shakha* (has capacity to produce food through heat and light rays) *and Krimi Nashak* (destroys harmful germs). These qualities make life easy, smooth and regular.

Just a few of these examples show clearly that Hindu *shrutis, agamas, puranas,* epics and mythology abound with hundreds if not thousands of stories which proclaim the Sun's glory and greatness. This fascination with the Sun starts with the *Vedic rishis* who were singing ever-ecstatic songs of the Sun's greatness. There is little doubt that our ancestors knew well the healing effects of the rays of the Sun.

*He is the remover of all weakness,*
*Healer of all illness,*
*Lord of all that stands and goes,*
*He slays the demons and guards the worshippers.*
*We meditate on the adorable glory of the radiant Sun,*
*May he inspire our intelligence*

*Rig Veda*

## Vedic Origins of Surya Namaskar

The earliest writings containing references to sun worship are in the *Rig Veda* and are dated to the third millennium B.C.E., though the exact date of origin is still in dispute. There are numerous references praising the Sun for the purpose of good health and prosperity. Some of these *Vedic* hymns were incorporated into *Nitya Vidhi,* the daily obligatory routine for Hindus, for the well-being of the individual through salutations to the Sun. This daily conduct was termed Surya Namaskar, literally "sun salutations". Physical prostration to the Sun while showing complete surrender of oneself to God is the main aspect of this practice. The forms of Surya Namaskar practiced vary from region to region and from school to school. Two such popular practices are *Trucha Kalpa Namaskarah* and *Aditya Prasna*.

*Trucha Kalpa Namaskarah* has its origins in the *Rig Veda*. Each mantra in the *Veda* is called a "*rucha*". A group of three *ruchas* is called a *trucha*. *Trucha Kalpa Namaskarah* is a method of performing Surya Namaskar using three *ruchas* from the *Veda*. After that *dhyana* mantra is recited:

ॐ ध्येयः सदा सवितृमंडलमध्यवर्ती नारायणः सरसिजासनसन्निविष्टः ।
केयूरवान् मकरकुण्डलवान् किरीटी हारी हिरण्मयवपुर्धृतशङ्खचक्रः ॥

*om dhyeyaḥ sadā savitṛmaṇḍalamadhyavartī*
*nārāyaṇaḥ sarasijāsanasanniviṣṭaḥ* |
*keyūravān makarakuṇḍalavān kirīṭī hārī*
*hiraṇmayavapurdhṛtaśaṅkhacakraḥ* | |

*Always worship the Sun, which is sitting at the center of his Galaxy on a lotus, wearing keyura, a makarakundala crown and holding a conch, chakra and having golden body.*

*Dhyana* mantra is followed by the performance of Surya Namaskara, accompanied by the chanting of twelve sacred Hindu mantras. These mantras are arranged in a specific way and consist of *trucha* taken from the 1st *Mandala*, 9th *Anuvaka*, and 50th *Sukta* of the *Rig Veda*. They were originally composed by Kanva *Rishi,* who maintained that by performing Surya Namaskar in this way the Sun would be pleased and would cure many diseases, such as heart trouble, leukemia, leprosy, jaundice, etc. For each of the twelve mantras one complete Namaskara consisting of twelve postures is to be performed. The ancient practice was to do nine full rounds or 108 Namaskaras in a day. Hindus consider it most auspicious to do it in this way. The meaning of the three *ruchas* (or a *trucha)* was as follows:

> *"O radiant Sun rising in the sky, please destroy the disease in my heart as well diseases of my external body. Let inner and outer diseases of my body be destroyed by the brilliantly shining Sun, the son of Aditi"*

At the end of the practice the *tirtha shloka* was recited as follows:

आदित्यस्य नमस्कारं ये कुर्वन्ति दिने दिने ।
जन्मान्तरसहस्रेषु दारिद्र्यं नोऽपजायते ॥
अकालमृत्युहरणं सर्वव्याधिनिवारणम् ।
सूर्यपादोदकं तीर्थं जिह्वाग्रे धारयाम्यहम् ॥

*ādityasya namaskāraṁ ye kurvanti dine dine |*
*janmāntarasahasreṣu dāridryaṁ no'pajāyate ||*
*akālamṛtyuharaṇaṁ sarvavyādhinivāraṇam |*
*sūryapādodakaṁ tīrthaṁ jihvāgre dhārayāmyaham ||*

*Those who perform Suryanamaskar daily, do not face poverty in life (good health), one does not face early death or suffer from diseases. Drink the water kept in front of the Sun.*

*Aditya Prasna,* on the other hand, uses verses which are taken from the first chapter of the *Yajur Veda,* the *Taittiriya Aranyakam,* which is also referred to as the Surya Namaskar. It is popularly practiced in South India. There are 132 *Anuvakas* in this chapter and it is the practice to recite and perform Sun salutations with prostrations after the recitation of each *Anuvaka.*

## Puranic Origins of Surya Namaskar

*Aditya Hridayam* is another ancient practice, which involves Surya Namaskar. It is the procedure of saluting the Sun that was taught to Shri Rama by the Sage Agastya before Rama's fight with Ravana. It is described in the "*Yuddha Khanda*", canto 107 of the *Valmiki Ramayana.* In total, there are 124 names praising the Sun in the whole practice. The names in verses 10 - 13 are given below:

आदित्यः सविता सूर्यः खगः पूषा गभस्तिमान् ।
सुवर्णसदृशो भानुर्हिरण्यरेता दिवाकरः ॥१० ॥
हरिदश्वः सहस्रार्चिः सप्तसप्तिर्मरीचिमान् ।
तिमिरोन्मथनः शम्भुस्त्वष्टा मार्ताण्ड अंशुमान् ॥११ ॥
हिरण्यगर्भः शिशिरस्तपनो भास्करो रविः ।
अग्निगर्भोऽदितेः पुत्रः शङ्खः शिशिरनाशनः ॥१२ ॥

*ādityaḥ savitā sūryaḥ khagaḥ pūṣā gabhastimān |*
*suvarṇasadṛśo bhānurhiraṇyaretā divākaraḥ ||10||*
*haridaśvaḥ sahasrārciḥ saptasaptirmarīcimān |*
*timironmathanaḥ śambhustvaṣṭā mārtāṇḍa aṁśumān ||11||*

hiraëyagarbhaù çiçirastapano bhäskaro raviù |
agnigarbho'diteù putraù çaìkhaù çiçiranäçanaù ||12||

In verses 15 - 20, salutations to the Sun are described. An example from the 15th verse is:

*The resplendent among the splendid. Oh! God, appearing in twelve forms (in the shape of twelve months of the year), salutations to you.*

## Tantric tradition

Tantric yogis use Surya Namaskar practice along with energizing breathing to absorb solar energy into their bodies. There is a whole branch of tantric science known by the name *Surya vidya*. An advanced form of such a tantric version of Surya Namaskar involves direct experience of the unity of the sun that exists both outside and inside our bodies.

## English Publications

The existence of the practice of Sun salutations for health in ancient India is not confined to Hindu texts and literature written by Hindu scholars. Early English publications also make reference to some of the ancient ways of Sun salutation. In "A Catalogue Raisonnée of Oriental Manuscripts", Rev. William Cooke Taylor noted that a short book with 71 leaves with "*Tricha calpa Vidhi*" from "*Aditya Puranam*" will be preserved. He describes the *vidhi* as "Modes of rendering homage to Sun, with praise and spells, the object being health or delivery from disease". He further notes the presence of

*Arghya Pradana, Surya Stotaram, Aditya Dvadasa Namam* - the twelve names of the Sun according to the monthly signs of the zodiac, *Surya Narayana Cavacham, Saurashtacshari mantram,* and many other elaborate rituals as the part of the *vidhi.* On page 148 of the same book, he mentions a shorter version called "*Laghu tricha kalpa Vidhi*".

# 4

# THE SUN ACCORDING TO SCIENCE

The Sun is the largest astronomical body and only star in our solar system. However, by comparison to other stars in our galaxy it is relatively small. It is a glowing, self-luminous globe of gas, held together by the forces of gravity. It has been estimated that its diameter is 1,392,000 km, with its average density being about one quarter that of the Earth. It is 1,300,000 times the size of the Earth with 109 times the Earth's diameter and 333,000 times its mass, which is 99.86% of the total mass of the solar system. Hydrogen accounts for approximately 75% of the Sun's mass, while the rest is mostly helium (23%), with only 2% left for other elements, etc. Its core temperature is about 28,000,000 $^0$F (15,555,538 $^0$C) while its surface temperature approaches 10,000 $^0$F (5,537 $^0$C). The mean distance of the Sun from the Earth is about 149,600,000 km. The Sun has no surface as such - it is all gaseous - yet due to the great distance between us, we experience an illusion of a surface.

The Sun is the source of all power in our solar system. Its gravitational power keeps the planets in orbit, while the Sun's visible light reflected from the surface of other planets allows us to see them. It is ultimately responsible for all creation, preservation and destruction of all animate and inanimate things on Earth. Without the heat of the Sun, our planet would be frozen and lifeless. The Sun's rays are responsible for light and heat, and by extension, the evaporation of water from the oceans and other bodies of water, the production of winds, the growth of plants and all other living species, and other innumerable functions vital to the existence of life on the Earth.

All power hidden in fossil fuels like coal, gas or oil, or in winds and water stored in dams and in rivers as hydraulic energy, is nothing else but a form of the power of the Sun. The Sun is the reason why we experience the change of night and day and of the seasons. Its energy is the source of clouds, rain, and all of the colors we see in the sky.

Finally, the fundamental role of the Sun in the development of life on Earth is expressed in the interplay of day and night or light and darkness. The 24-hour cycle is present in virtually all plants, microorganism, insects and animals, from the simplest single cell algae to advanced biological systems like the human body. All of these organisms, simple or complex, have their own internal time-keeping system, the circadian rhythm.

## The Sun as Sustainer of Life

According to *Vedic* teachings, there is a continuous interplay of six *paribals* (key components) in this world, namely: air, water, earth, *vanaspati srushti* (plant kingdom), *jiva srushti* (the kingdom of microorganisms and insects), and *prani srushti* (the kingdom of animals and humans). These six *paribals* can maintain a state of dynamic harmony only when they interact with the Sun; only then is life created. Therefore the Sun is the source of all; it is responsible for the existence and development of all living organisms on our planet. With the use of solar energy, plants can transform water and earth into substances like oxygen, hydrogen, carbon and carbohydrates (sugar and starches), fats, and amino acids, etc. The Sun's visible light is an essential component of photosynthesis and therefore is indirectly responsible for the manufacture of all food at the microcosmic level. Solar rays provide us with not only light and heat but also food, fuel and power, without which the planet Earth would be uninhabitable.

The Sun sustains our solar system by holding all the planets on their respective orbits with its immense gravitational power. At the same time, it radiates billions of watts of energy in a near-constant flood. This energy can be harnessed directly by humans in usable forms, like heat or electricity, or indirectly via other living organisms.

The nuclear reactions taking place continuously in the Sun are responsible for its very high temperatures. This energy is created by the conversion of hydrogen into helium, where four atoms of hydrogen are transformed into one atom of helium, with about 1% of matter left over and being transformed into an enormous amount of radiant energy. Every second approximately 4,000,000 tons of matter are converted into that radiating energy. The energy released in this way in the core of the Sun slowly makes its way to the surface and is dissipated into space, where it is transferred to us as the sunlight that we see and the heat that we feel.

The Sun's electromagnetic energy is emitted over the whole electromagnetic spectrum, from X-rays to radio waves. The white light that we see is a mixture of seven colors: violet, indigo, blue, green, yellow, orange and red. Visible sunlight is only a small portion of the full electromagnetic spectrum, with invisible infrared light lying on the left of the visible spectrum and invisible ultraviolet rays (UV) lying on the right. Infrared waves are responsible for the heat that we feel, and account for about 50% of the total solar radiation that we receive on the Earth's surface. These heat-producing infrared rays are the primary cause of our climate and weather.

The ultraviolet part of the electromagnetic spectrum covers the range from 10 nm to 400 nm and is divided into three main bands: UVC from 100 nm to 280 nm, UVB from 280 nm to 315 nm and UVA from 315 nm to 400 nm (the range from 10 nm to 100 nm is taken by EUV, SUV and LUV). Of these three bands, only the UVA band passes through the atmosphere and reaches the surface of the Earth almost intact. UVC is absorbed at a level of 100% and UVB at 90% during their passage through water vapor, oxygen, ozone and carbon dioxide. Visible light is the main and essential component of photosynthesis, which generates food for plants and by extension for humans and animals as well. Any deleterious effect of the Sun on life occurs almost entirely within the ultraviolet spectrum of the Sun's rays. The quality and quantity of UV at the Earth's surface depends on solar output and on the conductivity or transmission properties of the atmosphere. The UVB part of the solar spectrum is most significant from the biological point of view. It is controlled by the amount of ozone ($O_3$) in the upper parts of the Earth's atmosphere. First the ozone is created in the stratosphere (25 to 100 km) by short-wave UV (less than 242 nm UVR), and then the absorption of UV up to 320 nm converts the ozone back to oxygen. This mechanism prevents UV of a length less than 290 nm from reaching the Earth's surface. However, due to human industrial activities this self-controlling mechanism has been upset by chlorofluorocarbons, carbon dioxide, and other gases, causing the radical depletion of the ozone layer in some places by up to 50%.

The spectrum of ultraviolet radiation at the Earth's surface is impacted by temporal, geographical and meteorological factors. For example, from 20% to 30% of total UV rays are received in the period from one hour before to one hour after mid-day, with 75% of the total received between 9 am and 3 pm. The seasons of the year also have a significant impact on the amount of rays received at the Earth's surface. Near the equator seasonal variations are rather small. The further from the equator, the less UV reaches the Earth's surface and the higher the seasonal variation. Similarly, clouds can significantly reduce ultraviolet radiation, but care should be exercised in such conditions. While light, white clouds have almost no reducing effect; heavy dark storm clouds almost completely stop UV from reaching the Earth's surface. However, it is rare that even a heavy cloud cover would stop more than 10% of radiation present on a clear day. Altitude is another factor having a strong influence on UV, with each 1000 metres' gain in altitude increasing the UV influx by about 6%. UV reflection from certain ground surfaces should also be considered; normally it only amounts to about 7% of ambient radiation. However, freshly fallen snow can increase the UV ground reflection to a level of 30% of the ambient total, and gypsum sand, such as that found in Mexico near Cancun, to 25%.

## Applications of Ultraviolet Rays in Healing

Today, doctors use the Sun's rays in a number of ways to treat diseases. Some examples of this are sunbathing, phototherapy and chromotherapy. Sunbathing should be done during the early morning hours between 8 and 10 am, since later in the day the rays may be too strong. Patients should continue to sit under the sun's rays until profuse sweating commences. Then the sweat should be rubbed off and a lukewarm bath should be taken. Exposure to solar heat should be increased gradually day by day. If this procedure is continued in the mornings and evenings for some time, tuberculosis and other germs will be destroyed. A famous *Ayurvedic* doctor said: "Sunbaths should be practiced for keeping and enhancing health. In this way, sterility or impotency, leprosy as well as *apamaya*, are rapidly removed".

Phototherapy or exposure to UVB light - in particular to the 310 nm narrow band range of UVB light - is an effective long-term treatment for many skin conditions like psoriasis, vitiligo, eczema and others. UVB phototherapy does not require additional medications or topical preparations for therapeutic benefit; only light exposure is needed. A typical treatment regime involves short exposure to UVB rays 3 to 5 times a week at a hospital or clinic. Repeated sessions may be required before results are noticeable. Almost all of the conditions that respond to UVB light are chronic problems, so continuous treatment is required to keep them in check.

Chromotherapy, also known as chromopathy or chromo-hydropathy, is another method used to cure many common disorders. It was discovered about one thousand years ago by the famous physician Avicenna. In this method, the Sun's rays are captured in clean well water, which has been poured into bottles made of glass of a specified color. The bottles are corked and left in the Sun for three to four hours during the mid-day period. Such water can then be used internally or externally to heal many varied health problems, such as skin diseases, nervous and respiratory disorders, problems with urinary organs, rheumatism, gout etc. Another version of chromopathy is exposing the patient to rays of light reflected through colored glass, the color of which depends on the medical problem. One form of this technique used today in some sophisticated water filters ensures both the chemical purity of the water and the recharging of water molecules with solar energy.

Ultraviolet light from the Sun has antiseptic properties and can be used to sanitize tools and water.

## The Effects of Ultraviolet Light on Humans

Since ultraviolet rays have a low penetration factor on human tissues, noticeable effects of exposure to UV light in people are limited to the skin and the eyes.

Effects on the skin can be categorized as acute and chronic. Acute effects are of short duration while chronic effects are of long. Examples of acute duration effects are vitamin D production, tanning, and sunburn. Examples of chronic effects are skin cancer or photo-aging, both of which are caused by repeated and prolonged exposure to UV light.

The color of the skin is an important factor in determining the acuteness and severity of the skin response to UV rays. Usually, more pigmented skin is more resistant to UV light. For example darkly pigmented skin, such as found on Africans or South Indians, is not normally sunburned. Erythemal sensitivity can be judged at midday in summer with direct sun exposure for 45-60 minutes; based on the skin response, individuals can be grouped into six sun-reactive skin types. Sensitivity of the skin of the limbs is a quarter of that of the face, neck or trunk. Such anatomical differences are increased by the different levels of exposure to which different parts of the body are normally subject; for example, vertical and upright surfaces receive only 50% of ambient UV radiation, while horizontal surfaces receive close to 75%. In addition, erythemal sensitivity changes with age, with young and old people displaying much more sensitivity. There is no noticeable gender related difference in erythemal sensitivity.

Photo-aging is a characteristic of deep structural change in the skin with symptoms like deep wrinkles, dryness, sagging, loss of elasticity, accentuated skin furrows, and mottled pigmentation. In 80% of photo-aging cases the causative damage is believed to have occurred in the first 20 years of life. Sunscreen has been shown to inhibit this process if it contains protection against UVA and UVB light, and if the skin has the capacity to self-repair. Non-melanoma skin cancer (NMSC) is another affliction, which is caused by long exposure to UV light, and it is the most common type of human cancer. Malignant melanoma is another type of cancer derived from melanocytes (pigment cells) of the skin. The changing pattern of solar activity is believed to be the main factor in the increase of this kind of cancer.

The effects of the Sun's UV rays on the eyes can be divided into three, those on the cornea, on the lens and on the retina. The cornea is impacted negatively by UV light in two kinds of environment particularly snow fields and deserts or large beaches. The resulting condition is known as "snow blindness" (clinical name: photokeratitis). It will occur after about two hours of midday exposure to the Sun in snow covered areas, while in areas of sand about eight hours of exposure would be necessary. Some studies have shown a direct connection between exposure to UVB and the development of a certain type of cataract. A simple antidote is to use proper sunglasses with anti UVB protection. The retina can suffer irreversible photochemical and/or thermal damage. The strength of radiation from the crescent Sun during an eclipse with 99% of the Sun's surface obscured is sufficient to cause retinal burning, even when the level of illumination is equivalent to twilight.

## The Implication of Ultraviolet Rays for Suryanamaskar Practice

Since this practice is traditionally performed in the early morning, there are certain issues that need to be considered:

1) Traditionally it is practiced at dawn, at which time the impact of UV on the Earth is minimal.

2) If it is done at other times, especially during the mid-day period, it should be done in the shade (unless the location is far to the north or south of the equator, and the season is winter).

3) Since a rise in altitude influences the concentration of UV rays, people living at higher levels should take this fact into consideration when doing their practice.

4) People with fair skin need to give more care and attention to UV rays; dark people are less sensitive and less susceptible to the harmful effects of UV rays.

5) Clouds stop or reduce infrared radiation but not necessarily UV, especially when the clouds are light and white. Ignoring this fact may increase UV damage, since

the person may well not feel any heat while possibly still receiving close to the full amount of UV radiation, especially if relatively long periods are spent in the open.

6) During normal practice, UV exposure does not pose a threat since it takes so little time to complete an entire Suryanamaskar practice.

7) People with sensitive skin should apply sunscreen.

## Benefits of the Sun's Rays on Humans

- Promotes the production of vitamin D in the body.
- Increases the efficiency of the heart in pumping blood, and that can be observed on the improved EKG reading.
- Lowers blood pressure.
- Reduces the level of cholesterol.
- Reduces hypertension.
- Increases the level of estrogen and testosterone.
- Increases the production of solitrol, a hormone that affects mood[1].
- Stimulates the pineal gland, which produces many important secretions[2].

[1] Exposure to sunlight activates a hormone in the skin called 'solitrol' (also called the 'sun hormone'). This hormone is a form of vitamin D3, which works in an antagonistic way to melatonin. Together with melatonin it regulates the whole body, including the immunological system, mood, circadian rhythms, and seasonal reactions (Stumpf, 1988, pp.209-19).

[2] The pineal gland secretes melatonin at night for a length of time that is directly proportional to the period of darkness to which the organism is exposed.

- Assists in weight loss.
- Is an effective treatment for skin diseases like psoriasis, eczema, etc.
- Helps to ameliorate asthma and other lung disorders.

# PART - II

- Suryanamaskar and Physical Exercise
- The Practice
- Shavasana
- Mantras
- Psychic Centers
- Digestive Considerations
- Digestive Leukocytosis or Pathological Leukocytosis
- Toxins
- Hints

# 5

# SURYANAMASKAR AND PHYSICAL EXERCISE

The practice of Suryanamaskar as a complete and perfect blend of body movement, breath and concentration is used in many Indian schools and ashrams. It was considered by the ancients of India to be a form of *kriya* (purification), or body oblation, which would give an abundance of health, vitality and spiritual upliftment. The fact that some authors call it *kriya* indicates its strong purification qualities. The routine differs greatly from source to source with regards to the recommended pace of movement, number of repetitions, sequence of *asanas* and the emotional approach, i.e. whether as ritual worship or physical exercise. In ritual form, the movements are accomplished very slowly with devotion and mantra repetition; the central posture is the *Ashtanga Namaskar*. The exercise version, on the other hand, requires a high number of repetitions to be performed quickly, typically more than 200 rounds at less than 20 seconds per round.

Dr. Swami Gitananda from Ananda Ashram in Pondicherry

reported that he was able to identify 17 such distinct Suryanamaskar routines. Other sources mention even up to 50 such routines followed in different parts of India. Such richness of diverse forms of this sequence of *asanas* makes it very unlikely that Suryanamaskar would be a modern procedure invented in the nineteenth century [3]. Because they were frequently performed as a part of a ritual, these routines were often renamed, and now one can find such names as *Chandra Namaskar,Guru Namaskar, Hanuman Namaskar, KshatrianKriya,* etc. Of course, they differ with regard to the body movements used but the main idea of the original Suryanamaskar remains intact.

For example, in the introduction to his book *Guru Namaskara,* Swami Shri Raghavendra says that "Suryanamaskar is a method of worshipping the Sun, whereas Guru Namaskar is a method of worshipping Shri Maruthi (Hanuman)…It is also an ancient method of *sadhana* as Surya Namaskar". He also writes:

> "Our ancient *Rishis* called it *Upasana* or worship and founded an integral system that included those physical exercises also such as *asana* and *pranayama*. The practice of both

[3] Some Western scholars take a narrow view of the word 'origin' and question the ancient origins of Suryanamaskar. They hold the view that an old manuscript with the exact sequence of the whole practice should be present for it to be regarded as ancient, and therefore classify Suryanamaskar as a contemporary physical exercise, which was invented by Raja of Aundh. It is worthwhile to note that the Raja of Aundh himself never claimed to have invented Suryanamaskar and, furthermore, he stressed the ancient origins of this practice.

*Surya* and *Guru Namaskar* provide harmonious exercise to the entire body of the *sadhaka*. In addition, this practice provides the spiritual growth also, as it includes a system of worship which is supplementary to devotion, faith and spirituality."

Dr. Swami Gitananda in his book on Suryanamaskar discusses five styles: the Simple Suryanamaskar (11 movements) that goes back to *Vedic* times; a system as taught by the late Yogiraj M.R. Raja Rao (11 movements); the Rishikesh Series propagated by the disciples of the late Shri Swami Shivananda which was first expounded by Shrimant Balasahib Pandit Pratinidhi B.A. the late Raja of Aundh (variations from 11 to 14 movements); the Three-Part Suryanamaskar (27 movements or another variation with 33 movements); and Chandra Namaskar (16 movements). He concludes that "The oldest form of worship on this planet would have to be the worship of the core of our natural existence, the sun, the great star". After their morning meditations and ablutions, yogis would toss water towards the Sun's rays, do *pranayama*, recite mantras, gesticulate and genuflect to the Sun, which they considered to be god. However, the differences in the traditional styles are not that great and often quite insignificant. Besides the styles and variations described above Dr. Ananda Balayogi Bhavanani mentions in his book *Surya Namaskar – An expression of our gratitude to life* three different versions of Vedic Surya Namaskar, two versions of Aruna Surya Namaskar, Maha Sauri Surya Namaskar, and a couple of techniques used for propitiating the solar divinity. These latter two techniques are known by the names Jnana Surya Kriya and Surya Prana Mudra.

Most of the *asanas* in the sequence have themselves been documented in the literature. *Sashtanga dandavat*, the central *asana* of Suryanamaskar, has been practiced in India, from time immemorial, as a form of showing respect and complete surrender to God. *Bhujangasana* is described as one of the 32 most important *asanas* in the *Gheranda Samhita* (dated around 1650 C.E.), which describes the Yoga prevalent in North-East India. The *adhomukh swanasan* is described in the old wrestling text *Mallapurana* (dated before 1750). *Sarpasana* (*bhujangasana*), *gajasana* (*adhomukh swànnasana*), *uttanasana* and the series of postures done in tandem which are similar to Suryanamaskar are all described in the *Sritattvanidhi*, which was written on the request of Krishnaraja Wodeyar III (1799-1868) to capture the complete Indian traditional knowledge of his time.

The use of Suryanamaskar for physical exercise is also not modern. On page 61 of the book *A Short History of Aryan Medical Science* published in 1896, Bhagavat Simhaji says:

> "There are various kinds of physical exercise indoors and outdoors. But some of the Hindoos set aside a portion of their daily worship for making salutations to the Sun by prostrations. This method of adoration affords them so much muscular activity that it takes to some extent the place of physical exercise".

Historical sources say that in the seventeenth century the great national hero of India and of the state of Maharashtra in particular, Shivaji Maharaj, applied the practice of

*Suryanamaskar* to the training of his army of resistance fighters, when preparing it to fight against the Muslim invaders. Numerically much weaker, forced to act in secret, and using the principles of guerrilla warfare, they could not openly practice their skills. That is the reason why the sequence of exercises called *Suryanamaskar,* requiring no more than two square meters of space, were so useful. Shivaji Maharaj had learned the technique from his guru, one of the most well known sages and reformers from the state of Maharashtra, Shri Samarth Ramdas, who, in turn, as a young yogi had practiced it with great perseverance in the holy city of Nashik on the banks of the river Godavari. Ramdas mentions it in his philosophical treatise *'Dasbodh'*. Historical records mention that Ramdas practiced daily more than 1,200 rounds of *Suryanamaskar*. It is not surprising that someone interested in spiritual development should spend so much time and energy on physical training. In India almost all physical practices (*vyayama*) are rooted in spiritual values, and spiritual practice has long been considered a part of the physical training. The *Suryanamaskar* training enabled the partisans (Marathas), who were far fewer in number than their opponents, to win most of their battles against the much more powerful regular army of the Mogul rulers.

The benefits of a Suryanamaskar practice are so wonderful and so many that for example, in the late 1940s, Shrimant Bhavanrao Pant Pratinidhi (1868-1951), Raja of Aundh (1909-1947) made Suryanamaskar a compulsory part of the physical training program in his kingdom's schools. He helped to popularize Suryanamaskar as a simple physical exercise for the full development of individuals. Similarly, P. K. Bhattacharia, the director of the Department of Physical Education at Shri Aurobindo Ashram, says in his booklet:

> "... a complete cycle of Suryanamaskar consists of ten or twelve movements ...... through which one gets a good stretch and thorough exercise of the whole body. The body thus becomes strong, supple, agile and healthy. Suryanamaskar is a system of exercise for a common man."

In fact, some experts, including *Ayurvedic* physicians, consider Suryanamaskar to be "the crest jewel of exercises". It is so highly regarded that entire books have been written on this single practice.

Suryanamaskar's application and versatility make it one of the most useful and complete methods to bring about health and vigor while at the same time preparing adepts for the deeper processes of yoga. It is based on three elements: rhythm, energy and form. Form is evident in the 12 *asanas,* which are always performed in the same sequence. Such a steady and continuous performance of *asana,* which are coordinated with the breath, activates the subtle energy called *prana* in yoga. This steady and rhythmic flow reflects the rhythm of the universe, such as biorhythms of the body, which were expressed in the past by the science of the 12 zodiac phases. The rhythmic superimposition of the form and energy of Suryanamaskar on our psychosomatic organism is a transforming force since it activates the psychic body in a way that is completely different way from modern sports or games.

In this book, we will be concerned only with one form of the Suryanamaskar sequence known as the *Rishikesh Series* developed by Swami Shivananda of Rishikesh and later propagated among others by his disciple Swami Satyananda of the Bihar School of Yoga. The *Rishikesh Series* appears to be the leading style, especially in the North of India.

The basic principles of Suryanamaskar practice would not be complete without considering briefly some nutritional issues and concerns, and their relevance to a successful Suryanamaskar training. Nutritional issues are so important that the classical *hatha* yogic texts like the *Hathapradipika* or *Gheranda Samhita* deal with food issues in the very first chapter (*Prathamopadeshah*).

## Levels of Suryanamaskar Practice in Brief

There are several levels of practice and mastery of this technique. For example, *Ayurvedic* guidelines refer to three methods of practice, each one uniquely facilitating one of the three *doshas*: *vata, kapha* or *pitta*. Yogic guidelines, however, suggest four levels.

Beginners should start learning the sequence slowly, paying careful attention to each posture and its many salient features. Therefore, after assuming each and every posture, one should maintain it for several breaths before moving on to the next one. During this time, one should 'rotate consciousness' through each and every posture and correct any problems before moving on to the next one. This is the first and introductory level.

The second level starts when a practitioner has memorized all the postures, is able to co-ordinate each posture with his/her breathing and the flow of the practice is smooth and without jerky movements. At this level, the practice should mature to the point where major adjustments are not needed anymore, and only micro-adjustments may be required.

The third level starts when the co-ordination of movement and breath is automatic, so that all of the practitioner's attention may be focused on the mantras. There are *bija* mantras or special *Surya* (solar) mantras, which can be repeated aloud or silently during this third level of practice.

The fourth level is considered the most advanced and requires performing each round of the Suryanamaskar sequence in about 7.5 seconds, making 40 rounds per 5 minutes. According to a newly discovered scripture titled *AsanaYoga - Hathabhasyapaddhati* by Kapalakurantaka, one needs to do at least several hundred rounds in this manner. More advanced *sadhakas* may even increase the number of rounds to several thousand.

Suryanamaskar should never be treated as a mere physical exercise or as something incidental which simply precedes or follows Yoga *asanas*. Therefore, it is recommended that before beginning Suryanamaskar, we pray to *Surya* to bestow the good fortune of having only good thoughts, of hearing and speaking only good words, and of attaining a sound and strong body so that we may live a healthy life and achieve identity with *Paramatma*. One of the better known teachers of the past century, T. Krishnamacharya, often suggested the following greeting to be repeated inwardly in the heart before Suryanamaskar practice would start: "I honor the Divinity of my heart with all the warmth and cordiality of my mind".

## Suryanamaskar is for All

Any person with a sound body, from any walk of life, and with any background, may, from the age of eight, start doing the practice and continue throughout the entire span of life. It is not generally recommended for children below the age of eight to start the practice because they are always on the go and are very physically active. It can be done by men, women and children, young or old, slim or fat, whether in poor health (after a medical check-up) or in top condition, and of any creed or faith. The twelve positions will especially be beneficial to people who lead a sedentary way of life in their mid-30s and above. It is never too late to start Suryanamaskar, but for a young person it may be easier and take less time to master the positions and sequence. People who are overweight or are just skin-and-bones will come to develop a proper body size and shape after only a few months of continued practice. For example, the slim will gain strong and shapely muscles and perhaps gain some weight, while those who are overweight may lose some fat and instead gain firm muscles. Even people with disease or with permanently incapacitated lower extremities can experience some of the benefits of Suryanamaskar by using the specially modified form of the practice routine described in the appendix on page 260. On the other hand the elite form of *Suryanamaskar* practice as pranayama at a very advanced stage is described in the appendix on page 264 (*Purna-Suryanamaskar: intensive practice using the Mahayoga method*) and it is called *Purna Suryanamaskar*. For this advanced practice one can also use the Rishikesh Series sequence as described in detail in this book. Having learned the routine, you will be able to use it as a 'toolbox' to sculpt your body, mind, and spirit, whatever your objectives: for example, to develop strength or cardiovascular endurance, to increase flexibility, to lose fatty tissue, or to dive into deeper spirituality, etc. In setting such objectives, common sense is needed just as in every other activity of life.

## Number and Duration

Each Suryanamaskar cycle consists of two rounds and each round consists of twelve yogic *asanas* (postures) performed in one continuous flow. The sequence of *asanas* remains constant, so once learned it is easy to remember. The basic way to perform Suryanamaskar is to do it slowly at one's own pace, pausing and holding each posture for up to 5 seconds. More advanced practitioners may increase their speed gradually, reducing the hold in each *asana* so that the whole practice looks more like one uniform wave or flow. There are no set rules as to how many Suryanamaskar cycles should be performed. However, to attain the basic fitness benefits as defined by the World Health Organization, a daily practice of only 15 to 20 minutes should be enough, though 25 to 30 minutes would be optimal. This would be the equivalent of doing an amount from 12 rounds (6 cycles) of Suryanamaskar to 24 rounds (12 cycles). A beginner would start with only 2 or 3 cycles and would work up to the numbers specified below.

Children between the ages of 8 and 14 years of age would work up to performing from 12 to 24 cycles of Suryanamaskar per session once per day.

Adolescents between the ages of 15 and 18 years of age would work up to performing from 24 to 54 cycles (108 rounds) in one session per day. Experience has shown that Indian girls in this latter age group, after some time of practice, can, on average, easily perform about half of the recommended cycles.

All men, including young adult men, should perform a minimum of 54 cycles while women should perform a minimum of 27 cycles. This will ensure a proper fitness level throughout the full span of life. At more advanced levels of the practice, this number of cycles should not take more time than 25 minutes to complete. For example, a person in good health and with a properly trained body would take less than 15 minutes to complete 54 cycles of Suryanamaskar at the fourth level of performance. However, individuals seeking an optimal peak performance in their overall fitness should do many more cycles, depending on the available time and their health condition. Committed individuals can complete 504 cycles (1008 rounds) in only a few hours' time. World-class sportsmen use Suryanamaskar practice as their warm-up and general conditioning exercise, performing it in sets of several hundred. They attribute their long life in professional sports to their regular daily practice of Suryanamaskar.

When allocating time for practice, be sure to allow enough for 5 to 8 minutes of *shavasana* (corpse pose) at the end of the session.

To determine the appropriate number of cycles of Suryanamaskar to do, the golden rule is that the after-practice experience of enthusiasm and exhilaration should outweigh the experience of fatigue and exhaustion. Suryanamaskar is a powerful practice, therefore it is better to start humbly with a small number of rounds, and then slowly but steadily increase it, so that you can enjoy it all along the way.

## Helpful Points before We Start

1) The best time to practice is before the sun rises (*Brahma muhurta* time). If this ideal time proves impossible to keep, try to do it soon after getting up. The next best time is at sunset. However, if practice is not possible at either sunrise or sunset, try to do it as close as possible to these times, either in the morning or evening. Of course, any time of the day is better than none. The stomach should be empty, i.e. at least 2 to 3 hours should have elapsed after eating or 45 minutes after drinking. In other words, your stomach and digestive system should be light and at rest.

2) Suryanamaskar should be done after nature calls and you have bathed, but before you complete your daily worship, *sandhya vandana* or *pranayama*. That way, you will remain alertly aware during the later stationary activities.

3) It is best to practice Suryanamaskar in an open space with a free flow of air or in an airy room or hall.

4) The surface of the ground or floor should be flat and smooth, without any depressions or mounds. Crucially, the surface should not be slippery, which is especially important once you move to more advanced levels and start sweating heavily onto the ground or floor, which can make it extremely slippery. Using special yoga cotton mats is helpful (I recommend the *duree* mat); even rubber yoga mats can become soaked with sweat, absorbing it like a sponge, and thus becoming as slippery as uncovered ground or floor.

5) While performing Suryanamaskar in the open, face the Sun. Otherwise follow the general rule that all yogic practice is done with an alignment of East-West or North-South.

6) Warming up or limbering up prior to Suryanamaskar is unnecessary since the practice is designed to do it for you.

7) Take a shower prior to the practice and also after it, especially if completing many rounds has caused you to sweat. Room temperature water is the best. Alternatively, you may take a hot and cold shower. Showers are stimulating and invigorating, and are therefore preferable to a bath.

8) At the beginning it may be advantageous to practice in a group, which creates liveliness and enthusiasm, and is good both for motivation and the possibility of getting quick help. As you advance and individualize your practice, it is much better to do it by yourself. Yogis

have always done their practices privately since 'going within' is one of the most important features of any yogic practice.

9) The 12 *asanas* should be done in a smooth and relaxed manner. Jerky movements should be avoided. The quality of the practice is more important than the quantity.

10) When you start Suryanamaskar you may experience some tight muscles, joint aches or pain. You should withstand this type of discomfort because as soon as your body adjusts to the practice, it will pass. However, if you still feel pain after doing the practice for some time, return slowly to the original standing position, relax, and try it the next day again.

11) Wear the minimum clothing possible to permit your skin to breath and sweat freely, to allow your body unrestricted movement and to absorb the Sun's rays. Wearing minimal clothing is another reason to keep your Yoga private.

12) Feel receptive from within. I cannot emphasize strongly enough the importance of this inner *bhava* (attitude). Perhaps this is the most important point of the preparatory phase. You will be unable to receive anything unless you are receptive.

13) It is important that after performing Suryanamaskar, you allow yourself a few minutes to relax completely. *Shavasana* (the corpse pose) is the perfect *asana* with which to end your practice.

# 6

# THE PRACTICE

As you get ready to start your first practice, reflect on the difference between the exercise (*vyayama*) and a posture or a 'postural pattern' (*asana*). These concepts are often misunderstood.

## Asana vs. Vyayama

Most of us are educated and trained at home, in schools and in colleges, as well as in society to execute our decisions as voluntary actions and activities. These activities are external goal-oriented actions and behaviors, which both use and focus the sense organs and extremities on the external world. We are naturally motivated to engage in exercises to make the muscles of our body fit and strong for external work, e.g. by walking, running, jumping, kicking, pushing, pulling, lifting heavy weights, manipulating objects of all kinds, etc.

At the same time, Yoga stresses observing or witnessing what you are doing as well as what is happening inside the body as you do it. Even though we often move and are aware of voluntary actions, automatic movements take place all of the time and Yoga asks us to observe these movements too. Learning to witness these automatic movements along with their various psycho-physical attributes is an important yogic skill which may lead to perceiving and experiencing subtle happenings related to your survival activities, even when you are not actively involved with the external world. Learning this passive observation proves very helpful in the later, more advanced practice of various yogic techniques and methods.

Through yogic practices, you can learn to recognize the differences between these two modes of behaving. Understanding and reflecting on the differences between the attitude of the 'doer' and the attitude of the observer or witness can help you differentiate the experience of doing exercise from the experience of automatic processes happening inside your body. Maintaining this dual awareness during voluntary exercise will help strengthen your practice.

Practices can be done in a number of ways. The simple position of the body when in an *asana* is not sufficient to judge whether that form of exercise belongs to the system of Yoga or not. For example, consider the basic definition of *asana* and its potential implications on body positioning. Patanjali declares that *asana* should be comfortable and steady. The analysis of his *sutra "sthirasukhamasanam"* (P.Y.S. II.46) allows the ways of performing it as indicated in the box below:

As you can see the external appearance of the body position may look quite similar, yet out of the four possible ways

| | No tension (comfortable) | With tension |
|---|---|---|
| **Without movement** (steady) | classical Yoga (*asana*) | isometric Yoga |
| **With movement** | Yoga exercise | isometric exercise |

of performing the posture, only one can be qualified as an *asana* in the classical sense of the word. Such diverse ways of performing the same body position bring very different psycho-physiological responses and, over longer periods of time, adaptation.

Normally, while doing any voluntary action like physical exercise (*vyayama*), we have to make conscious decisions, which are then acted out. That fact by itself must involve the frontal cortex. Such decisions will be executed by the motor cortex, which is located close to the frontal cortex. As a result neurotransmitters and chemo-regulators will cause the outflow of nerve impulses to the muscles and glands affecting muscle tone and glandular secretions. We do not notice that reaction as it takes place completely below our level of awareness. However, we can experience these physical movements through various kinesthetic perceptions, which come from our muscles, ligaments, tendons and joint capsules. After the execution of a movement has been completed, muscle tone stays up for some time before returning to its tonic condition awaiting another 'command' from the central nervous system (C.N.S.). This period varies from individual to individual and depends on the organism's psycho-physiological condition.

| Exercise | Yoga | Suryanamaskar (Fourth Level) |
|---|---|---|
| Sympathetic nervous system predominant. | Parasympathetic nervous system predominant. | Sympathetic nervous system predominant. |
| Cortical regions of brain predominant. | Sub-cortical regions of brain predominant. | Cortical regions of brain predominant. |
| Rapid forceful movements. | Static positions and slow relaxed movements. | Fast relaxed movements. |
| Increased muscle tension. | Normalization of muscle tone. | Normalization of muscle tone. |
| High risk of injury. | Low risk of injuring bones, joints, muscles and ligaments. | Low risk of injuring bones, joints, muscles and ligaments. |
| Moderate to high caloric consumption. | Low to very low caloric consumption. | High caloric consumption. |
| Effort is maximized. | Effort is minimized, relaxed. | Effort is maximized. |
| Fatiguing (breathing is taxed). | Energizing (breathing is natural or controlled). | Energizing (breathing is natural or controlled); a 'pranic generator'. |
| Unbalanced activity of opposing muscle groups. | Balanced activity of opposing muscle groups. | Balanced activity of opposing muscle groups. |
| Competitive, goal-oriented. | Non-competitive, process-oriented. | Non-competitive, process-oriented. |

| Balance of awareness between external and internal* varies according to the nature of the exercise. | Awareness is internal* (focus is on breathing and the infinite). | Balance of awareness is primarily internal* (focus is primarily on breathing and the infinite). |
| --- | --- | --- |
| Scope for growth in externally related self-awareness. | Limitless possibilities for growth in internally related self-awareness. | Limitless possibilities for growth in internally related self-awareness. |

* 'Internal' awareness includes but is not confined to awareness of the physical body.

**TABLE 1:** Characteristics of conventional exercise compared to Yoga and Suryanamaskar for an accomplished practitioner in each case.

*Asana* differs from exercise as the muscles do not develop tension. *Asana* indicates a stabilized body in the most economical way. It is sustained and controlled from the cerebellum level instead of the frontal cortex, because the cerebellum is the structure of the C.N.S., which maintains posture, tone, and equilibrium. That way a great number of body positions can be executed either as *asanas* or as *vyayamas*. In *asana,* we remain ourselves (the 'being' aspect is emphasized over the 'becoming') while in exercise we want to 'become' someone like a runner, swimmer, etc., and we start to exteriorize ourselves.

Our inner attitude affects how we execute an activity. If we are trying to "get on with life" and be prepared for it, we have to exteriorize ourselves and so our muscle tone changes to tension. This residual tension does not ever disappear completely; it does not allow muscles to return to their original tonic state and so tension starts to accumulate over time. In this way, we start consciously to experience increased tension, stress, and eventually pain.

Yoga is a discipline, which favors perceiving, purifying and realizing our true self. Becoming a witness or an observer is an important step in that process. This attitude is geared towards recognizing tension, stress or pain and as a result of such recognition we start looking for a way out. By gaining skill in the practice, we can easily witness our thoughts, feelings or memories. The attitude maintained during Suryanamaskar practice is very important; we should strive to feel receptive from within. To receive, you must be receptive.

## Building Blocks of Suryanamaskar

The building blocks of Suryanamaskar are as follows: form (*asanas*), yogic breath (*pranayama*), concentration (*dharana*), mantras (*Surya* and/or *bija*), rhythm and energy, and a period of relaxation at the end of each Suryanamaskar session.

## Form

### Position 1

**Pranamasana** (Prayer Pose)

1) Stand upright at the front of your yoga mat facing the

Sun in a relaxed but attentive position.

2) Stand with your feet hip-width apart, so that your ankles rest comfortable beneath your hips approximately 10-15 cm (4-6 in) apart. When you start mastering the sequence you may bring your feet together, but this requires better balance.

3) Your heels, the back of your trunk and the back of your head should be aligned in a vertical line. Your chest should protrude forward while you draw in your abdomen.

4) Fold your palms in the *Namaskara Mudra* in front of your chest: your palms should press against each other with sufficient force, such that a sheet of paper could be held between them without letting anyone take it away.

5) Look forward towards the Sun and stand well balanced by equally distributing your body weight on the soles of your feet. If the Sun is not present, visualize it.

6) Assume a prayerful and receptive mood; your mind should be focused on the Sun.

7) Maintain normal inhalation and exhalation and focus your attention on your breath. Before starting your

first Suryanamaskar round, take a few deeper breaths. When you are ready, start with an exhalation. During the following rounds, you will do only exhalation in this posture.

**Benefits:**

This *asana* helps us reach a state of inner focus and calm, and strongly activates the *anahata chakra*. One of the definitions of Yoga is *samatva* that is balance, equilibrium, equality, sameness, evenness, etc. Through this *asana*, try to experience *samatva*, even in the very limited and restricted sense of weight distribution and transfer of body weight. By maintaining awareness, observe whether you are experiencing *samatva* or *asamatva* in your body. If you notice any imbalances working at the level of the body, then remove or correct them with the help of proper techniques, yogic or otherwise.

**Position 2**

**Hasta Uttanasana** (Raised Arms Pose)

1) While inhaling, raise your arms in front of you.

2) Stretch your arms forward while moving them out and then upwards. Arc your chest to increase the movement without moving the lower part of your body, while increasing tension in your buttocks.

3) Complete your inhalation at the same time you complete the maximum stretch backwards. N.b. that while stretching your arms back, your trunk and your head

should also follow the stretch.

4) Remember that it is a stretch back-ward and not a bend backward, which means the energy and the focus of the movement rests in the front of the body, not in the back. It should feel like someone is behind you, trying to lift you backwards by holding your wrists.

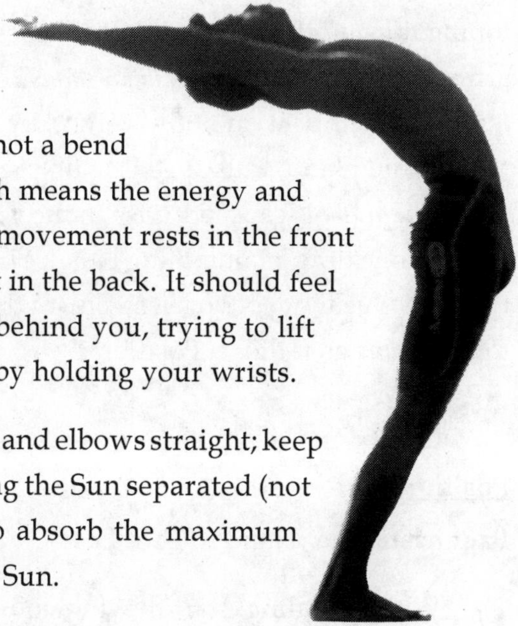

5) Keep your knees and elbows straight; keep your palms facing the Sun separated (not joined) trying to absorb the maximum energy from the Sun.

6) Your eyes should be fixed on a point in the general direction of (not look directly or stare at) the Sun and not follow the movement of your fingertips.

7) Remember to maintain a prayerful and receptive mood throughout the Suryanamaskar practice.

**Benefits:**

While the muscles of the neck and back are relaxed, the front of the body (chest and abdomen) is stretched. Combined with the deep inhalation, this gives an excellent massage to the organs of the abdominal area which improves digestion. At the same time, the elasticity of lungs and your vital capacity is increased. The flexibility of the spine increases as the upwards stretch gives it traction, which helps to maintain the cartilage discs (meniscus) between the vertebrae and tones spinal nerves. By toning the muscles of the abdomen, chest, forearms and upper arms, the benefits of *ardha chakrasana* are accrued. There is also a favorable impact on body weight, by virtue of activation of the thyroid gland, thus speeding up the metabolic rate. In this position, *prana* is caused to rise to the upper parts of the body. At the same time, maintaining balance in this *asana* extends the restricted meaning of yoga as *samatva* (balance or equilibrium) to this *asana* as it did in Position 1.

## Position 3

**Padahastasana** (Hand to Foot Pose)

1) While exhaling, start moving your arms, head and trunk forward and then downward. This movement should be initiated from the hip joints only, while the straight line from the hips to the fingertips is rigorously maintained.

2) When your upper body is parallel to the ground (at a 90 degree angle to your legs), check again that you form a straight line from your hips to your fingertips.

3) Remember that this is a *stretch* forward and not a bend forward, which means the energy and the focus are in the back. The

movement starts from the back of the body, from the back of your hips. The feeling is as if someone is trying to pull you forwards and then downwards by holding your wrists.

4) Keep your knees and elbows straight.

5) Your eyes should follow the movement of your fingertips.

6) Place your palms flat on the ground at your feet, approximately shoulder-width apart; your fingers can be spread out to enhance the grip of the floor. For the very flexible and those whose pace is relatively slow, imagine that one straight line runs from approximately the tip of the middle finger of both hands to the tip of the big toe of both feet. For those with less flexibility or whose pace is quicker, if it is more comfortable, use a line from the tip of the little finger or even from the wrist. Adjust your body as required.

7) Press your palms to the floor and push back your pelvis, then bring your head as close to your knees as possible, if possible touching your forehead to the knee caps.

8) Touch your chin to your chest if possible.

9) Complete your exhalation about the same time you complete the maximum stretch forward.

10) Remember to maintain a prayerful and receptive mood throughout the Suryanamaskar practice.

**Benefits:**

This posture combines the effects of the inverted postures with the effects of the forward stretching posture. It increases the suppleness of spine while at the same time improving the functioning of the abdominal glands and other digestive functions. It increases blood supply to the facial muscles, eyes and brain. It helps to improve the nervous system, concentration and memory. It massages all the abdominal viscera by increasing inner pressure of the abdominal cavity, thus pushing out the 'old' blood and allowing 'new' blood to replace it. The whole abdomen is toned, thereby eliminating many ailments such as constipation and other digestive problems while increasing digestive power. A healthy flow of blood passes to the spinal nerves, nourishing them as the inter-vertebrae space opens up. In this position, all the back muscles of the body are vigorously stretched (hamstring, calf, lower back and upper back) thereby relieving varicose veins and allowing blood to return more quickly to the heart. Women are benefited by having any prolapsed and menstrual irregularities relieved.

**Position 4**

**Ashwa Sanchalanasana** (Equestrian Pose)

1) While inhaling, start lowering your hips and at the same time press down hard on your palms. Stretch your left leg

backwards by sliding its toes along the floor in the final phase. Rest firmly on your left toes and your left knee.

2) While extending your left leg backward, push your hips down. At the same time, raise your trunk and your head.

3) While you are extending your left leg, bend your right knee forward.

4) Push forward your chest and stretch your head, neck and shoulders backwards as far as possible, arcing the spine backwards as far as possible.

5) Your palms and right foot should remain flat, approximately shoulder-width apart outside your right foot. There should be no movement or any change from Position 3. Again, for the very flexible and those whose pace is relatively slow, imagine that one straight line runs from approximately the tip of the middle finger of

both hands to the tip of the big toe of the forward foot. For those with less flexibility or whose pace is quicker, if it is more comfortable, use a line from the tip of the little finger or even from the wrist.

6) Remember that this is a stretch backward and not a bend backward, which means that the energy and focus of the stretch is in the front; movement takes place from the front of the body, not from the back. Pull your waist down while at the same time pulling your shoulders and head up and backwards.

7) Try to see the sky or the ceiling with your eyes facing upwards.

8) Complete your inhalation about the same time you have completed the maximum stretch backward.

9) In order to complete one full cycle, the next round should be done by stretching your right leg backward. Remember to maintain a prayerful and receptive mood throughout the Suryanamaskar practice.

**Benefits:**

The main stretch is in the pelvic region, which is pushed down and forward. This position activates *Surya nadi,* leading to a toning of sympathetic nervous system functions. It improves eyesight as you gaze up. It improves functioning of the thyroid glands as the throat is stretched up. It tones the lungs and improves the function of the abdominal glands. It tones calf muscles and thigh muscles. In this backward stretch, back muscles are toned at the same time as the front body muscles are stretched. Again, the viscera are massaged by increasing pressure in the abdominal cavity while taking a full inhalation.

## Position 5

**Parvatasana** (Mountain Pose)

1) While exhaling, stretch the entire length of your bent right leg along the side of your extended left leg by sliding it along the floor. Rest firmly on your right toes. In the initial phase of this position, both of your legs are straight, their knees are above the ground and the feet are supported on the toes while the feet are perpendicular to the floor. Head, trunk and legs should form a straight slanted line, and eyes should look down towards the floor.

2) Keep your knees and elbows straight.

3) In the second phase of this position, lift your hips as high as possible to bring your body to the "inverted V posture" without shifting your palms or toes. Place your feet fully on the floor so that the soles of your feet maintain full contact with the ground, pressing against it evenly.

4) Your head should rest between your upper arms with an effort to bring the chin as close to your chest as possible. Your spine should not be arced or curved in any way. There should be a straight line from your hips to your palms resting on the floor in one direction and a similarly straight line from the hips towards the heels in the other.

5) Push your chest and shoulders downwards.

6) Your eyes should be looking at your navel.

7) Remember that this is a forward stretch and not a bend, which means the energy and focus are in the back. The movement starts from the back of the body, from your hips.

8) Complete your exhalation about the same time you complete the maximum stretch forwards.

9) Remember to maintain a prayerful and receptive mood throughout the Suryanamaskar practice.

**Benefits:**

This *asana* strengthens the palms, wrists and elbows. The muscles of the forearms and upper arms are also strengthened. This posture helps to relax the entire spine. It enables one to keep the body, and also mind, in a balanced state. The calf muscles, Achilles tendons, hamstring and thigh muscles are toned and stretched, just as in *shalabhasana*. The flexibility of the soles of the feet is enhanced; the toes and other feet muscles become elastic and flexible. This *asana* helps to remove the varicose veins and it tones up the spinal nerves. It stimulates the *vishuddha chakra* and improves thyroid gland functioning as the chin and throat come closer, as in *sarvangasana*. In this position *prana* moves downwards with exhalation.

**Position 6**

**Ashtanga Namaskara** (Salute with Eight Parts Pose)

1) While maintaining exhalation, lower your body to the ground and assume a prone posture in the following sequence: bend your elbows and your knees, bring down your knees to touch the floor and bend your elbows further and place your chest and your forehead on the ground. At the same time, keep your pelvis, upper thighs and lower abdomen raised as high as possible, giving a strong stretch to the lower back.

2) In the advanced stages of practice, the knees are brought down to touch the floor as the last part thus supporting

most of the body weight by the shoulders and arms. This is the mode of practice for those desiring significantly to increase the strength and strength endurance of their shoulder girdle.

3) The name of this "obeisance" posture is derived from the eight points touching the ground: two each of the feet, knees and palms, and the chest and the forehead.

4) This position is central to the whole sequence of Suryanamaskar for a spiritual practitioner as this position expresses obeisance to the Divine with complete prostration.

5) Hold your breath throughout the duration of this posture.

6) Remember to maintain a prayerful and receptive mood throughout the Suryanamaskar practice.

**Benefits:**

By accentuating the normal curvature of the spine, this *asana* sends extra blood to the spinal nerves, thus rejuvenating them. It develops the chest and strengthens the legs, arms and shoulders. *Manipura chakra* is activated as the forehead is rested on the ground, leading to self control. *Jalandhara* and *uddiyana bandhas* take place effortlessly, which is conducive for *bahir kumbhaka* (stopping the breath after exhalation), leading to stability of mind. This allows the *prana* to move down to *manipura chakra,* where the merging of *prana* and *apana* takes place in the case of the advanced *sadhaka.*

**Position 7**

**Bhujangasana** (Cobra Pose)

1) While inhaling, start stretching your head, then your neck and trunk backward while at the same time pushing forward your trunk by squeezing your shoulder blades, pushing forward your pelvis down to the floor, and tensing your buttocks.

2) Raise first your head, and then continue with your neck, upper trunk and lower trunk, down to your navel. Continue until you fully arch your spine and your elbows are straight.

3) Lower the body from the waist; your feet should be parallel to the ground.

4) Keep your knees and elbows straight, and your buttock muscles firm in the final posture.

5) Try to see the sky or the ceiling with your eyes facing upwards.

6) Remember that this is a backwards stretch and not a bend, which means the energy and the focus are in the

front; the movement starts from the front of the body. This position is accomplished not by pushing up with the strength of your arms, but by pulling it up with your (deep) back muscles. Only in the final phase of assuming this posture may one use the muscles of the arms. NOTE: in the fourth level of performance, the speed of movement requires *bhujangasana* to be replaced by *sarpasana* (position of the young snake), in which the deep muscles of the spine are working only in the initial stage, and the final stage of the position is completed by working the muscles of your arms.

7) Complete your inhalation about the same time you have completed the maximum stretch backwards.

8) Remember to maintain a prayerful and receptive mood throughout the Suryanamaskar practice.

**Benefits:**

This is one of the best *asanas* as it stretches each and every vertebra from the top to the bottom of the spine as it releases tension in the back muscles and the spinal nerves. It is one of the very best postures to develop strength, elasticity and suppleness, and the general condition of the deep back muscles on which depends health, especially after the age of 40. The position also enhances the elasticity of the lungs. It builds up self-confidence and alertness. Since this position pulls the spinal column up towards the head and exerts traction on the lumbar end of the spine, it subtly stimulates *swadhisthana chakra*.

Detailed description of the following steps is not necessary since the description of Position 8 would be identical to Position 5, of Position 9 to Position 4, of 10 to 3, of 11 to 2, and, finally, of 12 to 1. It is important to remember that in order to complete the full cycle, the second round should be performed with the right leg being stretched all the way to the back in Positions 4 and 10.

## The First Level of Suryanamaskar Practice

A beginner should start learning the sequence slowly, paying careful attention to each *asana* and its many salient features. Therefore, after assuming each and every *asana*, maintain it for several breaths (at least 3 or 4) while consciously 'scanning' the pose and correcting any problems before moving on to the next one. At this level, take as much time as you want for each and every round. The most common time is between 30 and 90 seconds per round.

After learning the basic sequence and mastering the salient points of each *asana*, you can move to the second level. The best way of natural progression is first by increasing the number of Suryanamaskar cycles, and then by increasing their pace. In the second level, body movements are made more quickly since every movement corresponds to the breath, either inhalation or exhalation. The speed of the cycle will further increase in the fourth level, where instead of one motion per breath, there are three or four motions. However, before developing rhythm and flow, first work with the fullness and precision of your motion.

Gaining speed will take some time as your cardio-pulmonary system (along with other systems) adapts and builds endurance. You can evaluate the intensity of your practice by measuring your heart rate in beats per minute. Guidance on suitable heart rate ranges for training appears below in 'The Fourth Level of Suryanamaskar Practice'.

Many people may find Position 3 the most troublesome as they are unable to place their palms flat on the floor next to their feet while the knees are kept straight. This is usually due to a shortening of the hamstring muscles. After a few weeks of regular practice, the problem is easily overcome. One can also do additional loosening-up exercises, preferably in the afternoon or evening, when the suppleness of the body and flexibility are naturally at a higher level. Taking a warm or hot shower before beginning Suryanamaskar practice can also help with flexibility.

Another troublesome place for beginners is the transition from Position 8 to Position 9, where, due to lack of strength and flexibility, they cannot bring their foot forward and place

| Position | Asana (Traditional naming convention) | Translation | Asana (Krishnamacharya convention) | Asana (South Indian convention) |
|---|---|---|---|---|
| **Position 1** | Pranamasana | Prayer pose | Tadasana | Namaskarasana |
| **Position 2** | Hasta Uttanasana | Raised arms pose | Urdhva Namaskar | Urdhvasana |
| **Position 3** | Padahastasana | Hand to foot pose | Uttanasana | Hastapadasana |
| **Position 4** | Ashwa Sanchalanasana | Equestrian pose | Ashwa Sanchalanasana | Ekapada Prasaranasana |
| **Position 5** | Parvatasana | Mountain pose | Adho Mukha Svanasana | Dvipada Prasaranasana / Bhudharasana |
| **Position 6** | Ashtanga Namaskara | Salute with eight parts | Ashtangasana | Sashtanga Pranipatasana |
| **Position 7** | Bhujangasana | Cobra pose | Bhujangasana | Bhujangasana |
| **Position 8** | Parvatasana | Mountain pose | Adho Mukha Svanasana | Dvipada Prasaranasana / Bhudharasana |
| **Position 9** | Ashwa Sanchalanasana | Equestrian pose | Ashwa Sanchalanasana | Ekapada Prasaranasana |
| **Position 10** | Padahastasana | Hand to foot pose | Uttanasana | Hastapadasana |
| **Position 11** | Hasta Uttanasana | Raised arms pose | Urdhva Namaskar | Urdhvasana |
| **Position 12** | Pranamasana | Prayer pose | Tadasana | Namaskarasana |

**TABLE 2:** Displays possible names used for the same body postures (asanas)

it between the palms. A helpful suggestion may be to raise their buttocks (hips) as high as possible by going onto tiptoe and then 'swinging' the leg forward.

## Flexibility

Flexibility plays an important role in Suryanamaskar practice, as in much of *hatha* yoga. The ability to execute the *asanas* with a high range of movement is important for maintaining the proper Suryanamaskar technique. There are several factors that contribute to overall flexibility. They are muscle stretchability, which refers to the muscle's ability to increase its length without destroying its cells; elasticity, which refers to the ligament's ability to increase its length without causing itself damage; suppleness, which refers to the muscle's tension; and, finally, mobility, which refers to the degree of movement available in different planes. Only stretchability is highly trainable, while elasticity can be trained very little. Suppleness, or muscle tension, can be trained by strength and relaxation training.

Better flexibility allows both the economizing of movements and increasing their speed and force by lowering inner resistance. There are several types [4] of flexibility training, but

[4] There are two types of flexibility, 'general' or 'specific'. 'General' flexibility is not related to any sport or form of exercise in particular, whereas 'specific' flexibility refers to a specialized movement, which may in some cases be related to a particular sport or exercise. Flexibility training, or stretching, is divided into various categories, of which only those relevant here will be mentioned. One such category is 'passive' or 'active'. 'Passive' stretching is encountered when an external force, such as a partner or gravity, causes a movement to occur. This type of stretching creates the foundational flex-

for the purpose of Suryanamaskar the 'active-dynamic' type of flexibility training is the most important.

Flexibility is impacted by many factors such as time of day, temperature, prior warm-up, fatigue, diet, fasting state, amount of toxins in the body, emotional state, and spiritual energy (atmosphere), etc. There are several methods of improving flexibility:

- 'Ballistic' is the oldest type, with a quick succession of slight over-stretches and immediate release used to expand gradually the normal stretching limit.
- Using the neuro-muscular principle for stretching stimulus that follows isometric contraction (holding a fixed position against resistance), when the proprioceptors (various receptors located in the tendons, muscles, and ligaments) allow for a low resistance immediately after a muscle contraction. Isometric contraction should be maintained for 6 to 7 seconds and then be followed by 8 to 10 seconds of stretch.
- A slow stretch with a static hold of 4 to 8 seconds. (Maintaining the hold for any longer duration will not

ibility for 'active' stretching to be undertaken. In 'active' stretching the person concerned performs a movement without external assistance, a process which involves the contraction of the agonist muscles in order to stretch the antagonist muscles. For example, if, when standing upright, one leg is kept straight and raised in a forward direction, the antagonist (hamstring) muscles will be stretched without tension as the agonist (quadriceps) muscles contract. 'Active' stretching can be of two sub-types: 'static' (without movement) and 'dynamic' (with movement), hence the terms 'active-static' and 'active-dynamic'. Further information can be found in any book on exercise physiology or the science of training, for example McArdle W.D., et al., Exercise Physiology.

increase flexibility.) If no external force is involved, then this is an example of the 'active-static' type of stretching.

In Suryanamaskar all three methods can be used successfully for training. For example, most people on starting the practice find that their hamstring muscles and tendons have become somewhat shortened, and that they have a problem reaching the floor or ground with their fingertips while bending forward with their knees straight. A popular way of improving the length of the hamstrings is to use the 'ballistic' (also known as 'dipping') method. In this technique one comes up a bit and then uses passively the weight of the upper body to 'dip' to a lower than normal level, i.e. with a slightly increased stretch. Moving up and down in a 'ballistic' fashion for a minute or two every day improves significantly the performance of *Padahastasana* (position 3). Once the length of the hamstring muscles and tendons has been increased by means of the ballistic method the isometric method can be used. Take up the position for *Ashwa Sanchalanasana* (position 4) and hold the back knee steady and raised off the floor or ground (by no more than 1 inch or 25 millimetres) for 8 to 10 seconds and then rest it with full relaxation on the floor or ground while extending it backwards as far as possible. After a period of practice sufficient for these two methods to have produced a significant lengthening and strengthening of the hamstring muscles and tendons, the 'active-static' method can be introduced in attempting to perform a forward split. Initially it will be hard to perform the full splits, and it is important to support the body weight with the hands on both sides of the torso, in order not to over-stretch. Hold whatever position you can comfortably maintain for 4 to 8 seconds in an 'active-static' stretch, and then slowly and carefully release. Always remember to do these stretching exercises symmetrically, alternating whichever leg is in front. It is very important not to overdo flexibility exercises and to take your time, going rather slowly. Any significant injury of a muscle or tendon in the leg may well set you back many weeks, or even months, and is also likely to restrict severely most of your other physical activities.

These three methods can be greatly helped by following a proper (yogic) diet, which as a consequence will decrease the amount of toxins in the body and naturally increase flexibility, even without much exercise being taken. In fact, from a yogic point of view, there is much less point in forcefully working your joints, ligaments, and muscles into a greater range of movement if your diet has not been corrected. That is a secret that yogis have known for millennia. Indeed, there are various types of fasting, which further detoxify the body at the cellular and molecular levels, and lead to the achievement of additional and more refined enhancements in flexibility.

Perhaps the final refinement in reaching the greatest level of flexibility comes when a proper emotional state is achieved and stabilized by being in a spiritually charged atmosphere, such as is found in an ashram, a monastery or a holy place, when a real master is present. The author has had frequent experience of this phenomenon over many years during visits to various such places, particularly those in India.

There are a number of pointers worth remembering while exercising to develop flexibility:

- Practicing twice daily helps to increase flexibility faster. It is especially the second session in a day that assists making large gains in flexibility.

- Flexibility training should not be accompanied by a diminution of strength training; if it is, then there will arise the potential for a significant decline in muscle strength.

- Flexibility is best developed before puberty, but, if not maintained later on through the right kind of exercise, it will deteriorate.

- Fatigue has a negative effect on suppleness. It is, therefore, best to work on enhancing flexibility immediately after *warming up*.

- While training for flexibility, attention should be directed to the antagonist [5] muscles, with the aim of keeping them relaxed. If they become tense then they create resistance to the agonist muscles.

- Aim to increase flexibility gradually. Start with the 'passive' flexibility technique, then move on in turn to the isometric and to the 'active-static', before, finally, arriving at the 'active-dynamic', the most important for

[5] Antagonist muscles are the muscles that execute the movement of a joint in the opposing direction to the movement that is being performed. Often these muscles are unnecessarily tensed and in that way restrict the full range of the movement. Simply relaxing these muscles will allow increased flexibility as a natural consequence.

Suryanamaskar, and an intrinsic element of the dynamic form of the practice.

- 'Active-static' stretching helps to remove fatigue, so it is recommended to perform this type of stretching exercise immediately after *endurance* training.
- The tradition that women's bodies have better natural flexibility than men's has been confirmed by modern research.

## The Process of Bending and Stretching

In this process, the opposite (antagonist) group of muscles is put to stretch and they undergo relaxation to facilitate efficient contraction of the muscles and the resulting movement. However, these muscles may not always relax properly and so they may resist and not be able to move smoothly. This results in increased tension in the contracting muscles. When moving, we are guided by the contracting muscles and the tension is built up through that contraction to overcome the resistance of the opposite group of muscles. Working against resistance helps us to develop the body musculature, yet it also keeps our consciousness tied to the physical body.

In yoga, one of the aims of our practice is to transcend the body consciousness and to open and purify the various *nadis* (channels) to the free and unrestricted movement of *prana*. Therefore, different (postures) are used instead of exercises (*vyayama*).

In the second chapter of the *Yoga Sutras,* Patanjali defines *asana* as giving rise to a feeling of steadiness (*sthira*), comfort (*sukha*), effortlessness (*prayatna-shaithilya*) and allowing consciousness to explore infinity (*ananta-samapatti*). Such a state can be reached only when the physical body is 'out of the way', meaning that its muscles and organs are properly relaxed. Muscles tend to relax efficiently during passive stretching, as takes place naturally in massage or in water. In *asanas,* we work with the same guiding principle by 'letting go' in each and every posture to find areas in the body which are 'opening' or 'stretching' instead of 'closing'. Hence, Suryanamaskar stresses forward and backward stretching as opposed to forward and backward bending, as the former 'opens up' the body while the latter 'closes' it.

In everyday life it is the mind that tells the body and the body that tells the mind. In physical education training programs, the mind talks to and manipulates the body at all times. In contrast, in yoga sessions we try to establish a different relationship, one where it is only the body telling the mind, or, in other words, we try to remain in a receptive and listening attitude.

## The Process of Maintaining the Spinal Column

From early childhood onwards, the muscles of the spinal column (*merudanda*) are in constant activity executing any standing or other upright position. We tend to overlook the activities of our spine due to the focus on our extremities and their interactions with the external world. For that reason, we do not normally pay much attention to the spine and so do not sufficiently relax it when we lie down or rest, because our mind is still active in the external world. In yoga we try to release that tension which has accumulated in the body as well as in the mind. For example in various yoga postures, we try to stop the natural tendency of the body to go out through the extremities, and try to develop awareness of the stretching and relaxation.

To that effect, we work with the vertebral muscles, especially the deep vertebral muscles in the lower back. The condition of our spine is of paramount importance, especially for the condition of our deep back muscles after the age of forty. Thus, 'a man is as old as his spine'. As we start working with yogic techniques, we may discover that our spine is not very flexible and that many positions cause tension or even pain. In such situations, to overcome safely the tension, while at the same time continuing to make progress, we follow the rule of 'pleasant but bearable pain', which helps relax and release tension in muscles. In Part III of this book, we review scientific research findings that show significant improvements in the flexibility of the spine after yoga training, specifically after a regular Suryanamaskar practice which is shown to be extremely effective in the maintenance of core muscles.

Just as our extremities keep us connected to and related with various objects in the external world so the vertebral column at its center, our support structure for the trunk, relates to our Self. Higher yoga techniques involve working with the muscles that support the spinal column. Initially, this may seem to be very insignificant for our life in the external world, but in fact, the spinal column plays a central, crucial role. The practicing of different *asanas*, which practice corrects and adjusts our spinal column, helps us to sit in a more relaxed and more straight and balanced condition for longer periods of time, while at the same time helping to refocus our awareness on the Self (*Atma*).

Students who are interested in the *adhyatmic* (spiritual) aspects of yoga can refine their understanding by carrying out the following exercises to increase their awareness of the various aspects of Suryanamaskar practice:

- **Experience muscle stretching in different *asanas***
  This time, as you practice the sequence, monitor which muscles are being stretched in each *asanas* in the whole sequence.

This constitutes the first and introductory level of Suryanamaskar practice.

## The Second Level of Suryanamaskar Practice

The second level begins when a practitioner has memorized the form and sequence of the *asanas*, gained sufficient strength and flexibility to accomplish each *asana* correctly, and the flow of the practice is smooth and without any jerky movement. At this level, the practice should mature to the point where any major adjustments are unnecessary, and only micro-adjustments may be required. Most importantly, each a*sana* should be co-ordinated with the breath. At this level, Suryanamaskar is done as a *vinyasa*, such that there is co-ordination between the movement of the body and breath; each extension or expansion is associated with inhalation and each contraction is associated with exhalation. In other words, the movement rides on the rhythm of the breath.

Once you are proficient at this level, it is advisable to start your practice with 2 or 3 cycles of the slow, deliberate stretching and joint adjustment found in the first level practice. Performance of one *vinyasa* style round depends on your breath, but usually takes from 30 to 60 seconds. After each and every *asana,* there is a brief hold for 1 to 3 seconds. At this level, you should aim to do minimum of 12 cycles.

Preparatory exercises work with sensing, feeling and experiencing various aspects of breathing. These exercises are to be done slowly as in the first level so there is sufficient time to observe the breath.

- **Experience inhalation and exhalation in each *asana.***
  Hold each *asana* while inhaling and exhaling for a minimum of 2-3 breaths. With your full attention, follow the breath moving in and out of your body.

- **Experience the expansion and retraction of the body while breathing and changing *asanas.***
  The goal is three-fold: Find out how the different *asanas* modify breathing movements in different areas of the body, especially in the trunk, to discover areas where these movements are increased and where they are decreased, though never entirely absent. Recognize the areas where breath starts. Observe how the body changes

with each breath. Keep your breathing as normal, natural and spontaneous as possible and methodically examine the different areas of the trunk. Observe where you can or cannot experience respiratory movements. See if these movements make sense or not, and whether the body expands during inhalation and retracts during exhalation. Assess the intensity of these movements. If possible, try to recognize pressure changes within the body, especially which region is responsible for expansion and contraction while breathing. Monitor the breath in the neck and clavicle regions, and in the shoulders and the thoracic, abdominal and pelvic areas. Make sure that you are not blocking respiratory movements completely in areas of strong pressure. Experience the areas where respiratory movements are amplified; relax the whole back and let it move freely during respiration. Do this work with normal and then with deeper breathing without any strain.

- **Experience the filling and emptying of the body cavity in different *asanas*.**

  Direct your attention inside the body. If possible, try to recognize the presence of a space (cavity) between the two sides of the body. See if you can experience that this cavity is filled and emptied during breathing. Is the whole body cavity filled and emptied each time you change body position, or do you experience different body cavities (pelvic, abdominal or thoracic) becoming filled and emptied during different stages of the sequence? Try to pay attention to whether the whole cavity is filled and emptied, or if only a particular side or part of it exhibits this. Observe to which area of the body certain *asanas* draw your attention; some may give you the experience of more than one cavity. As you are observing, try to feel whether the body cavity seems to fill from the top down or from the bottom up.

- **Experience the sensation of the passage of air in the nostrils.**
  Practice the first sequence paying close attention to the sensation of the passage of air in the nostrils. Experience the passage of air over the upper lip and inside both nasal vestibules during normal spontaneous breathing. On subsequent rounds, see if you can gradually begin to experience the path this air of the in-breath takes inside the body as well as its ultimate destination during each posture. Such contact becomes the internally aroused sensation, which you may be able to experience.

Once you have successfully completed the above exercises, you can move on to the next step in the Second Level of Practice, which is breathing in time with the Suryanamaskar sequence. With every *asana*, which stretches backward, inhale. With every *asana* which stretches forward, exhale. This is also a *vinyasa*, which joins movement with breath.

After working in this fashion for some time and making the *vinyasa* natural and spontaneously co-ordinated, the next step is to learn *ujjayi* breath (*kumbhaka*), the preferred method of breathing during this practice. Before you join *ujjayi* with Suryanamaskar, start by practicing it while sitting. Assume a comfortable sitting body posture such as *sukhasana* (easy posture), *siddhasana* (perfect posture), *padmasana* (lotus posture), or, if needed, use a chair. When sitting in a chair, place your feet flat on the ground and keep your spine erect without touching or supporting your back on the back of the chair.

***Ujjayi Kumbhaka (Pranayama)***

1) In *ujjayi,* the passage of air inside the respiratory passages is felt at the glottis. There are two structures at the end of the trachea: one is called the glottis and the other the epiglottis. They close the respiratory pipe when we swallow, i.e. they protect the respiratory canal. The glottis rises when we swallow and presses against the epiglottis. You can place your palm on the throat and feel the glottis rising while you swallow. If you want to feel the passage of air at this point, you have to hold this part a bit closed, just as you may close one nostril at a time so that the sensations are increased in the open nostril.

2) The best way to learn it is by swallowing and, instead of completely releasing the contraction in the throat, release it partially and start breathing while maintaining the contraction.

3) Try this technique a few times before starting the formal practice. First breathe out, then swallow, relax the throat a little, and start breathing in through the opening between glottis and epiglottis, experiencing the

sensation of air in the throat. You will experience cool/ fresh air while inhaling and warm air while exhaling. At this point you will hear a delicate fricative sound arising from the area of the glottis.

4) Breathing normally, expand the whole trunk and body on inhalation and retract it on exhalation.

5) Swallow, and keep the glottis and epiglottis partially closed. As you do this, also maintain awareness of air inside the throat so that you may start feeling as if you are breathing from the glottis.

6) Feel the thoracic and abdominal cavities becoming filled and emptied at every breath from this point in the throat. Practice this filling and emptying in a smooth, uniform way. The sound you produce should be uniform, continuous and so subtle that it should be audible only to yourself. Make sure that you are not contracting your face or shoulders.

Once you have learned the proper *ujjayi* technique in a comfortable sitting position, you can start using it for your Suryanamaskar *vinyasa*. While doing the *vinyasa,* continue to observe the body: which areas of the body are filled and emptied while doing various *asanas*, whether your mind is absorbed by the hissing sound, whether you can trace the sensation of the sound in the body, where the inhalation ends and begins, what the after-effect of the practice is, etc.

This constitutes the second level of Suryanamaskar practice.

## The Third Level of Suryanamaskar Practice

The third level starts when you are comfortable performing the sequence of 12 *asanas* smoothly and without much strain in an exercise or a postural mode such that most conscious attention can be focused on the mantras.

This is the level where the practice enters the spiritual realm. Therefore, after mastering the use of *Surya* (solar) or *bija* mantras, one should also include the technique of focusing the mind on the various spiritual centers (*chakras*) while moving from one *asana* to the next (churning of the *chakras*). The list of these spiritual energy centers and their corresponding *asanas* is provided in the chapter on Psychic Centers, Churning the Chakras.

Start your practice with 1 or 2 cycles of the slow and deliberate stretching and joint adjustment from the first level practice before increasing your speed. Attend to your breath.

Special *Surya* and/or *bija* mantras may be repeated aloud with a whispering voice or silently during this third level of practice. A list of mantras with descriptive details is presented in the next chapter. The most popular are the 12 solar mantras, the 12 solar mantras joined with the 6 *bija* mantras repeated once or twice, the 108 *Surya* mantras and the *Gayatri* mantra. Depending on the speed of the practice, these mantras may be repeated before each round of Suryanamaskar or before each *asana* of the sequence.

Gradually increase your practice until you can perform 12 rounds of Suryanamaskar easily and comfortably. As always, when working with mantras, pay close attention to where in the body you experience their sounds as vibrations. In the beginning it is always a good idea to check with your teacher that you are pronouncing the sounds properly and correctly, as it is very important for the quality of vibrations.

Perhaps the most common practice it is to chant or repeat one of the 12 *Surya* mantras before each round of Suryanamaskar. After completing these 12 solar mantras, perform 12 rounds (or 6 cycles) of Suryanamaskar, the regular daily morning practice.

More advanced students may undertake the highly recommended 108 rounds of Suryanamaskar, which fits beautifully with the 108 *Surya* mantras. Alternatively, repeat the twelve *Surya* mantras nine times or the twelve *Surya* and *bija* mantras nine times. Students seeking a deeper spiritual effect should include the *bija* mantras together with the *Surya* mantras.

Mantra Yoga is a vast subject in itself and requires intensive study and practice with the help of a master. Mantras consist of special sound vibrations. They are not the ordinary sounds encountered in everyday life. Those ordinary sounds make the various vowels and consonants used to compose the words, sentences and language used for communicating our thoughts, feelings, and emotions, etc. to others around us. All are based on vibrations or sounds.

These ordinary sounds are meaningful and keep us connected with the outside world. Every object with a form (*rupa*) also has a name (*nama*) which indicates that object. However, with the different sounds of the mantras we stimulate our self yet without becoming attached to external objects. Each and every sound of a mantra has a distinct vibrational pattern.

On a physical level, all sounds are heard by means of vibrations in the air, which are sensed and experienced by means of minuscule bones in the ear. Thus, we experience the vibrations of different sounds as internal stimulation. When we work with the *Aum* mantra, the sound of the prolonged 'a' is designed to give inputs from the legs to the perineum. The prolonged vibration of 'u' connects you to the abdomen. And the prolonged sound of 'm' is felt in the upper chest, neck and head regions. The nasalized sound 'm' brings awareness to the head and face. In this way the whole body is "covered" with these sound vibrations. As we recite or chant the mantra *Aum,* this sequential pronunciation of the three sounds gives an internal experiential path from the legs and perineum to the top of the skull. *Bija* mantras, on the other hand, bring awareness only to specific different areas of the body.

Mantras can work differently in each individual, especially since pronunciation influences the internal experience. Therefore, before you start using a mantra during your Suryanamaskar practice, spend some time learning proper pronunciation as well as the technique for proper repetition. For this practice, assume a comfortable sitting body posture such as *sukhasana* (easy posture), *siddhasana* (adept's posture), *padmasana* (lotus posture), or you can use a chair. When sitting in a chair, place your feet flat on the ground and keep your spine erect without touching or supporting your back to the back of the chair. Most important is that your spine should stay erect in a mode of 'relaxed attentiveness' without straining or tensing your body muscles.

➢ **Working with the simple mantra sound *Om (AUM)***

Recite '*AUM*' with proper mechanics of the breath. As you chant or recite the 'A', experience its vibration in the feet and buttocks. During the recitation of 'U', experience its vibration in the area of the abdomen. When reciting 'M', experience its vibration in the upper part of the body.

Next, try to repeat the nasalized sound 'Ng' (as in 'sing', but with closed lips). As you produce this sound feel the vibrations throughout your body and become especially aware of the skull space. You may discover that the nasalized 'Ng' will be transformed into a cerebral 'Ng' like the vibratory sound produced by a bee. Allow yourself to be guided by this sound as high as possible in your skull.

At the end of this practice, you may recite or chant "*Om Shantih, Shantih, Shantih*" to ground yourself.

➢ **Working with *Bija* Mantras:**

As you work with the mantras, it is best to 'forget' any knowledge you may have acquired about them from books and allow your own experience to become the source of your knowledge. Now start reciting each *bija* mantra, trying to feel or experience which part of the body resonates with its vibrations until you have your own personal experience of the locus of each sound within the body.

- **<u>Working with *Surya* Mantras:</u>**
  As you work with the mantras, it is best to 'forget' any knowledge you may have acquired about them from books and allow your own experience to become the source of your knowledge. Now start reciting each *Surya* mantra, trying to feel or experience which part of the body resonates with its vibrations until you have your own personal experience of the locus of each sound within the body.

- **<u>Working with both the *Surya* and *Bija* Mantras:</u>**
  As you work with the mantras, it is best to 'forget' any knowledge you may have acquired about them from books and allow your own experience to become the source of your knowledge. Now start reciting each *Surya* and *bija* mantra set as shown in the table in the chapter on mantras, trying to feel or experience which part of the body resonates with its vibrations. Continue until you have your own personal experience of the locus of each sound within the body.

At this point, you are prepared to start using mantra sounds and vibrations in your Suryanamaskar practice. In the beginning, do not rush. It is better to go slowly and correctly. Repeat the same four exercises above in the same sequence, but do them in Position 1 (*pranamasana*) instead of sitting. Compare your experiences with each mantra you recite and choose for your own personal practice the set of mantras that you feel and experience most strongly.

This constitutes the third level of Suryanamaskar practice.

## The Fourth Level of Suryanamaskar Practice

The fourth level of performance is the most advanced, and requires much training and preparation before being able to perform each round of Suryanamaskar in 7.5 to 8 seconds time, for an average of about 40 rounds in 5 minutes.

The flowing sequence of any Suryanamaskar style can be considered a dynamic practice when compared to static *asanas*. So why use the name 'Dynamic Suryanamaskar' here? Most people watching this practice would agree that it calls for considerable intensity to move with the speed of 12 postures within less than 8 seconds in an average round during a single Suryanamaskar session, which can last for an hour or even longer. The intensity in this variation is present at all levels, not only the physical one. Thus this Fourth Level of Practice is the focus and an inspiration of this book, which underlines this inherent dynamism and intensity. No other exercise system seems to emphasize these two characteristics so rigorously. Practicing at this speed for more than two hours, a man weighing 80 kg would lose approximately 4 kg body weight in sweat!

## The Basic Process of Aerobic Training

At the advanced fourth level of Suryanamaskar practice it is useful to understand some basic concepts of aerobic training, since the stimulation of the body's structural and functional processes of adaptation becomes much higher than in the previous steps. These aerobic principles operate irrespective of the mode of exercise provided that the exercise concerned involves large groups of muscles. The types of such exercise are: bicycling, walking, running, jogging, rowing, swimming, skating, bench stepping, step climbing, and Suryanamaskar.

The American College of Sports Medicine (ACSM) has published guidelines for a "well rounded training program". Such a program should include flexibility exercises, including joint flexibility training, together with aerobic and resistance training. A balanced fitness program, according to ACMS, "cannot contain only resistance (weights) or only aerobic or anaerobic training, it also should consist of joint flexibility, which incorporates static and dynamic joint range of motion exercises of the major muscle / tendon groups". Analysis of the Suryanamaskar set shows that it fits beautifully into this definition, since it engages thoroughly all the major groups of muscles, from head to toe, unlike any other known physical activity.

In Suryanamaskar, performing potentially hundreds of repetitions can create a significant physical overload, which, while producing physiological enhancement, does require deliberate manipulation of three factors in the practice, namely, intensity, duration and frequency. The fourth factor that has an impact on the training response is the initial level of aerobic fitness. Those individuals with a lower level of physical fitness may expect the greatest improvement in a short period, while highly trained persons may experience rather small improvements. The concept of customized and progressive overloading of body systems is applicable to all types of exercise, regardless of whether we are just starting physical training or are already seasoned and experienced athletes. It is important to remember that individuals do not respond in the same way to the same training stimulus; there is a principle of individual differences, genetic and otherwise. For example, the same training may improve endurance by 50% in the case of middle-aged men with heart disease, by 10 to 15% in the case of active healthy adults, and by only 5% in the case of highly trained athletes.

While the science of physiological (sports) training is quite complicated and requires much scientific knowledge to be fully understood, an attempt will now be made to present a few useful points aimed at enhancing success with Suryanamaskar practice.

It has been proven that specific exercise elicits specific adaptations to create specific training effects. Thus the muscles trained effectively in running are different from those trained in cycling, swimming or upper body exercise. Likewise the absence of a training stimulus causes 'reverse' adaptation (the reversibility principle), and, after only one or two weeks, *detraining* or a reversal of metabolic and exercise capacity will be detectable, while, in the case of a person with a high level of fitness, over a period of several months without a training stimulus, very significant fitness losses will become apparent.

In our bodies there are two energy transfer systems that change with training: anaerobic (no oxygen used) and aerobic. The fourth level of Suryanamaskar belongs to the latter type. Some important changes due to training geared towards eliciting the aerobic adaptations are:

- Metabolic improved capacity (increased oxidation potential by increased size and number of cellular structures called mitochondria), which impacts fat and carbohydrate metabolism.

- Muscle fiber type and size; all fibers (slow and fast twitch) increase their existing aerobic potential (increase of myoglobin).

- Cardiovascular adaptations: the athlete's heart or cardiac hypertrophy (increased heart size). Heart rate is decreased, while the heart stroke volume increases to the overall effect of increased heart output. Both systolic and diastolic pressures are reduced.

- Increased amount of blood plasma.

- Distribution of blood improves; there is both a build-up of a more dense network of capillaries and enlargement of the cross-sectional areas of large and small arteries.

- More effective oxygen extraction from circulation blood (increases arteriovenous oxygen difference).

- Pulmonary adaptation increasing the tidal volume while decreasing breathing frequency, giving in effect increased oxygen extraction from the inspired air; increased ventilatory endurance.

- Lowering blood lactate levels.

- Change in body composition by reducing body mass and fat mass.
- Improved body thermoregulatory mechanism.
- Psychological benefits, where the occurring adaptation may be equal to or higher than other interventions (including pharmacological).

### *Training Intensity*

Training or overload intensity appears to be the most important factor in inducing a physiological adaptation. There are at least seven methods of expressing training intensity. The most precise is the method of measuring oxygen consumption, $VO_2$max, but it requires sophisticated and expensive equipment. However, research has demonstrated that there is a correlation between $VO_2$max (maximal oxygen consumption capacity of the whole body expressed in liters per minute) and maximum heart rate, to the extent that it is possible to estimate maximum heart rate with a likelihood of only an 8% error when $VO_2$max is already known. It has therefore become accepted that using maximum heart rate instead of $VO_2$max will provide a sufficiently accurate guide for practical purposes in determining maximum and training range heart rates. Monitoring the pulse during and immediately after exercise is the most practical way of ensuring that exercise intensity is both not excessive and not too little. For training to be effective it must meet a minimal intensity requirement.

## Maximum Heart Rate

Establishing the correct value of $HR_{max}$ is crucial for calculating training intensity. There is considerable disagreement as to how to predict that value and there are many formulae suggested by researchers, depending on a person's age, state of fitness, ailments, etc. Of course, the most precise procedure for the determination of maximum heart rate without measuring $VO_2max$ is by taking the actual measurement of heart rate itself. There are two methods that can be used. The simple one is to take the pulse immediately after several minutes (usually two to four) of 'all-out effort' in some specific type of physical activity. More technically complex and more accurate is the method of running a *cardiac stress test* on an EKG machine. Such a test lasts from ten to twenty minutes and is usually performed on a treadmill. The latter, but not the former, experimental method of establishing $HR_{max}$ is definitely preferable to using predicted values in the case of people with a medical condition, and especially for those with a heart condition. However, it should be noted that, even for those who regard themselves as reasonably healthy and fit, the former 'all-out effort' method of establishing the maximum heart rate, and therefore by calculation the training range, is likely to be excessively demanding, and therefore completely unsuitable for the vast majority of such people. In any case, it is a method that should only be used after obtaining approval as a result of undergoing a medical examination by a suitably qualified person, and when there is also suitably qualified supervision available. If such conditions are not met, as in many instances they will not be, the calculation method offers a safer, albeit less accurate, way of establishing the minimal threshold, and should always be preferred. Furthermore, the watchword whenever exercising should always be 'caution'. Whatever the figures say, your final guide must always be how you feel. Pain and or excessive discomfort are signals to stop exercising, take rest, and try again the next day, but only provided your body feels completely normal.

The recommended method for the calculation of maximum heart rate for healthy people has for several decades been to subtract age in years from 220, although this formula has neither high accuracy nor much scientific merit. Standard deviation or error for any age predicted $HR_{max}$ is ± 10 beats per minute, but according to several authorities its influence on establishing effective training is rather small. Thus for a person 50 years old:

$$HR_{max} = 220 - 50 = 170.$$

Various other formulae have been determined from research, and a very close approximation of those formulae, used sometimes by researchers and frequently by professionals, is the one immediately below. Consider again our 50 year-old person:

$$HR_{max} = 208 - (0.7 \times age), \text{ i.e. } 208 - (0.7 \times 50) = 208 - 35 = 173.$$

Both these methods of calculating $HR_{max}$ have been considered sufficiently accurate for those exercises where there is no upper-body muscle mass actively involved, such as running or cycling. However, whenever a large mass of upper body muscles is involved in the exercise, as in the case of Suryanamaskar, it has been determined that the calculated $HR_{max}$ figure should be adjusted downwards by 13 (beats per minute). For example, the calculation for the 50 year-old person would become:

$$HR_{max} = 208 - (0.7 \times 50) - 13 = 160.$$

## Training Range Heart Rate

There are also two main ways of calculating the individual's minimal training intensity heart rate.

*Karvonen Method*: $HR_{threshold} = HR_{rest} + 0.60\ (HR_{max} - HR_{rest})$, where $HR_{threshold}$ is the minimal heart rate required for a training effect to occur, $HR_{rest}$ is the heart rate measured at rest, and $HR_{max}$ is, as before, the maximum heart rate. For example, with a resting pulse of 76 and a maximum after exercise of 176, the calculation becomes:

$$HR_{threshold} = 76 + 0.60\ (176 - 76) = 76 + 60 = 136.$$

Although in its original formulation $HR_{max}$ was determined by the 'all-out effort' method, it subsequently became acceptable to apply the age based calculated figure to the Karvonen equation.

*Training Sensitive Zone*: on the basis of research this was established as being from 70 to 90% of the maximum heart rate. Thus the training sensitive zone, using the previously calculated maximum, for the 50 year old undertaking a form of exercise involving the upper body, such as Suryanamaskar, would be:

$$HR_{threshold}:\ HR_{max} \times 70\%, \text{ i.e. } 160 \times 0.70 = 112.$$

(The lower limit, $HR_{threshold}$, is also known as Target Heart Rate or Training Heart Rate {THR}).

Similarly the calculation for the 50 year-old's upper limit would be:

$$HR_{maxtrainingrate}: HR_{max} \times 90\%, \text{ i.e. } 160 \times 0.90 = 144.$$

Below is a table showing, *inter alia,* the maximal heart rate (100%) and training heart rate (70%) for aerobic training of fit and healthy men and women of different ages, calculated using the most common '220 minus age' formula. In parentheses are the heart rates adjusted for Suryanamaskar practice.

Generally, the higher the training intensity, the greater the training improvement. However, as we have seen, there is a minimal threshold level below which no training effect takes place. There may also exist a certain 'ceiling' above which no further gain will accrue. However, what is certain is that the more fit the individual is then the higher the threshold level that is needed in order to stimulate the training response. The suggested values in table 3 represent the safest and most optimal ranges established by numerous tests on many individuals seeking an optimal increase in their aerobic (endurance) training. Less fit, older, overweight individuals might be well advised to start with the 60% $HR_{max}$ figure and build up duration gradually to 45-50 minutes; such a duration would then provide a training response similar to that for a more fit individual exercising at 70% $HR_{max}$ for 20-30 minutes or to that for a highly fit person exercising at 90% $HR_{max}$ for ten minutes.

| Age | 60% level | 70% level | 90% level | 100% level |
|---|---|---|---|---|
| 20 | 120 (107) | 140 (127) | 180 (167) | 200 (187) |
| 25 | 117 (104) | 136 (123) | 175 (162) | 195 (182) |
| 30 | 114 (101) | 133 (120) | 171 (158) | 190 (177) |
| 35 | 111 (98) | 129 (116) | 166 (153) | 185 (172) |
| 40 | 108 (95) | 126 (113) | 162 (149) | 180 (167) |
| 45 | 105 (92) | 122 (108) | 158 (145) | 175 (162) |
| 50 | 102 (89) | 119 (106) | 153 (140) | 170 (157) |
| 55 | 99 (86) | 116 (103) | 148 (135) | 165 (152) |
| 60 | 96 (83) | 112 (99) | 144 (131) | 160 (147) |
| 65 | 93 (80) | 109 (96) | 140 (127) | 155 (142) |
| 70 | 90 (77) | 105 (92) | 135 (122) | 150 (137) |

**TABLE 3:** Maximal heart rates and training sensitive zone for aerobic training for men and women of different ages.

There is also a more subjective way to measure the intensity of Suryanamaskar by the rating of perceived exertion (RPE). See the table below:

| RPE scale | % Equivalent of $HR_{max}$ |
|---|---|
| Fairly light | 52 - 66 |
| Somewhat hard | 67 - 85 |
| Hard | 86 - 91 |
| Very hard | 92 and more |

**TABLE 4:** The Borg scale for estimates of relative exercise intensity.

### *Training Duration*

For aerobic improvement no threshold has been established for duration. It is likely, however, that aerobic improvement depends on the interrelation of duration, frequency, and intensity, or 'training volume'. While a training stimulus can occur in the case of people of poor fitness after only 5 to 10 minutes, for more advanced athletes it may require a duration of 20 to 30 minutes. But increased training volume does not necessarily produce greater improvements. For example, tests did not show any difference in swimming power, endurance and performance time between a group of swimmers who daily practiced for 1.5 hours and a group which practiced twice daily for 1.5 hours on each occasion (total 3 hours). However, it is possible to reach the overall conclusion that, when there is less intensity, then longer duration is required.

### *Training Frequency*

Studies are neither conclusive nor very precise, yet it was found that training of 2 days per week of a certain duration and intensity produced very similar results to training of 5 days per week of the same duration and intensity. However, some research shows that there is some advantage to be found with regard to cardiovascular improvement as frequency is increased. Similarly to the duration factor, the overall conclusion is that when there is less intensity, then greater frequency of training is required.

However, greater frequency or longer duration will not in themselves necessarily elicit more physiological changes, though they will, all other things being equal, require more caloric expenditure, and thus have an impact on the individual's body composition. To produce a significant effect of this kind the threshold with regard to frequency is 2 days per week, with duration of 60 minutes at a sufficient intensity to expend a minimum of 300 Kcal on each occasion. Otherwise neither anaerobic nor aerobic energy transfer systems will change in such a way as to develop their own capacity, or to affect body weight or composition. Thus a typical aerobic training schedule will require exercise to be undertaken 3 times per week.

Before switching your gears to high speed and becoming proficient at the fourth level, begin your practice with 1 or 2 cycles of the slow and deliberate stretching and joint adjustment from the first level practice, and follow that with several cycles of each of the techniques described in the second and third levels.

There are certain differences when practicing at this level:

- There is no conscious coordination of breath and body movements since the movements are much faster than the requirements for breath and oxygen.
- Depending on the strength and efficiency of your cardio-vasculatory and pulmonary systems, one round of Suryanamaskar may be accomplished in only 2 or 3 breaths instead of the 6 breath cycles used during the second or third levels of the practice.
- At this level, do not use the *ujjayi pranayama*; just ensure that the breath can move freely.

- Let the body dance to and follow the breath with its own inner intelligence; focus on just maintaining a receptive attitude while watching the flow.
- There are no short 'breaks' or stoppages following each *asana*; to an onlooker it should appear as a smooth, fluid, wave-like motion.
- Position 6 is done almost entirely 'in the air' without touching the ground.
- Position 7 is replaced by *sarpasana* or the young snake posture, which is a more dynamic version of *bhujangasana*. Externally it looks similar, yet internally it is quite different, executed rather from the shoulders and arms than the deep back spine muscles.
- The practice has the characteristics of an extremely potent *kriya* (purification procedure) having very powerful antitoxic properties. For this reason it is used in the *Ashtanga Kriyas* body purification system.

As a technique of solar vitalization, Suryanamaskar recharges our batteries, allowing us to live more fully and joyfully. It is like a '*pranic* generator' or a '*pranic* pump', which stores *prana* for future use while at the same time balancing the flow of *ida* (*Chandra*, moon energy or left nostril) and *pingala* (*Surya*, solar energy or right nostril). Check the flow of breath in your *Surya* and *Chandra nadi,* and if they are not equalized after some time of your regular Suryanamaskar practice, something must be wrong. This enhanced vitality prepares the practitioner for the *kundalini* awakening, so that its force can be withstood.

This fourth level of the practice is also called 'Dynamic Suryanamaskar' because these psychic or spiritual results manifest remarkably fast. This became obvious to the author one morning in mid 2005 when he was performing his regular 300 or so rounds. Being moved by intuition he decided to complete more than 400 rounds. Suddenly, about the 412th round he felt an immense force, which 'kicked' him at the base of his spinal column. That awakened force carried him smoothly and without any effort on his part to perform close to one thousand rounds in less than two hours! It seemed that he could have kept going on like that indefinitely, yet he had consciously stopped fearing that the next day he would be unable to move any part of his body. Needless to say, no such negative effects took place though he had surpassed more than three times his daily number of rounds. Instead, he observed very promising yogic effects of this uncommon manner of practice, among them tremendous lightness of body and strong total psycho-somatic-spiritual integration, and lack of tiredness, stress or tension. Contrary to his expectations he felt great clarity and alertness of mind for the following 48 hours, exuberant energy and great physical strength, very strong *pranic* currents along his back combined with overall happiness and contentment. Similar beneficial effects were reported in the 1970s by other Polish researchers, Professor Wieslaw Romanowski and Tadeusz Pasek of Jozef Pilsudski University of Physical Education in Warsaw, Poland, who stated that the psycho-prophylactic procedures of which the *asanas* in Suryanamaskar form a part, "aim at producing an ordered and stabilized sequence of functional states and relaxation characterized by a biological rhythm".

When observing this manner of performing Suryanamaskar, most Yoga students and teachers remark that it is either aerobics or some fast gymnastics and so has nothing to do with the original *hatha* tradition. However, the newly discovered scripture *Asanayoga - Hathabhasyapaddhati* by Kapalakurantaka states that one needs to perform at least several hundred rounds in this manner. It also says that more advanced *sadhakas* may even increase the number of rounds to several thousand. According to many authorities in *hatha* manuscripts, one of the important meanings of *hatha* is *strenuous* and *intense* or *rigorous*. Thus Kapalakurantaka brings out the hidden but true meaning of the tradition. Kapalakurantaka, who was also known as Kaurantaka or Paurantaka, is one of the *Maha-Siddhas* (accomplished masters) of the *Hatha Nath Parampara* (living tradition of the *Nath* sect), whose name is mentioned in the first chapter of the much-celebrated book on *hatha* yogic practices called *Hathapradipika*.

The author of this publication learned for the first time about this mode of doing Suryanamaskar practice from the late Swami Prakashananda Saraswati of Nashik and Saptashringi in mid-1976. He was a disciple of the well-known Swami Muktananda of Ganeshpuri, who also advocated this mode of practice, especially to young and vigorous adolescents and adults. However, the author did not change his mode of practice until receiving further encouragement to do so some five years later. Later still, several other accomplished masters, including Janglidas Maharaj, confirmed the value of this mode of practice.

This constitutes the fourth level of Suryanamaskar practice.

## The Ayurvedic Method of Suryanamaskar Practice

As stated in Mukunda Stiles's book *Ayurvedic Yoga Therapy,* there are three ways of practicing Suryanamaskar according to the *Ayurvedic* principles of *tridosha.* These three methods are described briefly below.

### Suryanamaskar Practice to Balance Vata Dosha

To balance *vata dosha,* Suryanamaskar needs to be performed slowly and deliberately, with a good sense of rhythm and with the Yogic breathing called *ujjayi* to balance the air and space qualities of *vata.* Practicing one cycle (two rounds) in this manner may take 60 seconds or even more; sometimes one round may last even 60 seconds. In this practice, the main focus on the sound of *ujjayi pranayama* produced by the glottis and on the slow, smooth, deliberate and rhythmic performance of the *vinyasa,* where one feels an internal wave of motion. This peaceful and smooth manner makes one more sensitive to inner thoughts and feelings, and encourages insight. Regularity will help to control levels of anxiety and fear. This type of practice is preferable in the winter months.

### Suryanamaskar Practice to Balance Pitta Dosha

To balance the fire and water quality of *pitta dosha,* this method focuses on energy and vitality. Little attention is paid to the breath, which just has to move easily and freely. The focus here is rather on moving with enthusiasm, speed and vigor to generate body heat. Therefore the speed recommended here is the fastest of the three *Ayurvedic* methods. This type of practice is very suitable for morning hours in winter and summer. It transforms anger, frustration or excess of sexual energy into a creative force with plenty of zest. The Fourth Level of Suryanamaskar Practice falls into this group.

**Suryanamaskar Practice to Balance Kapha Dosha**

To balance the earth and water quality of *kapha dosha,* the third method focuses on the physical and stamina aspect of the body by increasing its strength and purification. Much attention is paid to the strength developed during each posture, and to the accumulation of that strength during the repetition of the Suryanamaskar cycle. The length of time used for each and cycle is the longest of all three methods. Toning of the muscles is stressed against the stretching aspect, thus allowing for increased stamina. In this method, exhalation should be longer than inhalation, which helps practitioner achieve the perfect weight, fights lethargy and sadness, and increases faithfulness, hopefulness, humility, and courage. This type of practice is the best for autumn and spring.

# 7

# SHAVASANA

Every yogic practice ends with the relaxation posture called *shavasana,* also known as the dead man's pose or the corpse pose. This is one of two *asanas* used for relaxation in the *hatha* yogic curriculum. The other one, *makarasana,* is usually done only during the practice of prone postures, such as *bhujangasana, shalabasana,* and *dhanurasana,* i.e. while lying on the stomach. Relaxation postures provide rest and relieve tension found not only in the body but also in the mind. With this technique, complete rest and rejuvenation is reached in a matter of minutes. In the advanced stage, *shavasana* approaches the effects of *yoga nidra*.

The relaxation period which follows Suryanamaskar is equally important to the practice itself as it allows the body the chance to readjust its energies and remove toxins from the blood stream. During Suryanamaskar practice many physiological parameters increase, for example heart rate, blood pressure, the metabolic rate, brain waves and breathing rate among many other, which corresponds to the activation of the sympathetic nervous system. The relaxation calms these systems, balancing the earlier effects of the practice by lowering the heart rate, blood pressure, metabolic rate, brain waves or breathing rate among other parameters, which corresponds to the activation of the parasympathetic nervous system. In this manner through such combined activation of both systems the body is revitalized, stimulated and balanced. Rest in *shavasana* until your breath and heart rate return to their normal resting state and all muscles are without any tension. Depending on the skill, this may take 5 to 10 minutes' time.

*Shavasana* is a very useful practice, especially in the modern world where life is increasingly more demanding and stressful. It is one of the best-known techniques for addressing the problems of stress and tension. In the West, there are other similar techniques to *shavasana* or the more advanced technique of *yoga nidra,* for example, Johannes Schultz Autogenic Training, the Progressive Relaxation technique by Edmund Jacobson, Sophrologic Dynamic Relaxation by Alfonso Caycedo, Suggestology by Georgi Lozanov, Relaxation Training by Richard Lazarus, Relaxation Response by Herbert Benson, etc. However, all of these techniques depend on four basic conditions being met in order to achieve the condition of relaxed quietness:

1) Quiet and isolated place.
2) Comfortable body position (*asana*).
3) Focus of the mind.
4) Passive inner attentiveness or attitude of passive watchfulness.

From childhood we rely on movements of our extremities,

trunk, spinal column and especially facial muscles. Once these skills are developed, we use them throughout our school, professional, family and social lives. Our breath is used not only to oxygenate our body but also for talking, singing, smelling, etc. We use various sensory faculties to obtain knowledge from the external world. In other words, we are conditioned to be prepared for an extraverted lifestyle.

In yoga, we are taught to experience our body and being from within, without the interference of all these external factors. In the *Yoga Sutras, Maharishi* Patanjali says that '*asana*' means experiencing a steady and comfortable state of the body from within without manipulating our breath. We are to do nothing but maintain passive inner awareness of our bodies and our selves. So, while using such quiet body awareness, try not to interfere, just observe without emotional involvement.

To minimize uncomfortable experiences, make sure that your bladder and bowels are empty and that you are not hungry or thirsty. Make sure that your clothing is sufficiently loose and comfortable, not too hot or too cold, and that you have a clean blanket to lie on. If it is cold outside, you may need extra clothing or a soft blanket to cover yourself in order to be comfortable. In other words, try to foresee and pre-empt any likely disturbance while practicing *shavasana*.

## Simplified and Brief Description of Shavasana

**Technique:**

1) Lie on your back with your arms along your body.

2) Keep your legs straight and resting easily apart, about 40 to 50 cm (16 to 20 inches). Let your feet lie flat, your toes pointed slightly to the side.

3) Place both hands to the side, about 15 to 20 cm (6 to 8 inches) from your body. Slowly turn your head to the right and the left, and then keep it in a neutral position.

4) Close your eyes.

5) Breathe from the abdomen, and observe your breath.

6) Focus your attention on the flow of air at the tip of your nose.

**Useful Tips:**

1) Do not open your eyes; keep them closed.

2) Focus your attention inwards.

3) Do not move your body once you have assumed a comfortable position.

4) Allow yourself to relax as much and as deeply as possible.

**Benefits:**

1) Removes physical and mental fatigue.

2) Brings instant feelings of freshness and rejuvenation.

3) Regular practice reduces symptoms of stress and tension, such as high blood pressure, resting heart rate and breaths per minute, along with many other psycho-somatic reactions.

## Detailed and Full Description of Shavasana

**Technique:**

1) Assume the supine position described in the previous section.

2) Initially, while scanning the body, release any tension or stress which comes to your attention. Notice whether your body is warm or cold, blocked or open, painful or relaxed, etc. Attend to any tension, contraction, cramps, or pain, etc., in your body. Remember that you are not expected to visualize or imagine anything. Rather, you are to passively observe and experience the actual inner state of your body.

3) As you notice these different experiences, try to readjust that body part first by micro-movements then by gross movements. As you move to the next part of your body with your inner 'scanning', try to avoid revisiting the same area twice or making any additional voluntary movements.

4) Notice any gross movement or subtle micro-adjustment in any part of the body after you have performed a mental scan of it. Note the reason of the inner event which causes it.

## The 'Conscious Body Scanning' or 'Rotation of Awareness'

### Technique:

This describes a preferred sequential order to relax your body. Remember to start with your dominant side, for most people, this means the right side. Remember that as you 'rotate your consciousness' or perform a 'conscious scan' of your body, you may find tension or blockages somewhere. Try to remove them, or at least minimize them first through micro-adjustment and only later by gross movements.

1) Right leg: big toe →other toes in sequence →sole of the foot →top of the foot →heel →ankle joint →foreleg →calf muscle →knee joint →thigh (inner side, back side, outer side and front side) →groin →hip joint →buttock →whole of the right leg from the trunk to the sole and the toes.

2) Left leg: big toe →other toes in sequence →sole of the foot →top of the foot →heel →ankle joint →foreleg →calf muscle →knee joint →thigh (inner side, back side, outer side and front side) →groin →hip joint →buttock →whole of the left leg from the trunk to the sole and the toes →both the legs (toes to trunk).

3) Trunk: perineal region →pelvic region (front, right, left, back, and inside, if possible) →stomach region (four sides and inside) →chest region (four sides and inside).

4) Right arm: thumb and fingers of the right hand →palm

→back of the hand →wrist joint →forearm →elbow joint →upper arm →shoulder joint (front, outer side, top, back) →arm pit →pectoral area at the front of the chest →scapular area at the back of the chest →whole of the right arm from the neck to the finger tips.

5) Left arm: thumb and fingers of the left hand →palm →back of the hand →wrist joint →forearm →elbow joint →upper arm →shoulder joint (front, outer side, top, back) →arm pit →pectoral area at the front of the chest →scapular area at the back of the chest →whole of the left arm from the neck to the finger tips →both the arms from the finger tips to the neck.

6) Neck: neck region (four sides and inside).

7) Face:

   a external features of the face: chin, lower lip, upper lip, right cheek, left cheek, nose, eyelids, eyebrows, eyes, ears, jaws.

   b internal features of the face: mouth cavity (gums, teeth, hard palate, soft palate, uvula) →right nostril →left nostril →back of the eyes →ear cavities →whole of the face region.

8) Area of the vertebral column: cervical spine →dorsal/ thoracic spine (upper, middle and lower dorsal) →lumbar spine →sacro-coccygeal spine →whole spinal area.

9) Head: forehead →right temple →left temple →back of the head →top of the head →skull cavity, if possible →whole of the head region.

10) Glottis area: the 'speaking' muscles of the glottis.

11) The whole body: a quick final scan from the top of the head to the finger tips and the toes, including the spine.

12) Breathe deeply from the abdomen, and observe your breath.

13) Focus your attention on the flow of air at the tip of your nose and let it go.

As you progress, this conscious scan of your body can help you determine whether you are imagining things or are actually sensing, feeling and experiencing relaxation in different parts of the body. Initially you may find that your attention span is rather short and your mind easily goes elsewhere. If that is the case, bring it back to the conscious practice of your body scan. With practice, such unconscious 'journeys' will cease to occur. As you gain skill relaxing your body, you will find that this 'rotation of consciousness' will take a very short time and your body will be conditioned to go instantly into relaxation mode.

One of the secrets of deep relaxation is the relaxed state of your glottis muscles that are used for articulating your voice. They are directly connected to the mind. When there are no thoughts, then there will be no activity of these muscles.

## Preparatory Technique for Tensed and Stressed People

Some people are so stressed and tensed that they may find it difficult to do *shavasana*. In order to help them, experience a state of relaxation, first tense the muscles, one by one, to the maximum and then rapidly release that tension. A description of the technique follows:

Assume the supine position described in Simplified and Brief Description of Shavasana. You can introduce a gentle smile throughout this practice.

Place the legs, heels and toes in the *shavasana* position, and bring the arms to the side of the body, fists touching the thighs. Bring your legs together and your arms close to the trunk, and start tightening the whole body, from toes to head, part by part, according to the sequence suggested below:

1) Tighten the toes and feet; be sensitive to the soles of the feet.

2) Tighten the ankle joints and then the calf muscles.

3) Pull the knee caps and tighten them, and then tighten the thigh muscles.

4) Squeeze and compress the buttocks and pull them inwards.

5) Exhale, sucking in and tightening the abdominal muscles.

6) Tighten your fists.

7) Stretch the arms out and tighten them.

8) Inhale, expanding the chest and tightening it.

9) Compress and tighten your face fully.

10) Now your whole body should be tightened, but try to tighten it even more.... tighten...tighten.

11) After 20 to 30 seconds of this, release and relax the whole body - let it go.

12) Place the legs slightly apart, hands slightly away from the sides, just as suggested in the Simplified and Brief Description of Shavasana.

13) Relax the whole body completely with the techniques suggested in the Detailed and Full Description of Shavasana.

# 8

# MANTRAS USED FOR SURYANAMASKAR

## Surya or Solar Mantras (12)

ॐ मित्राय नमः ।

**om mitrāya namaḥ ।**

*Salutations to the Friend of All.*

This mantra is chanted in praise of the *Mitra* (friendly, friend of all) nature of the Sun, which makes life possible. Therefore he is lovable as a true friend and called *Jaganmitra*. We have seen earlier that life on Earth is possible thanks to the existence of the Sun, whose energy is essential for photosynthesis in plants, the beginning of the food chain. Invoking this mantra thus helps us be friendly with everyone, just as the Sun is with the universe.

ॐ रवये नमः ।

**om ravaye namaḥ ।**

*Salutations to the Shining One.*

This mantra is repeated in praise of the Sun (*ravi*: praised by all because it shines), who has the supportive nature to benefit all. This is the *tej* or glow of the Sun. The one who is worshipped in this way, because of the limitless blessings shone on all life, is called *Ravi*. The light of the moon, the heat of fire, or *yagna kunda* are all possible because of the *tej* of the Sun-God. The shining faces of true saints and sages have this glow on their faces, this is also due to the *tej* of the Sun-God. The seven chakras in the body which distribute energy throughout the body represent the same principle. By chanting this name we hope to imbibe these characteristics of the Sun.

### ॐ सूर्याय नमः ।

**om sūryāya namaḥ** |

*Salutations to the Inducer of Activity.*

This is the Sanskrit derivation of the word *Surya* (director or stimulator), the one who stimulates (directs) the world into action. In its dynamic aspect, *Surya* starts all daily activities which are essential to life; it is the symbol of cosmic energy. By chanting it we praise the stimulating nature of the Sun, hoping that at the same time this mantra will give us the strength and intelligence to become a stimulator of various activities around us. It is in this aspect that *Vedic* mythology paints the Lord of Heaven crossing the sky on a fiery chariot drawn by seven horses. The seven horses represent the seven levels of existence: materialistic, astral, heavenly *devas*, divine souls who transcended the ego, enlightened *siddhas* and the ultimate reality. The seven horses also represent the seven colors of the rainbow and the seven *chakras*. Here *Surya* symbolizes the light of supreme consciousness, which controls all these seven planes of existence.

ॐ भानवे नमः ।

**om bhānave namaḥ |**

*Salutations to Him who Illumines.*

The one who not only is illumined himself but also gives luster to the whole world is *Bhavane* (giving luster, light or beauty). This nature of the Sun first illuminates itself and afterwards gives light to everything around it. By chanting this mantra we can become enlightened, and once we reach that state, all around us may also become enlightened (lit.. 'to remove darkness'). The Sun is a physical representative of a divine teacher (*guru*) who removes the darkness of *avidya*, just as the darkness of the night is removed by dawn.

ॐ खगाय नमः ।

**om khagāya namaḥ |**

*Salutations to the One who Moves Across the Sky Daily and Creates the Basis of Our Time Measurement.*

The Sun's daily movements across the sky have created the basis of our measurement of time (*kha*: sky or space, *ga*: one who moves or stimulates our senses). Of the objects in the sky which appear to us to be moving, the Sun is by far the most prominent. It is, and has been, the cause of day and night for eternity. This mantra acknowledges the existence of the Sun, its rays and its warmth everywhere in cosmic space. It is considered that there is nowhere in the whole universe that the Sun's influence will not penetrate. Repeating this mantra can give us the strength to be as stable and permanent as the Sun is.

ॐ पूष्णे नमः ।

**om pūṣṇe namaḥ |**

*Salutations to the Nourisher of the World after its Creation.*

The Sun is the source of all strength just as nutrition is; it helps to provide *Pushan* (nutrition) to all life on Earth in direct and indirect way. Its basic characteristic is supporting life, the very existence of which depends on the Sun. The Sun is the source of all food, and food is the only source of energy that builds the body and makes it possible to act. Therefore one should be grateful to the Sun-God. Chanting this mantra allows us to tune in to that energy which supports and sustains life.

ॐ हिरण्यगर्भाय नमः ।

**om hiraṇyagarbhāya namaḥ |**

*Salutations to the One who Possesses Power to Develop Energy and Vitality.*

*Hiranyagarbha* is known as the golden egg in which *Brahma* was born as the manifestation of self-existence. It is the one whose central part is as bright as gold, who is fertile and who is the progenitor of all (*hiranyagarbha*: possessing power to develop energy and vitality in virile semen). The whole universe is contained in *hiranyagarbha* in its potential form prior to manifestation. He is the storehouse of all energies (macrocosmic mind and vital life energy). Therefore *Hiranyagarbha* is *manas* and *prana,* responsible for the systematic working of the organic parts of the world. Chanting this mantra allows us to become as pure inside as gold.

ॐ मरीचये नमः ।

**om marīcaye namaḥ |**

*Salutations to the Rays of the Sun.*

*Maricha* is the name of one of *Brahma's* sons, just as the rays emanate from the Sun by whose mere presence darkness is eradicated (*marichi*: destroyer of darkness, mirage, and disease). It is the aspect of the Sun, the rays and its heat that may form an image of water, but one cannot quench one's thirst with only an image. He creates all types of such illusions. When one is as bright as the Sun, no darkness can exist inside or anywhere around it. This concept of darkness relates not only to physical darkness but also to the mental equivalent, and anything, which can flourish in darkness. For example, various pathogens can exist in lower temperatures where there is darkness, such an environment being essential for their survival. The Sun's ultraviolet rays have the power to eradicate those pathogens. Another meaning of *marichi* is the one who makes one aware of his sins and it also indicates the power, which cures disease. The vibration of this mantra has the power to dispel darkness and its negative effects all around us.

## ॐ आदित्याय नमः ।

**om ādityāya namaḥ |**

*Salutations to the Eternal Celestial Light.*

This is one of many names given to *Mahashakti*, the universal mother. As the mother of all gods, she is limitless and inexhaustible; the creative power of the ultimate reality from which all other powers begin. The Sun is one of her children or manifestations; one born of Aditi is called *Aditya* (*Aditya*: attractor, one born of *Aditi*). Brihaspati is the husband of Aditi, and was priest to all the Gods. The Sun is the worthy son of these two, being made in the image of his celestial parents, Aditi and Brihaspati. He is the true follower of customs, traditions and commandments of his divine parents.

## ॐ सवित्रे नमः ।

**om savitre namaḥ |**

*Salutations to the Vivifying Power of the Sun.*

*Savitre* (begetter, arouser) represents the Sun before rising, before it can stimulate man to his daily waking activity. The Sun is the one which always activates others but He Himself is also full of activities. When the Sun rises in the morning all creatures, from worms and insects to birds and animals start their daily work. *Surya* is the Sun after sunrise, when activity has already begun. Chanting this mantra awakens the vivifying power of the Sun.

ॐ अर्काय नमः ।

**om arkāya namaḥ |**

*Salutations to the One who is Fit to be Revered.*

*Arka* (fit to be revered) is the name given to the one worthy of worship because of its own intrinsic qualities. *Arka* also means energy, and the Sun is the source of unlimited energy. This worship by mantra repetition allows us to gain these qualities of the Sun ourselves.

ॐ भास्कराय नमः ।

**om bhāskarāya namaḥ |**

*Salutations to the One who Leads to Enlightenment.*

This final salutation respects the Sun as a symbol of the revealer of great transcendental truth. As the One who illumines, as the One who is a glow (*tejas*), a light (*prakash*), or is refulgent (*bhaskara*), the Sun may grant our prayers so that we, too, may become as illumined as the Sun. He has imbued the entire universe with light; there is light inside and outside our body; He is the witness of all our acts, physical and mental. Therefore accept the Sun's help and perform your work happily. The Sun lights up the path on our journey to the ultimate goal of *moksha*.

## Bija Mantras

An alternative way to chant the mantras while doing Suryanamaskar is the series of six *bija* mantras *Hrām, Hrīm, Hrūm, Hraim, Hrāum, Hrah* which are repeated twice during one round.

| Asana (traditional naming convention) | Surya Mantra | Bija Mantra |
|---|---|---|
| Pranamasana | Om Mitraya Namaha | Om Hrām |
| Hasta Uttanasana | Om Ravaye Namaha | Om Hrīm |
| Padahastasana | Om Suryaya Namaha | Om Hrūm |
| Ashwa Sanchalanasana | Om Bhanave Namaha | Om Hraim |
| Parvatasana | Om Khagaya Namaha | Om Hrāum |
| Ashtanga Namaskara | Om Pushne Namaha | Om Hrah |
| Bhujangasana | Om Hiranyagarbhaya Namaha | Om Hrām |
| Parvatasana | Om Marichaye Namaha | Om Hrīm |
| Ashwa Sanchalanasana | Om Adityaya Namaha | Om Hrūm |
| Padahastasana | Om Savitre Namaha | Om Hraim |
| Hasta Uttanasana | Om Arkaya Namaha | Om Hrāum |
| Pranamasana | Om Bhaskaraya Namaha | Om Hrah |

**TABLE 5:** Asanas with corresponding Surya and Bija mantras.

Often the *bija* mantras *Hrām, Hrīm, Hrūm, Hraim, Hrāum, Hrah* are combined with the solar mantras, resulting in the table below:

| **Asana** (traditional naming convention) | **Bija and Surya Mantras** |
|---|---|
| Pranamasana | Om Hrām Mitraya Namaha |
| Hasta Uttanasana | Om Hrīm Ravaye Namaha |
| Padahastasana | Om Hrūm Suryaya Namaha |
| Ashwa Sanchalanasana | Om Hraim Bhanave Namaha |
| Parvatasana | Om Hrāum Khagaya Namaha |
| Ashtanga Namaskara | Om Hrah Pushne Namaha |
| Bhujangasana | Om Hrām Hiranyagarbhaya Namaha |
| Parvatasana | Om Hrīm Marichaye Namaha |
| Ashwa Sanchalanasana | Om Hrūm Adityaya Namaha |
| Padahastasana | Om Hraim Savitre Namaha |
| Hasta Uttanasana | Om Hrāum Arkaya Namaha |
| Pranamasana | Om Hrah Bhaskaraya Namaha |

**TABLE 6:** Asanas with corresponding Bija joined with Surya mantras.

Or sometimes the bija mantras *Hrām, Hrīm, Hrūm, Hraim, Hrāum, Hrah* may be repeated twice and then combined with the solar mantras as shown in the table below:

| **Asana** (traditional naming convention) | **Double Bija and Surya Mantras** |
|---|---|
| Pranamasana | Om Hrām Hrām Mitraya Namaha |
| Hasta Uttanasana | Om Hrīm Hrīm Ravaye Namaha |
| Padahastasana | Om Hrūm Hrūm Suryaya Namaha |
| Ashwa Sanchalanasana | Om Hraim Hraim Bhanave Namaha |
| Parvatasana | Om Hrāum Hrāum Khagaya Namaha |
| Ashtanga Namaskara | Om Hrah Hrah Pushne Namaha |
| Bhujangasana | Om Hrām Hrām Hiranyagarbhaya Namaha |
| Parvatasana | Om Hrīm Hrīm Marichaye Namaha |
| Ashwa Sanchalanasana | Om Hrūm Hrūm Adityaya Namaha |
| Padahastasana | Om Hraim Hraim Savitre Namaha |
| Hasta Uttanasana | Om Hrāum Hrāum Arkaya Namaha |
| Pranamasana | Om Hrah Hrah Bhaskaraya Namaha |

**TABLE 7:** Asanas with corresponding double Bija and Surya mantras.

At the end of Suryanamaskar practice, once all cycles are completed, it is customary to repeat the folowing mantra after these twelve mantras:

*"Om Shree Savitre Suryanarayanaya Namaha".*

## Surya or Solar Mantras (108)

These are the 108 names of *Surya,* which may also be repeated during Suryanamaskar practice:

*Om Arunaya Namaha, Om Sharanyaya Namaha, Om Karunarasasindhave Namaha, Om Asamanabalaya Namaha, Om Artharakshakaya Namaha, Om Adityaya Namaha, Om Adibhutaya Namaha, Om Akhilagamavedine Namaha, Om Achyutaya Namaha, Om Akhilagnaya Namaha, Om Anantaya Namaha, Om Inaya Namaha, Om Vishwarupaya Namaha, Om Ijyaya Namaha, Om Indraya Namaha, Om Bhanave Namaha, Om Indriramandiraptaya Namaha, Om Vandaniyaya Namaha, Om Ishaya Namaha, Om Suprasannaya Namaha, Om Sushilaya Namaha, Om Suvarchase Namaha, Om Vasupradaya Namaha, Om Vasave Namaha, Om Vasudevaya Namaha, Om Ujjvalaya Namaha, Om Ugrarupaya Namaha, Om Urdhvagaya Namaha, Om Vivasvate Namaha, Om Udhatkiranajalaya Namaha, Om Hrishikeshaya Namaha, Om UrjasvalayaNamaha,Om ViravaNamaha,OmNirjarayaNamaha,Om Jayaya Namaha, Om Urudvayavirnimuktanijasarakrashivandyaya Namaha, Om Rishivandyaya Namaha, Om Rugchutrea Namaha, Om Rukshachakraya Namaha, Om Rujuswabhavachittaya Namaha, Om Nityastutyaya Namaha, Om Rukaramatrukavarnaroopaya Namaha, Om Ujjvalatejasea Namaha, Om Rukshadhinathamitraya Namaha,*

*Om Pushkarakshaya Namaha, Om Luptadantaya Namaha, Om Shantaya Namaha, Om Kantidaya Namaha, Om Ghanaya Namaha, Om Kanatkanakabhooshaya Namaha, Om Khadhyootaya Namaha, Om Lunitakhiladaivatyaya Namaha, Om Satyanandasvaroopinea Namaha, Om Apavargapradaya Namaha, Om Arthasharanyaya Namaha, Om Aekakinea Namaha, Om Bhagavatea Namaha, Om Srushtistityantakarinea Namaha, Om Gunatmanea Namaha, Om Ghrunibrutea Namaha, Om Bhruhatea Namaha, Om Bhrahmanea Namaha, Om Aishvaryadaya Namaha, Om Sharvaya Namaha, Om Haridashvaya Namaha, Om Shourayea Namaha, Om Dashadiksamprakashaya Namaha, Om Bhaktavashyaya Namaha, Om Ojaskaraya Namaha, Om Jayinea Namaha, Om Jagadanandaheatavea Namaha, Om Janmamrutyujaravyadhivarjitaya Namaha, Om Ounnatyapadasancharaya Namaha, Om Rathasthayinea Namaha, Om Asurarayea Namaha, Om Kamaneeyakaraya Namaha, Om Abjavallabhaya Namaha, Om Anthabrahhiprakashaya Namaha, Om Achintyaya Namaha, Om Atmaroopinea Namaha, Om Achyutaya Namaha, Om Amareashaya Namaha, Om Parasmaijyotishea Namaha, Om Ahaskraya Namaha, Om Ravayea Namaha, Om Harayea Namaha, Om Paramatmanea Namaha, Om Tarunaya Namaha, Om Vareanyaya Namaha, Om Grahanampatayea Namaha, Om Bhaskaraya Namaha, Om Adimadhyantarahitaya Namaha, Om Soukhyapradaya Namaha, Om Sakalajagatampatayea Namaha, Om Suryaya Namaha, Om Kavayea Namaha, Om Narayanaya Namaha, Om Pareashaya Namaha, Om Teajoroopaya Namaha, Om Shree Hiranyagarbhaya Namaha, Om Hreem Sampatkaraya Namaha, Om Aim Ishtarthadaya Namaha, Om Ashuprasannaya Namaha, Om Shreematea Namaha, Om Sheayasea Namaha, Om Bhaktakotisoukyapradayinea Namaha, Om Nikhilagamavedhyaya*

*Namaha, Om Nityanandaya Namaha.*

*Om Shree Savithresuryanarayanaswaminea Namaha*

## Other Mantras

There are many other mantras that may be used for the practice, either at the beginning of each round or during the performance of the individual *asanas* used in Suryanamaskar. Some of them are: *Pranava* (*Om* or *Aum*), *Om Jyotir Namaha*, the classical *Vedic Gayatri*, the *Gayatri*-2, with its seven specific sounds: *Om Bhu, Om Bhuvah, Om Svaha, Om Mahe, Om Tapeh, Om Janah, Om Satyam*, or the less frequently used *bija* mantras *Lam, Vam, Ram, Yam, Ham, Am*; they are pronounced more like the following words: Lang, Nang, Rang, Yang, Hang and Ang.

At the end of the Suryanamaskar practice one can use yet another closing mantras called *Surya Mandala Stotram*:

आदित्यस्य नमस्कारं ये कुर्वन्ति दिने दिने ।
जन्मान्तरसहस्रेषु दारिद्र्यं नोऽपजायते ॥
नमो धर्मविधानाय नमस्ते कृतसाक्षिणे ।
नमः प्रत्यक्षदेवाय भास्कराय नमो नमः ॥

*ādityasya namaskāraṁ ye kurvanti dine dine |*
*janmāntarasahasreṣu dāridryaṁ no'pajāyate | |*
*namo dharmavidhānāya namaste kṛtasākṣiṇe |*
*namaḥ pratyakṣadevāya bhāskarāya namo namaḥ | |*

*One who performs Surya Namaskar regularly does not face poverty*

*[it relates to richness of health and intellect], does not face early death or suffer from disease. Oh! Lord Bhaskara, you are the dharma incarnated (you yourself are all the divine virtues). You are the witness to all my deeds, good and bad. You are the only God in shape and form. I bow to you (with all my body, mind and soul).*

# 9

# PSYCHIC CENTERS, CHURNING THE CHAKRAS

Yogic science, being a complete science, describes precisely and in detail the esoteric anatomy and physiology of the *jivatma* or individualized soul (Self). In brief, the *jivatma* consists of two principles, consciousness and inert matter. It is the consciousness that abides in and is hidden in the matter. This individualized consciousness is called *Atma* or *Atman* and lives in the material structure, which consists of three bodies: the physical or gross body (*sthula sharira*), the subtle body (*sukshma sharira*), and the causal body (*karana sharira*). The physical body has two parts: *annamaya kosha* (food sheath) and *pranamaya kosha* (vital air sheath). The subtle body, which is much subtler than the gross, consists of two parts: *manomaya kosha* (mind, emotional sheath) and *vijnanamaya kosha* (intellect sheath). Subtler still is the causal body, which consists of the *anandamaya kosha* (bliss sheath). These three bodies (five sheaths) are completely inert by comparison to *Atma*. Yoga has devised a method by means of which one can look at and observe these three bodies and gain conscious knowledge of them. It is called *Atma Vijnana* (science of the Self), which leads to *Atma Jnana*. Readers who are interested in further study of this esoteric science are requested to refer to other books specializing on the subject, such as *Science of the Soul (Atma Vijnana)* by Shree Swami Vyas Dev Ji Maharaj or to *Classical Hatha Yoga* by Shree Swami Rajarishi Muni.

In our psychic body (*pranamaya kosha*) there are many energy centers, the most important of which are the seven *chakras* (wheels). *Pranic* energy circulates through these *chakras* with a much higher intensity than is found elsewhere in the body. On a gross level, the scientific community locates these psychic centers on nerve plexuses and endocrine glands. Bridging the gap between modern medical sciences found primarily in the West with the science of Yoga is not easy; translating from one system to the other is a difficult task.

Activating *chakras* takes place when our mind focuses its attention at the physical area where they are located. Thus, it is important to learn where they are located. Below is the approximate location on the physical body (*annamaya kosha*), yet one needs to remember that they are really located on the pranic body, *pranamaya kosha*.

*Muladhara* - in men, it is located half way between the anus and genitals; in women, just behind the cervix.

*Swadhisthana* - located in the sacrum, in the front there is its set-off point located just above the pubic bone.

*Manipura* - in the spine area at the level of the navel but its set-off point is the navel itself.

*Anahata* – located on the spine at the sternum or the breastbone, with its set-off point on the lower part of the breastbone.

*Vishuddha* – located on the spine just behind the throat, its set-off point is at the base of the throat, between the collar bones.

*Ajna* – located in the center of the head; its set-off point is the halfway point between the eyebrows (*Bhrumadhya*).

*Sahasrara* – the top of the head, a 'thousand petalled lotus'.

As we perform Suryanamaskar, compression at the physical level stimulates the psychic centers connected with it. This happens regardless of whether we focus our mind in that place or not. However, adding that awareness greatly increases such stimulation, helping to awaken and purify that psychic center. As we join *mantra* repetition along with *chakra* awareness, we should develop a feeling that the *mantra* vibrates in the psychic center. With advanced practice, this feeling eventually becomes an actual experience of the *mantra* vibrating in the *chakras*.

During repeated practice of Suryanamskar cycles in a *vinyasa* mode, our mind, when *ida* and *pingala* are balanced, is focused repeatedly on these psychic centers in a preordained sequence. This practice, called 'churning of the *chakras*', charges the *chakras* with *prana shakti*, which 'ignites' them. Eventually, this culminates in spiritual awareness.

The following table shows the relation between the various *asanas* in the Suryanamaskar sequence with the *chakras* they activate:

| Asana (traditional naming convention) | Chakra |
|---|---|
| Pranamasana | Anahata |
| Hasta Uttanasana | Vishuddha |
| Padahastasana | Swadhisthana |
| Ashwa Sanchalanasana | Ajna |
| Parvatasana | Vishuddha |
| Ashtanga Namaskara | Manipura |
| Bhujangasana | Swadhisthana |
| Parvatasana | Vishuddha |
| Ashwa Sanchalanasana | Ajna |
| Padahastasana | Swadhisthana |
| Hasta Uttanasana | Vishuddha |
| Pranamasana | Anahata |

**TABLE 8:** Asanas with corresponding Chakra.

10

# DIETARY CONSIDERATIONS

*"Food is consciousness"*, state the Upanishads, one of the most revered scriptures of India. Other Yogic scriptures also stress the importance of proper foods, with *mitahara* (appropriate diet) being a central concept. In fact, proper food establishes the context for all yogic practices; it is so very important that it is dealt with in the very first chapter of famous yogic scriptures such as the *Hathapradipika* or *Gheranda Samhita*. The *rishis* who wrote these scriptures were not stupid or ignorant; these intuitive sages first experimented on themselves with the foods, which later enhanced their divine practices.

## Comparison of Western and Eastern Thought on Food

According to Indian scriptures and also modern science, food has the power to nourish and purify the body and soul. Therefore it either supports our activities or it pollutes our body, and through it our minds, which is equivalent to

inhibiting much progress in those activities.

The East and the West think differently about food. Western scientists are concerned primarily with the nutritive value of foods, so their analysis is based on protein, fats, carbohydrates, vitamins, minerals, etc. A balanced diet is recommended on the basis of quantity and proportions. The source of the food is de-emphasized and recommendation is based on the requirement or non-requirement of an item alone. Physical health is the main goal, and the impact of food on mind and behaviour is not generally considered important.

On the other hand, Eastern sages have focused on the impact of foods on our mind and behavior. The source of food is Brahma, and all living beings are born of and sustained by it. Hence the source, season, geography and psychophysical constitution of food are all important. Yogis, like Svatmarama, Charandasa, Gheranda, Vasishta, etc., included *ahara* as one of *mahavrata* components along with *ahimsa, satya* etc. The Indian concept of *ahara* is not limited to physical characteristics. It includes all types of intake from the environment, including our thoughts and the sensations of the sense organs. Life includes all *pancha koshas*. For that reason, Eastern sages recommend *yuktahara* or *mitahara*.

## Indian Thought on Food

Many cultures recognize that you are what you eat; that food in its subtle form becomes your thoughts, that food determines human mental attitude, and that that, in turn, determines human values. From the Indian point of view, food is responsible for our personality. Consider this quotation from the *Upanishads*:

> "On purity of foods depends purity of internal organs, purity of internal organs leads to stability of memory, and if memory is stable, the person remains free from all sorts of mental conflicts."
>
> *(Chandogyopanishad 7-26-2)*

This view is supported elsewhere in Indian literature:

> "Pure foods make *citta* pure, leading to the arousal of pure thoughts, resulting in the blissful condition of internal and external organs."

The subtle aspects of food which make it pure are as follows: the source of the food (pure or impure), the mental attitude with which it was cooked, the mental attitude with which it was served, the mental attitude with which it was consumed, whether we eat to live or live to eat, whether food has been shared or consumed alone.

Modern Western science would say that energy is necessary for the body, and that oxygen, water, and food supply us with that energy. However, Indian thought says that food transforms itself into *rasa,* which is of three types:

1) The essential, which provides nutrition to the subtle body (mind, intellect, ego, etc).

2) The less subtle, middle type works on or nourishes the seven *dhatus* of the body.

3) The third type is the waste material thrown out by the digestive system, lungs, skin, etc.

> "There are four food types: those which are chewed, sucked, licked and drunk."
>
> *(Chandogyapanishad VI/5/1 & Shiva Samhita V/73-74)*

## Yogic Food

Yogic *shastras* (teachings) explain that, as far as the body is concerned, *prana* is of five different sorts, some of which directly control the mechanism of food transformation into *rasa* and its absorption. Thus *prana* in the heart region is responsible for every intake of breath, *samana* controls the digestion and assimilation of food, and *vyana* distributes the *rasa* throughout the whole body. Excretion is accomplished by *apana*. *Udana* regulates our thoughts, emotions or learning and speaking capability. The body-mind complex functions well only when *yuktaharavihara* is observed, otherwise the very *ahara* that would otherwise be beneficial may cause many disorders.

There is a frequent question asked as to how much food a person should eat. Indian masters of Yoga have commented on this issue in many scriptures. For example the *Vashishta Samhita* (I/50) recommends the following quantity of food:

1) A *muni* should consume 8 mouthfuls.

2) A *sannyasi* and *vanaprasthi* should consume 16 mouthfuls.

3) A *grihastha* should consume 32 mouthfuls.

4) A *brahmachari* should consume as per his capacity and requirement.

Yogi Charandasa says that the appetite should be satisfied but at the same time there should be no physical lethargy after eating. The *Bhagavad Gita* (VI/17) recommends neither overeating nor under-eating; a balanced quantity should be maintained (*yuktaharavihara*). The two most important scriptures of *hatha* yoga, the *Gheranda Samhita* and the *Hathapradipika*, describe the same idea in their concept of *mitahara*.

- ½ of the stomach should be filled with solid food
- ¼ of the stomach should be filled with water
- ¼ of the stomach should be kept empty for the free movement of air.

Another important matter is what one should eat and what one should not eat. The selection of food items can be viewed from many perspectives, for example the philosophical, the *Ayurvedic* or the Yogic.

The philosophical perspective considers how the visible world is made. Therefore we need to consider the three basic qualities (*gunas*) in the universe, namely:

- *Sattva* – light in weight and illuminating, it is an indicator of purity, creativity and bliss.

- *Rajas* – stimulant, hyperactive and fickle, it is an indicator of impatience and pain.

- *Tamas* – heavy in weight, masking consciousness, it is indicated by ignorance, darkness and immobility.

On the basis of the dominating *guna*, foods are classified as *sattvika, rajasika* or *tamasika*. The *Bhagavad Gita* (B.G.) classifies these three food types as follows:

- *Sattvika* increases vitality, energy, vigor, health, joy and cheerfulness, which are savory and oleaginous ... *(B.G. XVII/8)*

- *Rajasika* is bitter, sour, saline, over-hot, pungent, dry and burning and produces pain, grief and disease. *(B.G. XVII/9)*

- *Tamasika* is stale, tasteless, stinking, cooked overnight, refused and impure. *(B.G. XVII/10)*

The *Ayurvedic* perspective is somewhat different, basing its theory of food classification on the *Ayurvedic tridosha* theory as follows:

- Either subsiding or aggravating *Vata*.

- Either subsiding or aggravating *Pitta*.

- Either subsiding or aggravating *Kapha*.

*Ayurvedic* foods are also classified on the basis of:

- *Rasa*, the taste, which is subdivided into six types (bitter, sour, pungent, salty, sweet, astringent).

- *Virya* , the effect of hot or cold.
- *Vipaka* , the heaviness or lightness of digestive force required.

*Ayurveda* recommends eating according to one's constitution and temperament. Making changes to food items according to the season and to natural laws is the key to a healthy life. Deliberate, willful violation of these rules (*prajnaparadha*) is a starting point for all kinds of disorders.

The Yogic selection of proper food items is more specialized than the above concepts. The two preceding classifications create a foundation upon which Yoga developed. Since the ultimate goal of Yoga is also different, this difference makes sense. In fact the quality and quantity of food is so very important that Yogic scriptures declare, "without controlling food habits, the practice of Yoga is futile". The meaning of Yoga is "to join", which here means "joining with the law of nature". In that context, the Yogic dietary regime has the following three objectives:

1) **To achieve the highest goal of Yoga**

   The role of food as conducive or non-conducive is considered. *Atyahara* (overeating) is non-conducive and *mitahara* is conducive. Food should be non-stimulating and non-irritating (i.e. the opposite of *rajasika*), and also not cause lethargy, sloth or sleep (*tamasika*).

2) **Just enough for bodily needs and health**

   Yogic food should not increase body weight. The foods should be sourced without causing anyone harm.

**3) The Yogic diet has preventive and therapeutic advantages**

Disease is caused not only by wrong food type, but also the frequency and time of eating, and the quantity and combination of foods play a role. The right choice of food is selected by taking into consideration body type, season, and geographical region.

The quality of food we consume can be wholesome or unwholesome. In the initial phase of yogic practice, one should consume *kshira* (rice boiled in milk and sugar). However, when one's practice is well established, no such regimen is binding. If *kshira* is unavailable, a yogi can eat food items as specified below:

> "Wheat, rice, barley and *shastika* rice, milk, ghee, sugar, butter, sugar candy, honey, dry ginger, the patolaka fruit, green gram and the rain water collected when sun is in *magha*..."

(*Hathapradipika I/62*)

> "Rice, flour or barley or wheat, green gram, horse gram, pure and free from husk. A Yogi should eat patola, surana, mana, kakkola, sukasaka, dradhika, karkat, rambha, dumbari, kantakantaka, amarambha, balarambha...he may eat leafy vegetables: balasaka, kalasaka, patola, patraka, vastuka and hamalocika."

(*Gheranda Samhita V/17-20*)

Even among these whole foods, selection should be made on the basis of food properties like:

- "Easily digestible, agreeable, soft and sticky, which nourishes the elementary substances of the body, which is desirable and proper."

  (*Gheranda Samhita V/29*)

- "Nutritious, sweet and unctuous, products of cow's milk, nourishing, of their own choice and suitable for the practice of Yoga."

  (*Hathapradipika I/63*)

The yogic scriptures also define very clearly what unwholesome food is:

- "Bitter, sour, pungent, salty or hot, green vegetables, sour gruel, oil, mustard, sesame and alcohol, fish, meat, curd, buttermilk, kulattha, berries, oil cakes, asafetida, garlic, etc."

  (*Hathapradipika I/59*)

- Bitter, sour, salt, pungent, scorched food, curds, buttermilk, heavy vegetables, liquor, palm nuts, jackfruits, kulattha, masura, pandu, kusmanda, vegetable stems, gourds, berries, kapittha."

  (*Gheranda Samhita V/23-25*)

The table below presents a summary of which foods are wholesome and which unwholesome:

| Wholesome | Unwholesome |
|---|---|
| From the point of view of *Rasa* - sweet is recommended. | From the point of view of *Rasa* - bitter, pungent, sour, salty have not been recommended. |
| From the point of view of effect - cooling food is preferred. | From the point of view of effect - heat producing food should be avoided. |
| From the point of view of digestion - light food is preferred. | From the point of view of digestion - heavy food requiring long digestion is to be avoided. |
| Foods which are subsiding *Vata, Pitta* or *Kapha* are preferable. | Foods which are aggravating *Vata, Pitta* or *Kapha* should be avoided. |
| Food items that are fresh, pure and agreeable are preferable. | Food items which are heated over again, stale, impure and non-agreeable should be avoided. |

**TABLE 9:** Summary of wholesome and unwholesome foods.

Since the recommendations for proper yogic food are quite elaborate, let us spend some time considering the benefits of such a proper yogic diet. The reasoning behind it is clearly stated in an old yogic encyclopedia, which is based on about fifty-one other yogic manuscripts. This encyclopedia is the *Hathatattvakaumudi,* which means *"Light on the Principles of Hatha Yoga"* and it was written somewhere between 1700 and 1800 C.E. Here there are a few selected *shlokas* (verses) recommending the yogic diet:

1) Consumption of pure food results in a purifying *sattvic,* effect, which also purifies the *nadis.* As a result of bad food, *apana* is not controlled, *mulabandha* is not perfected, feces cannot move out.

(*Hathatattvakaumudi IV/36*)

2) Impurities resulting from the consumption of bad food produce defects in the mind which are: *kleshas,* lethargy, and also obstacles such as diseases caused by the vitiation arising from *vata.*

(*Hathatattvakaumudi IV/36*)

3) In the initial phase of yogic practice, if one does not observe moderate diet, one may suffer from a host of diseases, and therefore success in Yoga will not ensue.

(*Gheranda Samhita V/16*)

4) All mental disturbances and bodily tremors occur and are aggravated by wrong diet.

(*Yoga Rahasya VI/6*)

5) Excess consumption of food causes increase of feces, which causes stuffiness and lethargy. Reduced intake of food quickly reduces feces, which causes repulsion in *dhatus.*

(*Hathatattvakaumudi IV/36*)

6) *Tamasika* & *rajasika* food items are the root cause of sleepiness, laziness, and diseases. Practitioners who adhere to rules of moderate diet face less trouble.

(*Hathatattvakaumudi IV/36*)

7) In the context of *nadisuddhi*, the observance of moderation in diet, speech and sleep is advisable. Conducive food items are *ghee, ksira* and sweet foods. The use of 'white' salt is prohibited in all yogic texts. Food items which are bitter, sour and pungent cause excess burning, therefore they should be completely avoided.

(*Hathatattvakaumudi IV/36*)

So far we have looked at the dietary discoveries and recommendations used by traditional Indian sciences for hundreds of years. They are very strongly correlated with any successful yogic practice, including the practice of Suryanamaskar. Without implementing them, it is hard to expect any significant progress in Yoga and meditation, especially by spiritual *sadhakas*. Hence I have decided to mention this subject in the Suryanamaskar manual. Please note though that this publication does not intend to be a dietary guide; the subject of proper nutrition and eating habits is quite vast and would deserve a separate publication. Yet I would also like to bring forward an extremely important scientific discovery made about eighty years ago in the West. It appears that, for one reason or another, our medical establishment has forgotten about it. I have chosen to include it here because without implementing the benefits of this scientific finding immediately in our proper daily diet, it will be very hard to move forward. The name of the 'forgotten secret' is digestive leukocytosis. Another issue of equal importance is the widespread incidence of food poisoning attributable to the practices of modern agriculture and the food industry.

# 11

# 'DIGESTIVE LEUKOCYTOSIS' OR 'PATHOLOGICAL LEUKOCYTOSIS'

A dictionary defines the term "leukocytosis" as an increase above the normal level (approximately 1% of blood by volume) in the total number of white blood cells (WBCs). Such an increase would normally be the result of the body's ability, when it perceives that it is under attack, to send white body cells to attack and destroy an invading organism, whether that organism occurs in association with malignancy, inflammation, allergic reaction, or infection caused by viruses, bacteria or parasites.

Until the Rudolph Virchow experiment in early 1897 it was believed that this immunological WBC reaction of the human body was only connected with harmful and dangerous situations. To Virchow's great surprise, however, he found that the WBC count would go up in completely healthy subjects after they had eaten food.

Such an immunological reaction was confirmed many times subsequently by various teams of researchers around the world. Nobody quite understood why the body treated food, which was supposed to nourish it, as an enemy and mobilized its immunological system several times a day, as though it were in a stressful and harmful situation of infection, exposure to toxic chemicals, or trauma. It appeared to be quite a wasteful management of the body's defensive resources, because, even in a situation of a common fever or cold, the body appeared to need to divert some of its resources to 'counteracting' improperly digested food. At that time a specialized name of 'digestive leukocytosis' was given to this little understood phenomenon.

Some thirty-three years later, in 1930, Paul Kouchakoff M.D., working at the Institute of Clinical Chemistry in Lausanne, Switzerland, was running a similar experiment and expecting similar results of an increased WBC count; yet he was unable to recreate the digestive leukocytosis reaction in spite of several attempts. After a thorough analysis he made a remarkable discovery: his subjects simply happened to have eaten some uncooked food just before the experiment. To confirm his initial observation he experimented with a great variety of foods, serving his subjects the same food, on one occasion cooked and then on another uncooked, and in each case he had the same results, namely that the cooked food caused the phenomenon of digestive leukocytosis while the uncooked did not. Kouchakoff, in trying to understand the problem, found that thermal processing (cooking) changed the bioactivity of the enzymes already existing in the food. After cooking, food became enzyme deficient because the higher temperatures simply 'killed' the enzymes. WBCs, on the other hand, rich in enzymes normally needed to digest viruses, bacteria or foreign pathogens in general, were in consequence being used by the body to make up the difference for the purpose of digestion. An interesting aspect of this discovery was that raw foods, which might have been expected to be subject to a degree of contamination, even after washing, did not evoke this reaction.

Kouchakoff deemed this response to food pathological because the body was using its immunological defensive potential for the purpose of digestion. He discovered that the phenomenon only occurred when the food was cooked over a certain temperature. Having tested many different foods, Kouchakoff found that this 'critical temperature' differed over a range of approximately 18°F (10°C). There was even a temperature for water, 191°F (87°C). The lowest temperature for a 'food' was for cow's milk at 191°F (88°C). His experiments determined that the critical temperature had to be exceeded for half an hour.

This pathological situation can be much helped by taking, for example, enzyme supplements, which will help to complete digestion in the first part of the gastro-intestinal tract and thus allow the digested food to be absorbed in the small intestine. Taking capsules with enzymes will also help the liver, pancreas and other organs to avoid overwork and, eventually, exhaustion. Many researchers are convinced that the organs of each individual person have a certain limited genetic potential to generate enzymes. Overuse and abuse of these vital organs will result in the limit being reached sooner, and thus may end up in premature death. Of course, the obvious option is to eat raw foods, which are naturally abundant in the specific enzymes that will support digestion, and, as Kouchakoff stated, will tend to nullify the adverse effects of cooked or adulterated food if consumed at the same time.

In the human intestine there are between 300 and 1000 different types of bacteria. Some are beneficial, of course, but for those that are not, undigested food can become their meal. During such a bacterial process many toxins can be produced as part of metabolic breakdown; starches and sugars, for example, may undergo fermentation while proteins, depending on their source, may be subject to putrefaction. These toxins will be diffused into the blood stream, where they will have to be dealt with by the immune system, if they are not to cause harm.

Enzymes are one of the component parts of foods. They assist in the process of autolysis (self-digestion). This phenomenon of autolysis has been known about for a long time. It is a confirmed fact that carbohydrates, such as fruits, vegetables or grains, contain a higher concentration of amylase, which is responsible for the digestion of carbohydrates, but lesser amounts of lipase, which aids the digestion of fats, or protease, which aids the digestion of protein. On the other hand, seeds and nuts, oils, and dairy foods, which are higher in fat content, contain relatively higher concentrations of the enzyme lipase, thus helping in the digestion of their fats.

A banana is a good example of how a food can self-digest its own ingredients. It consists of about 20 percent starch when green and not ripe. The enzyme amylase changes the banana into 20 percent sugar when the fruit is kept warm for a few days, and it then becomes speckled with brown 'sugar' spots. The banana's amylase is effective on banana starch, but it is much less so on other starches, such as potato starch. The autolysis process functions in all foods, including meat.

Professor Artturi Virtanen, a biochemist from Helsinki and Nobel Prize winner, demonstrated that enzymes are released in the mouth from raw vegetables when they are chewed; they come into contact with the food and start the process of digestion. What is interesting is that these food enzymes are not denatured by stomach acid, as suggested by some researchers, but remain active throughout the digestive tract.

The process of oxidization, occurring during long shelf storage, improper food processing, or cooking at a temperature exceeding the critical figure, has the ability to change irreversibly the internal structure of the proteins out of which the enzymes are built. After any such change the enzymes lose the capacity to perform their original function and such food becomes deficient. Such loss is clearly likely to contribute to illness in the long run because of the increased demand on valuable metabolic enzymes to aid digestion. As we have seen above, and contrary to popular belief, digestion of cooked food demands much more energy than the digestion of raw. To demonstrate this, many tests were run on various animals, where the animals were fed the same types of food as normal, except that the food was cooked instead of being raw. For example, a calf was still given its mother's milk, except that the milk, instead of coming directly from the udder, was first commercially processed (pasteurized and homogenized). In another case a tiger was fed cooked deer. The reaction of the animals to such denaturalized food was more dramatic than in the case of humans. After about a week of the experiment they developed such a bad problem with their gastrointestinal tracts that they, most unfortunately and regrettably, died. Perhaps humans do not die because they go through a long and slow adjustment period to denaturized food.

The fact that digesting cooked food takes more energy than digesting raw can be observed easily by running a simple experiment at home. Try eating the same type and amount of food on one occasion cooked and then the next uncooked. Use, for example, oat flakes or an apple, and observe that, after the cooked version of the food, you feel much heavier and often sleepy, while after the uncooked version you feel alert, fully energetic, and ready to go. The reaction of the body being sleepy is easily experienced after consuming a 'hearty' and heavy dinner, when, in addition to most foods having been cooked, they will also have been improperly combined.

Our detrimental habits of cooking food, some of which has already been processed with agricultural and food industry chemicals, of eating junk food, of drinking alcohol, and of using drugs of various kinds, result in a call for large quantities of enzymes from our genetically predetermined supply. Illnesses such as simple colds or fevers deplete this supply further. A body in such an enzyme-deficient and therefore weakened state is a primary target for all types of disease, such as heart disease, cancer, or diabetes, and for other degenerative problems of the kind that have become so common in the West. However, this problem is no longer confined to the West, as more and more nations in the developing world, due to their increasing affluence, have begun to adopt the more 'advanced' Western diet and life-style. The well-known Dr. Dean Ornish sums this up as: "You eat like US, you live like US and you die like US." The statistics show an unrelenting decline in this regard. For example, in the last two years India has become the world leader in diabetes, hardly a sought-after distinction by any nation. Furthermore, although there are many clinical reports from around the world demonstrating that alternative healing methods of exclusively raw food diets can cure most diabetes cases within a month, the majority of sufferers are convinced that they must continue using insulin until their 'natural' end.

## The Effect of Raw Food versus Cooked Food on the Human Immune System

As described above it was a Swiss research team led by Dr. Paul Kouchakoff which made the remarkable and important discovery that unaltered and natural foods do not cause an increase in WBC count, unless cooked for a certain length of time at a temperature exceeding the relevant critical level. Even then, if accompanied by raw foods of equivalent or higher critical temperature, the increase in WBC count does not occur. They also discovered that the consumption of food that was processed by the food industry (refined, mixed with chemicals as additives and/or preservatives, pasteurized, homogenized, etc.) always caused a rise in the number of white cells in the blood, unless accompanied by at least two raw foods of higher critical temperature than the processed food.

Following the Rudolph Virchow experiment in 1897 this little understood phenomenon of increasing WBC count in healthy people after eating was given the neutral name of 'digestive leukocytosis'. Later, having gained an increased understanding of its causes, Kouchakoff and his team re-named it 'pathological leukocytosis', since it was regarded as a non-normal response on the part of the body to highly altered food. Unless accompanied by an appropriate amount and kind of raw food, each food after heating, even if originally unprocessed, would cause an increase in WBC count, and if the food concerned had first been subject to any other kind of denaturalization, as in the manufacturing process, then it was treated by the body as some type of pathogen or a trauma, and not only would the WBC count increase, but the proportions of the various types of WBC would also be changed, as can occur in illness.

It also became clear that food enzymes can be destroyed by long storage or by improper food processing. The worst offenders of all were foods which had been refined, pasteurized, homogenized, or treated with additives for preservation or flavour. Refined foods include white flour of any kind, white sugar, white non-whole-grain rice, and some wheat and barley, etc. Pasteurization is a process in which milk or juice is flash-heated to high temperature in order to kill bacteria and other pathogens, and also to delay spoilage. Homogenization is a process also seen in milk and juice production, in which high pressure is used to break up fat globules in milk and to reduce microbiological activity in raw juice. Treatment with additives can involve the adding of chemicals to delay spoilage or to enhance texture or taste. In other words, the worst offenders were the foods which were the most changed from their original natural state.

If you still doubt the extent to which your health depends on the food you eat, read the famous report, *The China Study* (Campbell, 2006). This describes the largest survey ever run on the relationship between mortality rates and diet and lifestyle, conducted on 6,500 people in 65 rural counties of China over 20 years. This study and its overwhelming statistics proved beyond any doubt that human well-being and health depend on the consumption of the right kinds and amounts of unaltered and natural food.

## 'New' Western Thought on Food

Further evidence to support that conclusion appeared in a report in The Huffington Post on 1 June 2012:

> The Ornish [dietary] program affects gene expression - turning on genes that prevent disease and turning off genes that promote breast cancer, prostate cancer, colon cancer, and heart disease. Over 500 genes were

beneficially affected in only three months. Ornish also directed a study with Nobel Prize winner Dr. Elizabeth Blackburn that showed the Ornish diet and lifestyle method increases telomerase by nearly 30 percent in three months. (Telomerase is an enzyme that repairs and lengthens telomeres, the ends of our chromosomes that control how long we live.) "Our genes are a predisposition, but our genes are not our fate," Ornish explained. "Some people think, 'Oh, I have bad genes, there's nothing I can do', what I call 'genetic nihilism'. They often become inspired to know that there's a lot they can do - not to blame, but to empower.

Practicing hundreds or thousands of Suryanamaskar rounds at the fourth level requires much training, with similarities to the amount of effort required in professional sport. If the practitioner is able to maintain an average speed of about 7.5 seconds per round throughout the whole practice session, and so perform 1008 rounds in a little more than 2 hours, it is very likely that the loss of body weight will be about 6 to 8 pounds. By any standard such performance brings the practitioner close to the performance level of the best and most highly trained sportsmen in competitive sport.

Perhaps one of the toughest races known in sport is the 'Ironman' competition that combines a 4 km (2.4 mile) swim, a 180 km (112 mile) bicycle ride, and a 42 km (26.2 mile) run (marathon). It makes sense, therefore, to look more closely at what top professional sportsmen do in order to bring their psychophysical performance up to such levels. Not so long ago it was hard work and talent that made a sporting star. Nowadays, in the age of technology, when the exchange of information is very quick, any new training routine or edge in training methods very quickly becomes widely known and copied. As a result differences in training tend to be minimal and natural talent is at a premium. Exercise physiologists have found that almost invariably the deciding factor in the difference between the elite athlete and the moderate performer is the recovery rate. In other words, the speed with which the sportsman's organism can fully regenerate itself after competition or training is ultimately responsible for the best performance. Important parts of that recovery and regeneration process are both the ability to attain very deep levels of relaxation and also the standard of nutrition supplied and absorbed. Experience has shown that the right diet can account for up to 80 percent of the total recovery process. Optimal nutritional choices thus become the means to attain peak performance. This idea can be carried beyond the field of professional sports. For the non-sportsman also, achieving a standard of what may be called 'premium nutrition' would provide the basis for a productive, full and enjoyable life from birth to its natural end. Such a person would learn how to thrive in life.

Through personal experimentation, which has included long periods of fasting and detoxification, I have discovered that, when I have used the right foods, my performance has reached levels that have amazed me. If, on the other hand, I have had no access to my preferred diet for a while, my personal performance has invariably deteriorated to a significant degree. Through experimentation I have realized that the perfect form of food for me is organic, whole, and plant-based, with most of it being consumed fresh and raw. This is the diet consisting of 'super-foods'. By studying selected books containing accounts of world-class nutritional experiments, I have realised that most people believe in unsubstantiated myths about food, such as:

- Human beings must eat meat to get all the nutrients.
- Animal proteins are optimal for building human body and muscles.
- Reducing animal products, such as meat or dairy, will cause weakness and will facilitate the development of illnesses such as osteoporosis, anaemia, etc.

In fact, the wonderful effects of using the so-called super-foods in the daily diet would be likely to surpass your highest expectations. Among the many benefits you would notice would be a diminution in the effects of aging and a reduction in your equivalent biological age; body fat would decrease to a more normal level; coffee, tea or white sugar would not be needed to boost your energy; your mood and mental clarity would be enhanced; depth of sleep would improve; your immune system would become so strong that you would visit doctors rarely or not at all; cholesterol would decrease to a healthy level; and your desire to eat junk foods and snacks in-between meals would cease, etc. The very tangible improvements taken from this 'high-performance' nutritional method would for the most part be retained, even if the diet occasionally included fish or some other animal-based product.

# 12

# TOXINS AND OTHER HARMFUL SUBSTANCES IN FOOD

The average European consumes annually about 54 kg of one or more of the 8000 additives and preservatives used by the food industry today. Perhaps the most popular are Aspartame (E951) and Monosodium Glutamate (E621).

Aspartame is made from three well-known poisons: 50% phenylalanine, 40% aspartic acid and 10% methanol (wood alcohol). It has been shown to cause brain cancer, diabetes, emotional disturbances, epilepsy, cellular mutations, etc. in laboratory animals. It is a stimulant as well, which damages the central nervous system. Clinical reports from many institutes around the world have proved that fact beyond any doubt.

According to North Carolina University researchers, Monosodium Glutamate increases the chances of obesity by at least 3 times. Jozef Pilsudski University of Physical Education in Warsaw has tested this widely-used substance and found that it negatively impacts neuro-muscular conductivity, causes heart palpitations and increased sweating, causes feelings of anxiety, stress, stomach pains, and migraine headaches, increases blood pressure, negatively impacts sensory perceptions, etc.

India is one of the largest users of chemical fertilizers, pesticides, herbicides, etc in the world. In his book *The Vision of Natural Farming,* Bharat Mansata mentions Baskar Save quoting surveys that show that Indians regularly eat food with the highest amounts of toxic pesticide around the world - "forty times more than what average Americans or Europeans ingest with their food". This research shows that in that process, they risk heart disease, brain, kidney and liver damage, and cancer.

In 1984 the UN Food and Agriculture Organization (FAO) analyzed more than 1,500 samples of Indian pulses, milk, cereals, oils, and meats from different parts of the country. Almost all of the samples were contaminated with DDT (synthetic pesticide) and BHC (other than gamma isomer pesticide), which have been banned in the USA since 1972. Delhi citizens were tested and were shown to have the highest amount of DDT in their body fat - up to 20 ppm (parts per million) while the World Health Organization (WHO) declared that 1.25 ppm of DDT was hazardous. Dr. Krishna Murthy, Chairman of the Scientific Commission that probed the Bhopal tragedy, said:

> "What we are seeing is just the tip of the poisonous iceberg. And even that seems serious enough for us to sit up and take corrective action".

A 1987 report prepared by the American Environment Protection Agency (EPA) revealed the presence of more than 20 hazardous pesticides in the ground water of at least 24 states. However, in California, they have found at least 57 different pesticides in the ground water. The National Academy of Sciences estimates that pesticide residue in food will cause at least 1,000,000 deaths in the present generation.

## Impact of Chemical Fertilizers on Nutritional Value of Food

The nutritional value of our foods has been declining steadily over the years due to the chemical farming prevalent in today's agriculture. For example in a Health Capsule on August 1, 2006 the Times of India reported the following: .....between 1936 and the present day, there has been a 24% drop in calcium, a 28% drop in magnesium, a 10% drop in potassium, a 22% drop in iron and a 81% drop in copper in fruits and vegetables... A researcher from the agricultural department of Banaras Hindu University in Varanasi said that the current organic content of the top soil in the area of Varanasi is only 0.5%, while historically it was always at the 3.5% level. That is the reason why all plants growing in that area are stressed by not getting enough quality nutrients.

The figures concerning the decline of various constituents of various foods appear to be rather low when compared with those in a report produced in 1996 by the Food Laboratory of Karlsruhe, Germany. The laboratory ran a comparison investigation to establish the existence of any nutritional differences occurring within a period of ten years that is between 1985 and 1996. Most of the popular grains, vegetables and fruits were tested for the nutrient content of eighty nutrients. For example, for broccoli it was found that there was 68% less calcium, 52% less folic acid and 25% less magnesium. Potatoes lost 70% of their original calcium content and 33% of their original magnesium content. Apples lost a huge 80% of vitamin C and bananas lost 84% of folic acid, 96% of vitamin B6 and 24% of potassium. Spinach lost 68% magnesium and 58% vitamin C. (Please note that these numbers are selected to show the point and they are not all inclusive of the changes of all eighty nutrients. Those interested can find full information through the internet or can purchase the laboratory publication.)

Recently the University of California published their own report after 10 years of experiments with tomatoes. Their research has shown that on average, organic tomatoes have twice as many nutrients, including the very important (bio) flavonoids, also known as phytochemicals, when compared to chemically grown tomatoes. This 'discovery' is very significant because an increased presence of flavonoids is strongly correlated with better resistance to cancer. At this point it is worth noting that the bioflavonoids 'die', i.e. are destroyed, when cooked or frozen. Their bioactivity depends on the temperature of the environment, which must be in the range between 32°F (0°C) and 111°F (44°C). Also bioflavonoids tend (about 95%) to condense in the skin of the fruit or vegetable and about 1.5 mm (1/20 in) under the surface, which means that by peeling the fruits or vegetables, we remove the most beneficial part of the plant.

At the same time, researchers from the University of California at Davis ran comparative studies on the kiwi fruit grown in Marysville, California. They found that organic kiwis had 17% more polyphenols (anti-oxidants) and 14% more vitamin C when compared to non-organic kiwis. In addition, they found that organic kiwis have much higher levels of almost all nutrients.

Similar reports have come from Europe. For example, experiments run at the 725-acre farm at the University of Newcastle, England have shown that organically grown vegetables and fruits have up to 40% more anti-oxidants than the non-organic ones. Similar differences were found in the levels of other nutrients like iron or zinc. The report noted even higher differences in the level of anti-oxidants in the milk of organically fed cows finding a level that was 50-80% higher than in regular commercial milk.

In addition, a group of researchers from the University of Michigan, Ann Arbor, USA ran a meta-analysis of 293 research cases which demonstrated that natural organic farming is not more expensive than "chemical" farming. In fact, they stated that, in developing countries, organic farms can provide up to three times more food than 'chemical' farms, and that, in rich and developed countries, organic farms can compete successfully with standard chemical farming.

Taken together, these facts show that the quality and purity of the food we eat, or in other words, the nourishment and perhaps even the toxins we take in with the food we eat, are of paramount importance to our well-being. The importance of proper food cannot be overemphasized. Therefore a wise person, acting intelligently, will try to avoid situations that are hopeless, such as when the proverbial bucket is being filled with water but holes at the bottom are so large that they would drain the water even faster than it could be filled. So if you want to experience a rapid improvement in your health, general fitness, and spiritual progress, first look at your eating habits and correct them wherever necessary.

Now-a-days food poisoning is encountered all too frequently. It is often caused by a combination of 'chemical' farming, processed foods (addition of food additives and preservatives, and restriction of the amount of nutrients for reasons of cost), wrong food combining, and cooked food intake (without a compensating minimum of 51% daily intake of raw food). The result is the absolute necessity of detoxifying of the body. The need for a process of natural detoxification was recognized long ago, well before food became as heavily denatured as it is now. This was the insight of the three fathers of Western medicine, Hippocrates, Galen and Paracelsus. The latter, for example, declared: "Fasting is the greatest remedy - the physician within". All of three of them prescribed fasting as the most potent detoxification technique. However, it is essential to note that there is a world of difference between fasting and starvation. Rudolph Ballentine, M.D., founder of the Center for Holistic Medicine in New York City, sums up this difference lucidly by saying: *"The destruction of starvation, and the cleansing and repair that happen in a well-managed fast, are polar opposites."* During a properly executed fast large amounts of metabolic waste, toxins and poisons are removed naturally through organs such as the liver, kidneys, lungs, and skin. Through a fast undertaken according to scientifically established principles we can rejuvenate and prolong significantly the life of both animals and humans. Experiments have shown that regular and periodical fasts have doubled (or more) the life-span of certain animals. What was of great significance in these findings was not only that the length of life was increased but that, most importantly, the quality of life was also dramatically improved. Finally, it should be emphasized that fasting is not supposed to be some type of masochistic 'technique' to strengthen the ego. Rather, if used judiciously in appropriate circumstances it can be most potent both as a remedy and as a preventative.

In fact, the most valuable recommendations to improve the food that you eat do not cost more money. Doing what is necessary just takes some knowledge and motivation. Certain corrections can be made at almost no cost.

Before you read the practical hints below, based on the information presented at the beginning of this chapter, read the following thoughts, which have stood the test of time:

> "Humans live on one-quarter of what they eat; on the other three-quarters lives their doctor."
>
> *(Egyptian pyramid inscription, 3800 B.C.)*

> "Let food be thy medicine."
>
> *(Hippocrates, 460 – 377 B.C.)*

"Very few people know what real health is, because most are occupied with killing themselves slowly."

*(Albert Szent-Gyorgyi, Ph.D., Hungarian-born American biochemist; Nobel Prize in medical science)*

# 13

# HINTS TO IMPROVE YOUR EATING HABITS

1) Stop the use of any and all forms of polished rice. Start buying only UN-POLISHED whole grain rice. It should be cheaper to buy unpolished rice because the procedure to obtain it is much shorter and much less demanding. Refining of rice or all other grains means removing the germ or the part of grain from which a new plant can grow along with the outer bran layers. Removing the bran together with germ also removes all the oils of the grain which could go otherwise rancid and spoil the flour. Without the germ and the bran its long shelf-life is assured along with finer textured and higher rising bread. Additionally the white and refined cereals have become a status symbol.

2) Stop the use of white, industrial salt (sodium chloride). It is an inorganic chemical compound which is totally useless and harmful to the body. It is the next to sugar as a leading additive that contributes to ill health and

disease. It is the presence of salt which traps and holds water. From ancient times, Indian *rishis* have strongly disapproved of its use. If you must use salt, use only *kala namak* (Indian black rock salt), sea salt or any other natural or rock salt.

3) Stop the use of refined white sugar since it has no nutritional value; it has no enzymes, no phytochemicals, no fibre, no proteins, no minerals, no vitamins and no fat. Our body needs glucose or fructose instead of sucrose of which consists the refined white sugar. The sucrose is obtained in a chemical reaction by bleaching it with calcium phosphate to obtain sparkling white color. After all it should be much cheaper to buy *gur, jaggery,* brown sugar or molasses (sugar cane or beet) than the refined sugar, since its production is much easier and is far less expensive. Clinical reports about the destruction white sugar causes the human body are devastating. The health dangers, which ingesting sugar on habitual basis creates, are certain. Simple sugars have been observed to aggravate asthma, cause mood swings, provoke personality changes, mental illness, and nervous disorders, cause cancer, diabetes, and heart disease, grow gallstones, increase hypertension, and cause arthritis. Because refined sugars lack minerals, vitamins and fiber, and have such a deteriorating effect on the endocrine system, the body must draw upon its own micronutrient stores in order to be metabolized into the body. When these storehouses are depleted, metabolization of cholesterol and fatty acids is impeded,

contributing to higher blood serum triglycerides and cholesterol, and promoting obesity due to higher fatty acid storage around organs and in sub-cutaneous tissue folds. Therefore major researchers and major health organizations (the American Dietetic Association and the American Diabetic Association) agree that sugar consumption in America is one of the three major causes of degenerative disease. One can only presume that it is not very different elsewhere.

4) Stop the use of white, non-whole grain flour of any kind, most especially of the white wheat flour used for chapattis and other breads. Grains in general tend to acidify the system but refined flour acidifies infinitely more. Today's wheat is very different from the one used by our ancestors. In order to increase crops cross-pollination was used and the amount of gluten content has doubled in this wheat hybrid. Nowadays the name 'wheat' could be considered to be just used by convention. The wheat plant has been changed by the 'green revolution' into one that has 42 chromosomes, and could be considered a completely different plant from the original one, grown for hundreds of years, which had only 14 chromosomes. Gluten makes the grain nice and chewy but it also is the cause of allergy; wheat is one of the eight most allergy common foods. Its starch is ten times more difficult to digest than potato starch. Modern wheat is responsible for a great number of complication like acidity, headaches, irritable bowel syndrome, dandruff, fatigue, joint inflammation, diabetes, heart attacks, etc... etc. among many others.

The list of diseases is very long; recommendations for what and what not to do are discussed in detail in the book by William Davis entitled 'The Wheat Belly'. Most people are not gluten sensitive where it will cause illness. However, if you have to eat wheat choose only whole-grain wheat flour.

5) Limit very pungent foods spices (hot and irritating) used in your food. Such spices cause dullness and activate the *tamas* quality, while active and healthy people need to encourage the *sattvic* qualities in order to make better progress.

6) Stop the use of groundnut oils, especially of soya oils. No refined oil of any kind should be used at all. Minimize or better, entirely stop, eating fried foods. In addition, today's soya grown in India is almost entirely genetically modified (GMO) and thus poses a great danger to humans. Experiments by Russian Professor Irina Ermakowa proved beyond any doubt the negative impact of modified soya on laboratory rats and by extension, on humans. Among the many negative effects discovered, worth mentioning particularly is that in only the third generation, the rats showed the following differences: a total loss of fertility; a longer time to reach maturity; degenerative changes in the testicles, liver and pancreas; and early death.

Similarly shocking results with genetically modified corn (NK603) were noticed after two years of experiments at the university in Caen, France by Professor Gillies Seralini's team. This research has been published only recently in 2012 in *The Food & Chemical Toxicology Journal* and has been called "the most detailed research on GMO foods, which was ever published as far as the health results are concerned. The problem with previous testing was that it never lasted over the three month period while the devastating results start showing up after the fourth month of eating GMO foods." This experiment has shown unusual growth of cancer, especially in female rats, vast and devastating results in internal organs, especially liver and kidneys, and premature death. "One can expect that consumption of GMO corn and herbicide called Roundup has a serious negative impact on human health" said Dr. Antoniou, a molecular biologist from King's College, London. The same corn is used for example in breakfast flakes (cereals) and other snacks, tortillas, and corn syrup itself.

7) Use of cow's milk should be limited or banned altogether. Hundreds of clinical reports from around the world show many, many negative effects of ingesting milk products and commercial milk products especially. One of the many negative effects, which contradict popular belief, is the washing out of calcium from the body, thereby significantly weakening the bone structure. And it is a well accepted scientific fact that the homogenization of milk is a primary culprit in arteriosclerosis. For example, in humans, among the many negative reactions, it is the excess of casein in cow's milk that causes production of homocysteine, which blocks veins and arteries and causes overall weakness of connective tissue. Milk casein

is responsible for the enormous creation of mucus, which is collected in the intestines and stops other nutrients from being properly absorbed by the body. Note that milk casein is used to produce strong glues and buttons.

8) Try to buy organic, ecological vegetables and fruits, which were grown without chemical fertilizers, pesticides, herbicides, etc. Clinical data show a devastating impact on the body and a plethora of later diseases when humans use chemically grown plants. Their nutritional value is substandard; sometimes laboratory tests show up to five times less nutritional value than their organically grown counterparts.

9) The importance of water quality should be addressed and properly understood. Our interest in clean, natural water should go well beyond chemical purity as it should also include the physical purity of the water, evidenced by the water crystals. In addition, it should be charged with solar and cosmic energy as natural water is. The importance of this cannot be overstated, yet it is almost unknown to most people, including medical staff. People do not pay enough attention to water despite the fact that the human body consists of more than 70% water. There is a huge weight of medical evidence that good, living, pristine, energized and unpolluted water can be the cause of 'miraculous' cures, yet very few people use that knowledge.

10) Stop drinking soda drinks (coca cola, pepsi cola, limca, etc) as they contain the highly poisonous *Aspartame*, which is used as sweetener instead of sugar to lower the

caloric intake. *Aspartame* is made of three well known poisons and is sold under many different names.

11) Coffee or black tea is only a stimulant. Neither provides any real nutrition, and therefore they are not good. The same applies to other intoxicating drinks like alcohol. So it is best to stop using alcohol entirely or at least drink a little only in the later part of the day.

12) Eating and snacking when not fully hungry should be strictly avoided. Do not eat too often; adults should have at the most two cooked meals per day, preferably one. One should not eat within 3 hours after a full meal. Follow the rule that whenever you are very hungry you eat and that you drink when you are thirsty.

13) Eating agreeable and limited food according to the yogic concept of *mitahara* should be strictly followed. Consider food to be godlike, and before your first bite offer it to God. Do not rush while eating; masticate each morsel thoroughly until it is liquefied before swallowing.

14) Eat at the minimum 51% raw foods in a day. It will 'pacify' your immune system response, which will no longer treat food as an 'enemy' to fight. Pay the utmost attention to how you combine your foods. Look at every meal that you take from the point of view of nutritional value instead of how tasty it is.

15) Do not eat during physical tiredness or mental restlessness. Never eat when negative emotions are running high, for example when angry, afraid, grieving, etc.

# PART - III

- Review of Research
- Personal Experiences
- Benefits of the Practice

# 14

# REVIEW OF PSYCHO-PHYSIOLOGICAL EFFECTS OF SURYANAMASKAR PRACTICE

This chapter contains reviews of relevant research reports which can be useful to the practitioners of Suryanamaskar. One of the main reasons to undertake the practice of Yoga in general and Suryanamaskar in particular is to keep fit. Therefore it is a legitimate concern to ask how these ancient practices can influence physical fitness parameters like strength, strength or cardiovascular endurance, flexibility, body mass index (BMI), and our physiology and our psyche as compared to other types of exercises like swimming, cycling or jogging.

In 1995 Professor Ramesh Bijlani included a special chapter on yogic physiology written by Dr. Mukund V. Bhole in his textbook on human physiology for medical students, *Understanding Medical Physiology*. And in 2002, the bi-monthly U.S. magazine *Yoga Journal* published an article by

Alisa Bauman which described the physiological principles involved in yoga. She reported that a university sports lab at the University of California at Davis tested three yogis for strength, endurance, flexibility, BMI and lung capacity, etc. and found that the yogis' BMI was comparable to the BMI scores of elite athletes involved in such endurance events as marathon running and cycling. Their flexibility compared very favorably with top athletes in the fields of ballet and gymnastics. Their endurance and strength was observed to be near or within the normal ranges. And their lung capacity and cardiovascular endurance was in the range of fairly active athletes.

At the core of yogic practice in general and Suryanamaskar in particular is the chanting of mantras. In Suryanamaskar there are special solar and/or *bija* mantras, which are to be repeated in advanced stages of practice. In 2001 Barnardi et al. published a comparative study on the effect of the rosary prayers and yogic mantras on autonomic rhythms in the British Medical Journal. They wanted to know whether such rhythmic prayers or mantras could, in addition to modifying baroreflex sensitivity, reinforce and synchronize inherent cardiovascular rhythms. This study clearly demonstrated that when recited with the speed of six times per minute, both rosary prayers and yogic mantras had a powerful and synchronous, positive influence on cardiovascular oscillations with increased baroreflex sensitivity.

In the mid 1990s, Japanese professor Dr. Masaru Emoto, Russian professor Dr. Konstantin Korotkov at the Russian Academy of Natural Sciences, professor of medicine Dr. Vyacheslav Zvonnikov, and Dr. Vlail Kaznacheev of the Russian Medical Academy, Dr. Rustum Roy of the State University of Pennsylvania, and many more established that sound vibration impacts the structure of water. Thus, the great mantras that came down from ancient *rishis* have been shown to change water molecules to the most exquisite and beautiful hexagonal water crystals, thereby increasing its overall energy capacity. Water molecules arranged in this perfect hexagonal shape are easily used by the body for various metabolic processes, so instead of only irrigating our cells, they can hydrate our body and profoundly effect on our overall health and performance. For example, the water taken from the Andes Mountains in Venezuela has an energy level of about 40,000 times that of the regular water used by most people in typical urban environments. Indigenous people in the Andes suffer from few diseases and enjoy very long lives without old age debility despite of the difficulty in obtaining highly nutritious foods at altitudes over 5000 metres. Traditional Tibetan medicine has been using this knowledge of the structure of water for centuries; for them, mantra chanting for patient recovery is nothing new or unusual. They say that the chanting corrects the patient's water and the patient is healed.

The body's circadian rhythms are set by the environment and by our lifestyle. The inner rhythms express not only our inner needs but also correspond to outer demands and forces. Professor Wieslaw Romanowski of the Department of Physiology, Jozef Pilsudski University of Physical Education, Warsaw, Poland writes: "Movement and rhythm are characteristic of the universe in which we live...In living organisms, certain rhythmic functional changes occur depending on the periodicity of processes occurring in the outer environment, and are known as exogenous (external) rhythms. There also exists a specific rhythmicity in the biological unit - endogenous (internal) rhythmicity". According to the science of biorhythms, these rhythms can be divided according to their frequency into three groups: (1) low frequency, such as annual, seasonal or monthly cycles; (2) moderate frequency, such as respiratory, heart or digestive cycles; and (3) high frequency, such as the pulsation of enzymatic systems or atoms in crystals. In this study of Suryanamaskar, we are interested in moderate frequency cycles, and "superimpose" on these physiological rhythms a new factor: an ordered, systematic, sequential, energizing, cleansing set of postures, breath, mantras and concentrations on energy centers (*chakras*). In addition, sound vibrations set certain life rhythms in our psychosomatic apparatus. One of the most important body cycles is the one connected the three essential functions maintaining our life, namely digestion, absorption and elimination. Though these three functions go on continuously in the body, there are times in the 24-hour cycle when one function is predominant over the other two. They are of approximately eight hours duration. Digestion or appropriation takes place between 12 noon and 8 p.m., absorption or assimilation takes place between 8 p.m. and 4 a.m. and the elimination takes place between 4 a.m. and 12 noon. The best time for Suryanamaskar practice or in fact for other yoga or any other physical exercise is during the elimination phase, that is between 4 a.m. (*brahma muhurta*) and 12 at noon phase. Less favorable is the period of digestion assuming that stomach has been empty for a minimum 2 to 3 hours. However one should not practice Suryanamaskar or any *hatha* yogic practices during the assimilation phase of the cycle.

Although the body of scientific experiments concerning various mainstream yogic practices grows worldwide, especially in India and in the United States, research on Suryanamaskar is still not a burgeoning field. I have tried to present here descriptions of the few studies specifically related to the practice of Suryanamaskar. Reading them, one should remember that there are many different ways of practicing the Suryanamaskar routine and that the psycho-physiological results are very much related to the mode of practice. For example, some may do only 4 or 5 rounds very slowly while others may choose to do it faster and with many hundreds of rounds. Thus, even though they follow the same set of sequential *asanas*, the overall effect is quite different.

Sinha et al. critically observed the energy cost and different cardio-respiratory changes which occur during the practice of Suryanamaskar (SN). Twenty-one male volunteers from the Indian Army were chosen to practice selected yogic exercises for six days a week for three months. The yogic practice schedule consisted of *hatha* yogic *asanas* (28 min), *pranayama* (10.5 min) and meditation (5 min). In this schedule, participants practiced *kapalabhati* (rapid breathing) for 2 minutes followed by *yogamudra* (a yogic posture) for 2 minutes. After that, they rested until oxygen consumption and heart rate (HR) returned to their resting values. Following this, subjects performed SN for an average of 3 minutes and 40 seconds. After completing three months of training, participants performed the entire yogic practice schedule in the laboratory during their training session and experiments were carried out. Their pulmonary ventilation, carbon-dioxide output, oxygen consumption, HR and other cardio-respiratory parameters were measured during the actual practice of Suryanamaskar. Oxygen consumption was highest in the eighth posture (1.22 ± 0.073 L/min) and lowest in the first posture (0.35 ± 0.02 L/min). Total energy cost throughout the practice of Suryanamaskar was 13.91 kcal at an average of 3.79 kcal/min. During practice, the highest HR was 101 ± 13.5 beats per minute. Sinha et al. concluded that, as an aerobic exercise, Suryanamaskar seemed to be ideal since it involves both static stretching and the slow dynamic component of exercise within lactate or anaerobic threshold, therefore giving optimal stress on the cardio-respiratory system.

Ray et al. studied the effects of training in *hatha* yogic exercises on aerobic capacity and PE after maximal exercise was observed. Forty men from the Indian army (aged 19-23 yr) were administered maximal exercise on a bicycle ergometer in a graded work-load protocol. The oxygen consumption, carbon dioxide output, pulmonary ventilation, respiratory rate, heart rate (HR) etc., at maximal exercise and PE score immediately thereafter were recorded. The subjects were divided into two equal groups. Twelve subjects dropped out during the course of study. One group (yoga, n = 17) practiced *hatha* yogic exercises for 1 hour every morning (6 days in a week) for six months. The other group (PT, n = 11) underwent conventional physical exercise training during the same period. Both groups participated daily in different games for 1 hour in the afternoon. In the 7th month, tests for maximal oxygen consumption ($VO_2max$) and PE were repeated on both groups of subjects. It was observed that the absolute value of $VO_2max$ increased significantly ($p < 0.05$) in the yoga group after 6 months of training. The PE scores after maximal exercise decreased significantly ($p < 0.001$) in the yoga group after 6 months but the PT group showed no change. The conclusion was drawn that the practice of *hatha* yogic exercises together with games helps to improve aerobic capacity in the same way as the practice of conventional exercises (PT) together with games. The yoga group performed better than the PT group in terms of lower PE after exhaustive exercise.

Clay et al. studied the metabolic cost of *hatha* yoga. In order to determine the metabolic and heart rate (HR) responses of *hatha* yoga, 26 women (19-40 years old) performed a 30-minute *hatha* yoga routine of supine lying, sitting, and standing *asanas* (i.e., postures). Subjects followed identical videotaped sequences of *hatha* yoga *asanas*. Mean physiological responses were compared to the physiological responses of resting in a chair and walking on a treadmill at 93.86 m/min [3.5 miles per hour (mph)]. During the 30-minute *hatha* yoga routine, mean absolute oxygen consumption ($VO_2$), relative $VO_2$, percentage maximal oxygen consumption (%$VO_2$ R), metabolic equivalents (METs), energy expenditure, HR, and percentage maximal heart rate (%MHR) were 0.45 L/min, 7.59 ml/kg/min, 14.50%, 2.17 METs, 2.23 kcal/min, 105.29 beats/

min, and 56.89%, respectively. When compared to resting in a chair, *hatha* yoga required 114% greater $O_2$ (L/min), 111% greater $O_2$ (ml/kg/min), 4,294% greater %$VO_2R$, 111% greater METs, 108% greater kcal/min, 24% greater HR, and 24% greater %MHR. When compared to walking at 93.86 m/min, *hatha* yoga required 54% lower $O_2$(L/min), 53% lower $O_2$(ml/kg/min), 68% lower %$VO_2R$, 53% lower METs, 53% lower kcal/min, 21% lower HR, and 21% lower %MHR. The *hatha* yoga routine in this study required 14.50% $VO_2R$, which can be considered a very light intensity and significantly lighter than 44.8% $VO_2R$ for walking at 93.86 m/min (3.5 mph). It was found that the intensity of *hatha* yoga may be too low to provide a training stimulus for improving cardiovascular fitness in spite of previous research suggesting that *hatha* yoga is an acceptable form of physical activity for enhancing muscular fitness and flexibility.

Hagins et al. were interested to see if *hatha* yoga practice would satisfy recommendations for intensity of physical activity, which improves and maintains health and cardiovascular fitness. Since little is known about the metabolic and heart rate responses to a typical *hatha* yoga session, there were three main purposes of this study: (1) to determine whether a typical yoga practice using various postures meets the current recommendations for levels of physical activity required to improve and maintain health and cardiovascular fitness; (2) to determine the reliability of metabolic costs of yoga across sessions; and (3) to compare the metabolic costs of yoga practice to those of treadmill walking. This was an observational study where 20 intermediate to advanced level yoga practitioners, age 31.4 ± 8.3 years, performed an exercise routine inside a human respiratory chamber (indirect calorimeter) while wearing heart rate monitors. The exercise routine consisted of 30 minutes of sitting, 56 minutes of beginner-level *hatha* yoga administered by video, and 10 minutes of treadmill walking at 3.2 and 4.8 kph each. Measures were mean oxygen consumption ($VO_2$), heart rate (HR), percentage predicted maximal heart rate (%MHR), metabolic equivalents (METs), and energy expenditure (kcal). Seven subjects have repeated the protocol so that measurement reliability could be established. He found that, across the entire yoga session, the mean values were, for $VO_2$ 0.6 L/kg/min, HR 93.2 beats / min, %Max HR 49.4, METS 2.5, and energy expenditure 3.2 kcal/ min. Results of the ICCs (2, 1) for mean values across the entire yoga session for kcal, METs, and %MHR were 0.979 and 0.973, and 0.865, respectively. He has concluded that metabolic costs of yoga, which averaged across the entire session represent low levels of physical activity, are similar to walking on a treadmill at 3.2 km/hr, and do not meet recommendations for levels of physical activity for improving or maintaining health or cardiovascular fitness. He has also concluded that yoga practice incorporating Suryanamaskars exceeding the minimum about of 10 minutes may contribute some portion of sufficiently intense physical activity to improve cardio-respiratory fitness in unfit or sedentary individuals.

Raju et al. conducted a study on the effects of yoga on exercise tolerance in normal healthy volunteers. The subjects were twelve normal healthy volunteers (6 males and 6 females) undergoing yoga training for 90 days and were studied for the effect of yoga on exercise tolerance. Their ages ranged from 18 to 28 years. The volunteers were taught only *pranayama* for the first 20 days and later on yogic *asanas* were added. A sub-maximal exercise tolerance test was done on a motorized treadmill by using Balke's modified protocol at the start of the experiment, after 20 days (Phase-I) and after 90 days of yoga training (Phase-II). Pyruvate and lactate in venous blood and blood gases in capillary blood were estimated immediately before and after the exercise. Minute ventilation and oxygen consumption were estimated before and during the test. It was found that post exercise blood lactate was elevated significantly during initial and Phase-I, but not in Phase-II. There was significant reduction of minute ventilation and oxygen consumption only in males in Phase-I and II at the time when the volunteers reached their 80% of the predicted heart rate. Female volunteers were able to go to higher loads of exercise in Phase-I and in Phase-II.

Chaya at al. conducted a study of the effect of long term combined yoga practice on the basal metabolic rate of healthy adults. The purpose of this study was to investigate the net change in the basal metabolic rate (BMR) of individuals actively engaging in a combination of yoga practices (*asanas*, meditation and *pranayamas*) for a minimum period of six months, at a residential Yoga education and research center in Bangalore. In this study, the measured BMR of individuals practicing yoga through a combination of practices was compared with that of control subjects who did not practice yoga but led similar lifestyles. It was found that the BMR of the yoga practitioners was significantly lower than that of the non-yoga group and was lower by about 13% when adjusted for body weight ($p < 0.001$). This difference persisted when the groups were stratified by gender; however, the difference in BMR adjusted for body weight was greater in women than men (about 8% and 18% respectively). In addition, the mean BMR of the yoga group was significantly lower than their predicted values, while the mean BMR of the non-yoga group was comparable with predicted values derived from 1985 WHO/FAO/UNU predictive equations. In conclusion, this study shows that there is a significantly reduced BMR, probably linked to reduced arousal, with the long term practice of yoga using a combination of stimulatory and inhibitory yogic practices.

Malhotra et al. have researched the beneficial effect of yoga in diabetes. Twenty NIDDM subjects (mild to moderate diabetics) in the age group of 30-60 years were selected from the out-patient clinic of G.T.B. hospital. They were on a 40 days' yoga *asana* regime under the supervision of a yoga expert. The thirteen specific yoga *asanas* done by Type 2 Diabetes Patients included suryanamaskar, *trikonasana, tadasana, sukhasana, padmasana, bhastrika pranayama, paschimottanasana, ardhmatsyendrasana, pawanmuktasana, bhujangasana, vajrasana, dhanurasana* and *shavasana*, which are believed to be beneficial for diabetes mellitus. Serum insulin, plasma fasting and one hour postprandial blood glucose levels and anthropometric parameters were measured before and after yoga *asanas*. The results indicate that there was significant decrease in fasting glucose levels from basal 208.3 ± 20.0 to 171.7 ± 19.5 mg/dl and one hour postprandial blood glucose levels decreased from 295.3 ± 22.0 to 269.7 ± 19.9 mg/dl.

Sisodia studied the effect of Transcendental Meditation on selected physiological variables and co-ordinative abilities in judo on sixty judokas studying at various standards at L.N.I.P.E. and Jiwaji University, Gawalior. The variables chosen for the study were: reaction ability, orientation ability, different balance and rhythm ability, and physiological variables such as aerobic power, vital capacity, resting respiratory rate, resting heart rate. Body composition and 't' tests on all the subjects were applied. On the basis of the results, the following conclusions were drawn:

1) In the case of aerobic power performance, Transcendental Meditation did not improve performance significantly in comparison to the non-meditators.

2) In the case of vital capacity, Transcendental Meditation did not show significant improvement among experimental groups as compared to the control group.

3) In the case of total body fat percentage, Transcendental Meditation did not show significant change in comparison to non-meditators.

4) Balance ability in the experimental group improved significantly when compared to the control group.

5) With regard to lean body weight, Transcendental Meditation was found to be ineffective for the experimental group when compared to the control group.

Rychlik has conducted a study of physiological characteristics of a training session in the system of *Ashtanga Vinyasa* (Power Yoga). A single training session of *ashtanga* yoga consists of a dynamic part with Suryanamaskar (up to 50 rounds of Suryanamaskar per session) and a static part with standing postures, followed by sitting postures, calming down postures, isometric postures and final relaxation in *shavasana*. The main goal was to verify the impact of a session on the pulmonary and cardio-vasculatory systems and the analysis of the intensity of the various parts of the whole session, including aerobic and anaerobic capacity. The subjects were seven men 27 ± 3.16 years old, who practiced yoga for 6.1 ± 2.2 years, with body weight 73.37 ± 8.95 kg, body height of 178.73 ± 4.55 cm. All subjects were vegetarians for a number of years. The parameters measured were: (1) body height, weight and composition; (2) VE, $VO_2$, $CO_2$, RQ, f, energy cost with the K4 Gas Analyzer; (3) spirometer test of VC, MVV with Lung Test 1000 measuring instrument; (4) anaerobic power and capacity test (Astrand and Wingate tests). The obtained results were as follows: (1) while aerobic capacity represented average level, mean value was for $VO_2$max ml/kg/min = 43.77, SD = 14.36.; anaerobic capacity (mean for the group): mean power = 7.49 W/kg SD = 0.49, maximal power = 9.64 W/kg SD = 0.51; (2) spirometer tests VC =109.17%, SD =12.29; MVV =129%, SD =9.7; (3) training measurements: HR =128.7 ± 17 b.p.m. (67% ± 9% HRmax); VE = 32 ± 7.3 l/min.; $VO_2$ = 19 ± 3.6 ml/min./kg; energy expenditure = 6.5 ± 1.4 kcal/min. The results showed that the subjects had an average aerobic and anaerobic capacity, however the spirometry was higher with VC =109% and MVV =129%. The intensity of a single training session was average at 129 b.p.m. and oxygen absorption at a rather low level (19 ml/min./kg) with low energy expenditure (6.5 kcal/min).

Sudarshan conducted a randomized wait-listed control study which was aimed at assessing State Anxiety, Trait Anxiety, and Perceived Stress and emotional intelligence after the practice of Suryanamaskar at the work place. Selected subjects for the practice were corporate employees who were compared with other regular employees of the same corporation. The subjects were normal healthy (n = 102) employees from VWF Industries, Mysore, of both genders, were aged between 21 and 60 years, and were randomly assigned into two equal groups, i.e., Yoga Group (51) and Control Group (51). The participants were administered GHQ 12 (General Health Questionnaire) and excluded if scores were > 2. Another exclusion criterion was age; subjects were excluded when their age was below 21 and above 60, and in some cases, subjects with health problems were excluded from the study. One group was taught Suryanamaskar while the other group was doing their routine work. The Spielberg State Trait Anxiety Inventory (STAI) and Perceived Stress Scale (PSS) questionnaires were administered for Anxiety Stress to both groups before and after 21 days. It was found that the data were normally distributed ($p > 0.005$) and the baseline was matched ($p > 0.05$). Repeated Measures ANOVA showed significant difference across group over time on State Anxiety ($p < 0.001$), Trait Anxiety ($p = 0.032$), Perceived Stress ($p = 0.039$) in the yoga group as compared to the control group. It was concluded that Suryanamaskar practiced for 20 minutes helps to reduce anxiety and stress, and the results suggested a possible role to improve quality of work among employees.

Stec conducted a study where the Repeated Measures Design was used to determine the effects of Dynamic Suryanamaskar on anthropometric and physiological variables of selected physical education students at Banaras Hindu University, Varanasi. The subjects were twenty male B.P.Ed. students from the Physical Education Department, Faculty of Arts at Banaras Hindu University. The subjects were tested on selected physiological and anthropometric variables. The physiological variables were: anaerobic power, cardiovascular endurance, positive breath holding capacity, negative breath holding capacity, vital capacity, resting heart rate, resting blood pressure, and resting respiratory rate. The anthropometric variables were: body height, body weight, total body fat percentage, lean body weight, in-breath chest circumference, out-breath chest circumference, and flexibility. The supervised intervention of the Dynamic Suryanamaskar practice included twelve poses and was designed for 45 minutes per session for six days a week for six consecutive weeks. To determine the effect of Dynamic Suryanamaskar on physiological and anthropometric variables of selected physical education students at Banaras Hindu University, Varanasi, One Way ANOVA was used at a .05 level of significance. Least significant difference (L.S.D.) Post Hoc Test for comparison of the paired means of the trials was used. The analysis of variance showed that there was significant difference in relation to cardiovascular endurance (F = 4.443), positive breath holding capacity (F = 3.474), negative breath holding capacity (F = 5.874), vital capacity (F = 2.193), differential chest circumference (F = 5.244) and flexibility (F = 2.136). The 'F' values were found to be significant since these were required to be at 2.13 at .05 level of significance at 7.152 df. The analysis of variance showed that there was not a significant difference in relation to anaerobic power (F = 2.054), resting heart rate (F = .898), systolic resting blood pressure (F = .422), diastolic resting blood pressure (F = 1.880), resting respiratory rate (F = 1.686), body weight (F = .386), fat percentage (F = .882), lean body weight (F = 1.808), in-breath chest circumference (F = .272) and out-breath chest circumference (F = 1.343). The 'F' values were found to be not significant since these were required to be at 2.13 at .05 level of significance at 7.152 df.

Rakesh et al. conducted a comparative study of Suryanamaskar and physical exercises on flexibility, attention and concentration in adolescents. For this longitudinal prospective randomized control study normal healthy (n=82) male schoolchildren of 12-16 years' age (13.31± 1.07), from Vivekananda International Public School in Bangalore were randomly assigned into two groups Yoga and Control after signing informed consent forms. The inclusion criteria were age, sex and health. They were taught Suryanamaskar (SN) and Physical Exercises (PE) respectively. Sit-and-Reach (SAR) and goniometry tests for spinal flexibility and six letter cancellation test (SLC) for attention and concentration were administered to both the groups before and after twenty-eight days. Results have shown that the data were normally distributed ($p > 0.05$) and baseline was matched ($p > 0.05$). Paired 't' test (two-tailed) showed that there was a significant change between pre- and post-study values in both the groups (Yoga, $p < 0.001$ and Physical Exercise, $p < 0.001$) on all the variables in both the groups. There was a significant change between the groups ($p < 0.001$) in SLC, SAR and goniometry (forward and backward). In summary, this study has shown that Suryanamaskar practiced for thirty minutes daily improves spinal flexibility, attention and concentration better than PE in students of twelve to sixteen years of age.

Fondran studied the effect of Suryanamaskar yoga practice on resting heart rate (HR) and blood pressure (BP), flexibility, muscle endurance, and perceived well-being in healthy adults. She has used the traditional *Rishikesh Series* of Suryanamaskar, which consists of 12 *asanas* in the sequence. The 30 participants (24 females, 6 males; mean age 34 years) were randomly assigned to a yoga or control group using the fishbowl technique of random assignment with replacement. After a 3 hour introduction to proper Suryanamaskar techniques, the subjects were directed to perform daily two sessions of Suryanamaskar routine for 10 minutes, each followed by a 5 minute relaxation period, 5 times per week for a period of 6 weeks. When performing the routine, subjects were instructed to hold each posture for the duration of one inhalation or exhalation depending on the movement being performed. Each routine consisted of eight rounds of practice followed by a five minute rest period where they were to lie still in a supine position (*shavasana*) and to follow their natural breath. The entire self-directed yoga practice took approximately 15 minutes to complete. Pre- and post-period measurements were conducted for HR, BP, hamstring flexibility, upper body muscle endurance, and perceived well-being. Inferential statistics with repeated measures methodology (2-way ANOVA) was used to analyze the data. The results have shown significant increase in flexibility with an improvement of 2.9 inches ($p = .000$) and 4.4 push-ups ($p = .003$) after yoga was the training program, with little or no change in the control group. The final conclusion was that Suryanamaskar is effective in increasing hamstring flexibility and improving upper body muscle endurance.

Modak et al. published a book in Marathi in 2010 entitled *Suryanamaskar – from the scientific and medical point of view*; which is a compilation of several studies. In one paper written together with Sudhakar Joglekar which was entitled "Suryanamaskar – one extraordinary viewpoint" he reports the following: (1) it increases the supply of blood from 2 liters to 25 liters per minute; (2) it decreases free fatty acids thereby decreasing overall cholesterol, which chokes the blood vessels, causes the heart problems and increases the blood pressure in the brain; (3) it improves and regulates breathing and blood pressure; (4) it regulates five functions in the brain (speech, touch, smell, etc.); (5) it improves the working of "biological clock", that is the effect of day and night on the brain and body; (6) it regulates the pituitary gland therefore through it influences the whole endocrine system; (7) in 1990 some world famous scientists studied the effect of the sound of various mantras. They found that the *Gayatri* Mantra was the most effective and created over 10,000 sound waves. On the bases of this method he studied sound signals and has done graph tracing and analyzed it by a multi-dimensional voice program (model 5105).

Patwardhan Vinita has studied the effect of Suryanamaskar on human psychology. As far as the emotions are concerned, the Suryanamaskar practice activates the lower parts of the brain, such as the thalamus and hypothalamus, which are responsible for the emotions and which regulate the autonomic nervous system and limbic system. The lower parts of the brain control such emotions as anger, worry, nervousness, etc. The impact of Suryanamaskar on the intellect (*buddhi*) is also positive, as the practice sharpens the mind and intellect. It was found that the consistency of Suryanamaskar practice improves self-confidence and decreases nervousness, anger, and tiredness.

Godbole Avinash and Milind Modak studied "Abnormal Suryanamaskar". The reported advantages of the practice are: (1) it is especially useful in achieving body compactness (sound body); (2) it makes muscles and joints more dynamic and improves their working; (3) it is very useful for people training games and martial arts; (4) since it requires more effort and demands more calorie consumption, it thereby makes the body more powerful and firm.

Khire Usha studied "Importance of Mantra in Suryanamaskar". By 'mantra' are understood sound waves, which contain 'immortal' power. All names of Suryanamaskara begin with the *Omkara*. It consists of all sounds from 'a' to 'z', it gives life to all *chakras* situated in different parts of the human body, and it makes the *chakras*' activities well managed and organized. (1) In the research conducted at Kaivalyadhama (Lonavla) it has been observed that the energy has been created in the body and the minute waves have been experienced in the body.

(2) At Prashanti Kutiram (SVYASA) in Bangalore the chanting of the mantra "*Omkara*" during meditation reduced the number of heartbeats and stabilized the working of the heart. Meditation with the *Omkara* proved positive on the capacity of intelligence. (3) In the age of modern research with the use of computerized and electrical gadgets like EEG, polygraph etc. it showed that *Omkara* stabilizes EEG and it has proved its usefulness for treatment. (4) With the help of modern equipment the frequencies of 400 Hz, 406 Hz and 6 Hz were made heard and it was found that the frontal and occipital lobes working has been improved and increased significantly. (5) At Dhyan Prabodhini an experiment was conducted with 30 adults who were exposed to *Omkara* mantra; it was found that the subjects' quality of life has improved. (6) In an experiment conducted with school and college students it has been observed that, due to use of the *Omkara* mantra, meditation and concentration have improved and also emotional stability has increased.

Datar Arun Chintamani has studied Suryanamaskar and found that it is the king of exercises because of many positive effects which are attributed to this practice: (1) it gives exercise to all muscles of the body; (2) it gives exercise to all joints; (3) it increases body power and breathing capacity and improves the body figure; (4) it avoids disorders of the backbone (*merudanda*), and if any disorder is already there, it will help in healing it to a great extend; (5) it also cures breathing disorders; (6) it improves the posture thus increases the height of youngsters; (7) it regulates the breathing, the heart becomes more active, and it increases lung capacity;

(8) it makes the mind more active and it sharpens both mind and intellect.

Koholi Pavan has studied Suryanamaskar from the point of view of games and sports. Since in Suryanamaskar there are eight yoga *asanas* besides *pranayama,* which regulates the breathing, and the *Omkara,* in addition to other mantras, it naturally has become the best all-around type of exercise. Experiments conducted with Dr. Tehar at Singapore Sports Science Centre proved that Suryanamaskar can be not only a slow speed exercise but also a type of high speed exercise, and in the latter mode it could use up as much as 281 kcal compared to 238 kcal during fast running for the same length of time.

Gurjar Moreshwar compared Suryanamaskar to gymnastics and quoted Greek philosopher Plato (before 427 B.C.), who used to say that without the use of gymnastics and music there is no importance to education, as gymnastics is a must for good health and music for the development of the soul. Gurjar has observed that the same principle operates in Suryanamaskar, which includes chanting of mantras and exercising of various parts of the body in order to attain both a sound mind and a healthy body. If we look carefully, then we will find most aspects of yoga and *asanas* of Suryanamaskar have been part and parcel of gymnastics.

Risbud Shriram compares Suryanamaskar to Chinese Yoga called Tao. Sound waves of the body require exercise and that is done by mantras. When the mantra chanting is done scientifically, the air is breathed out creating useful waves giving positive massage to the internal body. It improves blood circulation. The *Omkara* gives the best experience of God. The source of power is *kundalini,* which is situated in the *muladhara chakra* in an inactive form. The *Omkara* activates the *kundalini,* whose power goes up to the *sahasrara chakra* situated at the top of the head.

Vidyavachaspati Shankar Abhyankar looked at Suryanamaskar and the *Omkara* as *adhyatmic* practice or *sadhana.* He says that Suryanamaskar is the real *sadhana* of *atma* and power. He says that it has hidden power and capacity for all-round development of a human being. It only requires a firm belief, regularity in practice and confidence.

As an example of what is possible, in the Modak book *Suryanamaskar – from the scientific and medical point of view;* Joglekar Bhau states that due to his regular Suryanamaskar practice in his young age he had energy to work daily 16 - 17 hours and now in his old age when he is eighty he still can work for 12 hours per day.

Konar at al. researched the cardiovascular responses to the head-down and body-up *asanas* like *sarvangasana* (the candle posture or shoulder-stand). This research reports echocardiographic analysis on SVGN in eight male subjects before and after the practice of such inverted posture *asanas* twice daily for two weeks. The report shows that resting heart rate (RHR) and left ventricular end diastolic volume (LVEDV) were significantly lower after two weeks' practice. Statistically non significant tendency towards a mild regression of the left ventricular was noticed as well. Also the CV responses to sharp 45 degrees head-down-tilt (HDT) on a tilt table were not changed after this *asana*. Consequently there was no orthostatic intolerance during a five minute period of 70 degrees of head-up tilt (HUT). Since Suryanamaskar is a combination of spinal bends and stretches where the head continuously changes height in different positions, even some indirect study like the one quoted above may reveal the possible impact of the practice on human physiology.

Stec carried out a 3 month study (2014), where, in order to reduce the effect of confounding variables, the Solomon Four Group Design was used to determine the effects of Dynamic Suryanamaskar on 42 variables, grouped as physiological, psychological, anthropometric and physical fitness parameters. The testing was conducted on the basis of training a randomly chosen group of male students (n = 105), aged 17.15 ± 1.42 years, from an Indian high school located in Maharashtra, and comparing the results against those of a similarly chosen but untrained control group from the same school. The following were the tests used and parameters measured: the physiological variables were: Positive Breath Holding Capacity, Negative Breath Holding Capacity, Vital Capacity, Resting Respiratory Rate, Resting Blood Pressure, Resting Heart Rate, Hemoglobin Level, RBC (Red Blood Cells) Count, MCH - Mean Corpuscular Hemoglobin, MCHC - Mean Corpuscular Hemoglobin Concentration, WBC (White Blood Cells) Count, Platelets Count, MCV - Mean Corpuscular Volume, Packed Cell Volume (HCT - Hematocrit), TC - Total Cholesterol, TG - Triglycerides Level, VLDL – (Very Low Density Lipoprotein) Level, LDL (Low Density Lipoprotein) Level, HDL (High

Density Lipoprotein) Level; the psychological variables were: Stress Level (2 tests; PSS and STAI-Y1), Anxiety Level (STAI-Y2), Emotional Well-Being Level (EQ); the physical fitness variables were: Strength, Strength Endurance, Sit & Reach Test, Bridge-Up Test (2 tests), Cardiovascular Endurance, Anaerobic Power; the anthropometric variables were: Body Height, Body Weight, Lean Body Weight, Total Body Fat Percentage, Body Mass Index (BMI), In-breath Chest Circumference, Out-breath Chest Circumference, Differential Chest Circumference. Statistical analysis of the dependent variables was carried out by: one-way analysis of variance (One -Way ANOVA), analysis of covariance (ANCOVA), and t-Test ($p < 0.05$). Application of the 12-week DSN training resulted in after-training effects in which 41 out of the 42 tested variables indicated a beneficial effect, with statistical significance being at least at the .05 level ($p < .05$). Only in the case of one parameter, WBC count, was no significant change shown. Statistically significant results were as follows: increase in body height, reductions in body weight, lean body mass and BMI; increase in the deepness of respiration and expansion of the chest, longer duration of apnea, increased vital capacity and a decrease in resting breathing frequency; increased motor skills; increased strength and flexibility of the 'corset' muscles in the trunk; the increased occurrence of hypotension and bradycardia in their non-symptomatic forms; improved aerobic capacity of the blood; no changes in the white blood cell count, but there was a reduction in the number of platelets and an increase in mean corpuscular volume; a reduction in cholesterol and the so-called 'bad' lipoproteins (LDL) and an increase in the concentration of 'good' lipoprotein (HDL) fractions; a reduction in stress level and anxiety level; an increase in the level of emotional intelligence. To summarise, the use of DSN training showed a statistically significant positive effect on both physical fitness and mental health. The results indicated potential benefits for weight reduction and control, respiratory system efficiency, posture, human motor skills performance, back pain, prevention of cardiovascular disease, endurance training, immune system functioning, adaptation to difficult life situations, and for creative activity and problem solving. These findings call into question the conclusion of the ACSM (American College of Sports Medicine) that practising yoga is ineffective in maintaining health related fitness.

Suryanamaskar is a practice with alternating forward and backward spinal bends and stretches. As such it has not only an effect on the spine but also upon every part of the body, which is either directly or indirectly involved. This practice actively exercises muscles by stretching and toning up every major muscle group in the body, most joints are moved through a large range of their maximal motion, the spine is elongated allowing improved circulation in that area and spinal cord nourishment and stimulation of the nerves, pressure on the abdomen region gives massaging effect to all the internal organs, therefore improving digestion. The forward stretches tend to stimulate the parasympathetic nervous system while the backward stretches stimulate the sympathetic nervous system. The lungs and intercostal muscles develop increased range of movement when inhalation is expanded with the backward stretches, and exhalation is deepened with forward stretches, therefore the mobility of the thoracic area significantly increases. It helps to relieve symptoms of menopause. All glands are equally activated and stimulated. The general body posture is corrected and improved.

Reports on the effects of yogic practices on aerobic capacity, cardio-respiratory changes, and cardio-vascular endurance are comparatively few. Where such research does exist, it usually concentrates on the effects of the whole yoga practice, of which Suryanamaskar forms a relatively small part. Furthermore, Suryanamaskar styles can differ enormously from school to school, not only with regard to the number and kind of *asanas* used, but also with regard to the speed with which each round is performed. Dynamic Suryanamaskar (DSN) requires both high intensity and high speed. Since Dynamic Suryanamaskar is largely unknown and thus not widely practiced, research dedicated to it is scarce. Still, one could hypothesize that the psycho-physiological effects described elsewhere in the Yogic literature show up more quickly with the more intensive practice.

The following is a summary of the results of a survey conducted by Yoga Biomedical Trust in 1983-84. Three thousand individuals with very varied health ailments who were prescribed yoga as an alternative therapy were surveyed. The results show that yoga was very effective for treating alcoholism, back pain, nerve or muscle disease, anxiety, arthritis, ulcers, and for managing heart disease and cancer.

The complete results are shown in the table below:

| Ailment | Number of Cases Reporting | Percent Claiming Benefit |
|---|---|---|
| Back Pain | 1,142 | 98 |
| Arthritis or rheumatism | 589 | 90 |
| Anxiety | 838 | 94 |
| Migraine | 464 | 80 |
| Insomnia | 542 | 82 |
| Nerve or muscle disease | 112 | 96 |
| Menstrual problems | 317 | 68 |
| Premenstrual tension | 848 | 77 |
| Menopause disorders | 247 | 83 |
| Hypertension | 150 | 84 |
| Heart disease | 50 | 94 |
| Asthma or bronchitis | 226 | 88 |
| Duodenal ulcers | 40 | 90 |
| Hemorrhoids | 391 | 88 |
| Obesity | 240 | 74 |
| Diabetes | 10 | 80 |
| Cancer | 29 | 90 |
| Tobacco addiction | 219 | 74 |
| Alcoholism | 26 | 100 |

**TABLE 10:** Percentage of patients claiming improvement due to yoga practice.

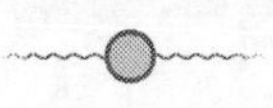

# 15

# PERSONAL EXPERIENCES

Among many other people perhaps Balasaheb Pant Pratinidhi (1868-1951), Maharajah and Ruler (Chief) of the tiny princely state of Aundh, Maharashtra, (near Pune), from 1909 until 1947, deserves the highest credit for the popularization of Suryanamaskar in modern times. It was mainly due to his own efforts that the he was able to convince his subjects of the usefulness of this simple system of keeping fit at every level, and he instituted a state regulation that made Suryanamaskar compulsory at all the schools of the Aundh State. Balasaheb Pant Pratinidhi strongly identified himself with the following statement:

> "I don't believe in over-muscled men. I believe in the harmonious development of the entire body. It is much more important to see 10,000 men, women and children go through a series of carefully planned exercises than to watch some professional athlete beat the world's record in some useless attainment by one tenth of a second."

(Physical Culture, February 1927)

There follow some accounts by people who have experienced the beneficial effects of systematic and regular Suryanamaskar practice. They show that women and girls doing the practice of Suryanamaskar also benefit much from it. We start with some reports recorded about 1928 and extracted from the book "Surya Namaskar" written by the Chief of Aundh. The very first extract is by the Maharajah himself.

## BALASAHEB PANT PRATINIDHI, THE CHIEF OF AUNDH

"Before setting his eye on the Suryanamaskar, the Chief of Aundh studied famous *kushti* (wrestler) competitors and physical culturists of his time, purchased required equipment, read the books on the subject and for ten years practiced these systems continuously according to the instructions, with the results that 'the chest measurements remained the same while that of the waist and abdomen decreased in size.' However, only after undertaking the regular and continuous practice of the Suryanamaskar he noticed 'remarkable lightness of his body, buoyancy of mind, and a general feeling of youthfulness, which must be experienced to be understood. But the highest benefit of all is that during the past 17 years, we have been absolutely free not only from fevers and other ailments, but never even suffered from cold or cough.' He believed that besides the physical benefits there are also spiritual benefits for those interested to do the Suryanamaskar along with the solar and *bija* mantras."

## RANISAHEB

"Girls and women doing Surya Namaskars according to our method are being tremendously benefited in bodily and mental health.

Some of the benefits derived by the Ranisaheb from Surya Namaskars are:

1) Strength of the Spine and Back. Before she took the exercise about three years ago, she felt pain in the upper part of the spine, whenever she studied or worked for an hour or so in a sitting position. Now though she has been studying or working harder and longer in the same position, she feels no pain in that part or anywhere else.

2) Normal Alimentary Canal. She suffered now and then from stomach troubles, constipation, etc. They have all gone now.

3) Normal Menses. A number of menstrual complaints have disappeared since she began this exercise: hemorrhage continued as long as eight days, attended with severe pains. Now it is normal in quantity and duration, and without pain.

4) Pain about her waist afflicted her now and then, but it has all gone now.

5) Weakness subsequent to childbirth disappears more rapidly than before.

6) She looks younger for her age."

## MRS. SAUBH SITABAI KIRLOSKAR

"She had started the Suryanamaskar about three years before the experience was written down:

1) All pain in the back and waist has disappeared.

2) Almost all the menstrual complaints, she suffered during the past 35 years gradually vanished and all tendency to prolapsus or falling of the womb quite disappeared. This shows that Suryanamaskar, when regularly and systematically done, produces beneficial effect upon the uterus or womb.

3) There were no more rheumatic complaints.

4) Most of the superfluous fat melted, rendering her limbs firm, strong and pliant.

5) Muscles in her arms, legs, and bust became firmer, stronger and more prominent.

6) Chest measurements increased by two inches.

7) Improvement in the quality of the blood. Complexion became appreciably ruddier; nails showed a redder tint.

8) Falling of hair stopped.

9) Perspiration lost its unpleasant odor.

    a. Digestive organs began to function better.

    b. Not even cold or cough ever since."

## MR. R. K. KIRLOSKAR

"He has been doing the Suryanamaskar for five years before writing this report. He was doing daily one hundred Suryanamaskars in about thirty minutes. Before starting this practice he was usually taking two meals per day but after a few months since the commencement of the Suryanamaskar he did away with the evening meal.

1) Absolute freedom from any physical complaint or ailment. He has had during this period not even cold, which before came on him at least once per year.

2) He has not during the past five years suffered even once from worms, for which he had to take Santonine once or twice every year.

3) The pain at the base of the neck and about the waist, which troubled him now and then has completely disappeared, thus showing that this exercise strengthens the spine and back and waist.

4) Digestive organs are functioning more satisfactorily.

5) His energy, physical and mental, is like that of a young man of forty-five."

That ends the extracts from the book "Surya Namaskar" by the Chief of Aundh.

There now follows a report of Shri Shri Raghavendra Swami. The account below is a summary based on the experiences he describes in his book on Suryanamaskar.

## SHRI SHRI RAGHAVENDRA SWAMI

As he describes himself in his own words:

> "A bundle of diseases as a boy, I was a veritable bag of skin and bones. Only my face said to have good features testified to the fact that I belonged to human species! None of the elders at home dared to interfere with whatever I did because I would cry myself to death even if someone raised his voice against me, let alone spank me! Thus it came about that my very ill-health helped me to grow wild. What with medicines from the Kerala indigenous doctors, talismans from roadside quacks and *ex voto* services to every conceivable diet at every conceivable place, I went on living. I developed epilepsy studying in the high school. I was like an abscess over a wound. As if this was not enough, my heart grew weak......True, I walked like a walking corpse as a student."

As a student, he briefly met a great *siddha* of the South India, Shri Shri Swami Nityananda (in later years, the master at Ganeshpuri near Mumbai) and received his grace. That meeting changed his life. Unfortunately, Nityananda disappeared without a trace.

After many turbulent wanderings in search of God and meeting many ascetics, mendicants and *sadhus*, Raghavendra Swami met a great *hatha* yogi who was a master of Western and Eastern physical culture who practiced Suryanamaskar, *pranayama* and *asanas* every day. Raghavendra Swami would pester the *hatha* yogi with words like "I want to see God, please, show him to me". The response was very swift: "God does not show Himself for the mere asking. It requires hard effort, endeavor, faith and health. You need a strong body." Raghavendra Swami continued his studies under the direction of the *hatha* yogi for a few more years and his body became healthy and strong, yet his search for God continued.

In his search of God, he met many eminent personalities of India such as Swami Kuvalayananda of Lonavla, Swami Shivananda of Rishikesh, Professor Manikya Rao, Babasaheb Pant Pratinidhi, the Ruler of Aundh, etc. During all these years he experimented intensely with various systems of physical culture, yet throughout his life he never stopped doing his daily Suryanamaskar. Raghavendra Swami encouraged all to practice a high number of Suryanamaskars. He himself reports that he has been doing over one thousand Suryanamaskars daily for twenty years and now, when he is over 80, he is still performing 108 rounds on a daily basis. He says:

> "If a person like me, disease-ridden from infancy, a walking corpse, a scarecrow as a boy, could through Suryanamaskar build a body which is younger than that of a youth and look upon the ceaseless work as a stimulation and exhilaration, why could not our young men and women, strong and healthy to start with, achieve if they took to Suryanamaskar."

In his *gurukula ashram* at Malladihalli in the state of Karnataka hundreds of boys and girls practice Suryanamaskar daily together as a large group on a field.

The remaining reports in this chapter are contemporary and were collected from practitioners having had experience with Suryanamaskar for at least six months.

## ROXANNE KAMAYANI GUPTA, (58), PH.D., ITHACA, U.S.A.

*Author of A Yoga of Indian Classical Dance (Inner Traditions: 2000)*

I began my practice of Suryanamaskar in India where I had gone at the age of 19 to study Indian Classical Dance. Yoga began as a complement to my dance, as it is the best way to stretch and strengthen the body. I loved Suryanamaskar, as it is like a dance in its flowing aspect. I soon came to integrate the spiritual qualities of yoga and Indian classical dance and understand the meditative aspects of both disciplines. After my marriage and returning from India, I began teaching yoga one week after the birth of my son in upstate New York in 1974. In those days many people had hardly heard of yoga. From the beginning Suryanamaskar was a central feature of my yoga classes.

But my Suryanamaskar practice took on even greater significance for me in 1986 when I had the good fortune to meet Shri Apa Pant, son of the Maharaja of Aundh, the man who first popularized this exercise in the early 20th century. From Shri Apa Saheb I learned the accompanying mantras and correct way to perform this exercise. He also challenged me to perform the exercise every morning without interruption to see how it would change my life. I did so and was very pleased with the discipline and focus that it brought to my life. Since then, in all my classes Suryanamaskar is a major component. I explain to students that it is the most versatile exercise because it can be performed slowly to calm one's nerves, or with more speed to increase circulation and body temperature. In the West not all persons are fit enough to perform it correctly. Older women in particular cannot always lower their full body weight on their hands. So I have for them developed a variation whereby this can be done more easily.

I have also learned other variations of Suryanamaskar whenever possible. Some are very beautiful and more challenging than the original. Although I do not practice the Iyengar style, accompanying Apa Pant on a tour, I had the opportunity to witness and video the Suryanamaskar performed by Master Yogi B.K.S. Iyengar himself. Because Suryanamaskar as we know it today is in fact a relatively recent historical development, I do not feel that the original is in any way sacred, or something that should not be changed. The difference between the Bihar School and the Iyengar method, as well as the 'original' Suryanamaskar performed by the Maharaja of Aundh does not take away from each of their efficacy.

For me what is equally important to the physical aspects of the exercise is the mental state in which it is performed. It is important for me to understand it as a ritual, albeit modern, for invoking solar conscious energy. It engages the mind and spirit not only the body. It puts us in touch with nature and with our inner selves. I believe Suryanamaskar has been revealed to the world at the exact right moment, when our integrity as human beings in threatened from all sides. It is a protection and a pro-active response for the times in which we live. No wonder it is the world's most famous Yoga exercise.

## ANDRÉ RIEHL (61), AVIGNON, FRANCE, DEEP YOGA INSTRUCTOR

In 1976, when I was 24 years old, a friend from my school days and I decided to walk from France to India as a pilgrimage. Doing this, it took us a little more than six months to reach the country we had been dreaming about for years. All those days of the journey we used to wake up early and start walking, often at dawn. And every day we walked, proceeding towards the east, we could see the sun rising. Every morning it was a glorious sight. In the West a sentimental romantic feeling is associated just with sunset, and so it was a new experience to see the sun rising every day in its great splendor, and to feel a sensation of pure joy for being bathed in the light at those particular moments.

Having arrived in India, after some weeks I came into contact with a wandering ascetic with whom I was going to share the days, months and years ahead. He was a very unusual sadhu, named Kashmiri Babu, who wore a green robe. He preferred to live in the forest, not caring at all about any social life, and apparently communicating with animals more easily than with human beings. He liked to sit all day long, listening to Indian music on a radio, under a large tent erected on bamboo poles. He lived in a spontaneous way, frequently wandering around, never staying more than a month in any one place. This was to become a transforming relationship for me, lasting many years, as his knowledge seemed to be endless, and my desire for learning was the same.

But, despite the range of his knowledge, his interests were not at all mundane, and he would never discuss anything other than spiritual matters. He was also very strict regarding the sadhana itself, never accepting any refusal from my side. He was, however, quite impressed by the fact that my friend and I had walked for all those months, and I was also very impressed by all the fields of knowledge at his command and by his capacity, as it seemed to me, to read my mind!

Once he asked me what had been the most important spiritual experience of the trip. I explained to him about those sunrises' bringing joy and uplifting feelings. His answer came suddenly: "You have to learn to bow in front of the sun and the correct way to give yourself fully to the light!" He then taught me some flowing movements, which had to be done in harmony with the breath. It was almost a year later that I came to know that the movements were called "Surya Namaskar".

My body was stiff at first and I took the practice as a kind of gymnastic exercise. But he was very strict and soon told me that I had to practice from just before dawn, so as to welcome the morning light, until breakfast, which was at about nine o'clock, which meant a session of 2½ to 4 hours! Some days, being totally exhausted, I almost fainted. He would then scold me, saying: "If your body is not able to be used like a disciple, how will you learn to surrender to Surya, how will you pray to the Lord of the Universe?" I was spellbound, facing this bodily fatigue and not really understanding what he meant.

Months went by, and then he asked me to do the same practice in the late afternoon until night fell. Some time later a session at midday was added. Eventually one night he came to wake me up, saying that I was now ready to learn the deep practice of Surya Namaskar, and that I also had to practice it when the sun had totally gone, which meant at precisely midnight every night. I accepted this again, hoping for a kind of secret teaching that he would pass on to me. Then came the teachings of kumbhakas, mantras, drishtis, and bhakti prayers that were all to be added to the physical practice.

It did not take much time before I sensed that, altogether, this very complete practice was awakening in me a very powerful energy, to such an extent that, on some days, it was as if the energy itself was doing the practice. It was at this point that my teacher told me that Surya Namaskar was not at all a physical exercise but was a kind of prayer, to be done with all aspects of the human organism, the physical body, the understandings of the mind, and a heart full of love for the essence of life, which was Light. He said:

"Surya Namaskar is a spiritual practice involving all your life to meet the wholeness of Life. Never reduce it to body movements. Make it larger and larger until it is the Infinite doing Surya Namaskar Itself, using your body as a tool for reverence".

It took years to realize what he meant. What I can say about it now, is that there seems to be a living force, felt as pure light, running through every aspect of life, and of course within all the layers of the human being. This light is operating in unexpected ways almost impossible for human thought to comprehend. But this is a reality: there is a movement of light giving full strength and power to all our cells.

When this is felt, from time to time at least, the whole movement of our life loses all those meanings invented by thought, and we are put in a state where only clarity resides. In this clarity there are no more questions and no more answers, but there is only a very pure movement of light, which is like a prayer to itself. Then and then only can the understanding of Surya Namaskar be said to be completed.

## Questions and answers.

*Could you go a bit more into the technical details of the practice? How many rounds did you perform?*

There was not, ultimately, a specific number of rounds to be performed, because the Master did not consider Surya Namaskar to be a physical exercise but rather a kind of asana puja directed to Surya. But in the beginning, it was 12 only, then increasing in stages, by adding another 12 rounds each time, to 24, 36, 48, etc., up to 108. From that point on there was no more counting, just going on until the Master told me to stop. He was present all the time, always watching, sometimes more closely, sometimes less. It was as if he was checking my inner state. The order to stop would come suddenly.

The practice was increased in steps to 4 times a day, before dawn, at midday, by sunset and at midnight. Each fully extended practice session took between about 2½ and 4 hours. It took about 3 years to build up to that length of time. The presence of the Master was enormously important in practising for such long periods every day. When I was apart from him I found I was unable to sustain such duration and intensity.

All sessions were physically the same, but the bhava (mental state) was different according to the time of day: calling for the light in the early morning, full joy at midday, giving thanks for the light at sunset, and accompanying the hidden light at midnight.

*Was the co-ordination of breathing and movement essential or could the body simply be allowed to move as fast as it could without trying to co-ordinate the two?*

Co-ordination with the breath was essential. Kumbhaka (breath retention) was used as part of the process of intensifying the practice. This was developed in stages over about 2 years:

1. Breathing in and out in a co-ordinated way with the movements.
2. Adding short kumbhakas (both full and empty) in-between the movements.
3. Each round performed with lungs full kumbhaka (antara kumbhaka).
4. Each round performed with lungs empty kumbhaka (bahya kumbhaka).

When the whole 12 movements were done with kumbhaka

(breath in or out), emphasis was placed on repeating a mantra with the movements and on making quick changes in the object of dharana (concentrating on fixed places and the process of movement).

*How fast, in seconds, were you doing one round?*

I do not know exactly, but perhaps 10 to 15 seconds when the round was accompanied by kumbhaka. The speeding-up came by itself, but only because of adding the kumbhakas. Going quicker was a must to avoid asphyxiation!

*Was your routine the same as the one described in the book? Were there any differences, including in asanas?*

The asanas were the same.

*Were you doing other asanas to complement the Surya Namaskar practice or was it self-sufficient according to that sadhu?*

No other asana, but sun pranayamas, sun dharanas and sun mantras were done.

*Has the sadhu stressed that the flow of air in the nostrils should be even (as Swara yoga states) after a properly performed Surya Namaskar practice?*

The practice did bring perfectly equal breathing between the two nostrils, but he stressed the fact that Surya Namaskar at its higher levels had to stop the breath altogether, and that when the breath had stopped, I should go on for 1 more round (12 asanas) and then stop moving completely, and just stand still and stare at the sunlight [n.b. **not** the sun itself] in the daytime or at the inner light during nighttime. This stopping of the breath happened a number of times, perhaps 10 in total, and in the beginning I thought I was going to die, which made him laugh a lot!

*Has the practice of Surya Namaskar put you into deep meditative states?*

Yes. It improved both concentration and meditation. Concentration in the sense that adding more and more mental points on which to focus brought both a stronger faculty for facing and staying with any type of mental question and also a lessening of mental confusion or diversion when looking for clear answers.

Meditation in the sense that the quality and quantity of energy produced by such intense practice sometimes acted spontaneously and naturally to suspend the mind and bring about a state of natural lightness, silence and vastness, that I call meditative. Sometimes it brought also states of pure joy without object, and a clarity of being which was linked with the source of all life. That happened only with the cessation of the breath.

## BRONISLAW SWIATKOWSKI (59), MANAGER, WARSAW, POLAND

I have been regularly practicing Suryanamaskar for the last 24 months. I do a minimum of 24 rounds daily. However, on irregular basis, on and off, I have been doing this sequence for the past 30 years. The style I do is the *Rishikesh Series* from the Bihar School of Yoga (Swami Satyananda). Sometimes I perform even up to 108 rounds, but that is not very often. I always do the sequence in the morning around 6 a.m. and I start rather slowly and deliberately as a *vinyasa,* coordinating the body movements with my breath. I use Suryanamaskar as a nice way to wake up my body fully and welcome the day.

I perform several rounds of Suryanamaskar several times in a day, when I work at home at my computer. Thanks to it my general well-being improves, I feel that the feelings of heaviness and stiffness in my spine and other joints are gone, and it improves my blood circulation and my breathing, I feel my brain and mind being refreshed.

Here are the benefits I have noticed after the regular practice for the past year:

1) My lumbar area (lower back) back pains have disappeared.
2) My spine gained suppleness and flexibility, I can easily reach the floor with my palms while my legs (knees) are straight.
3) There is an overall feeling of my body being supple, relaxed and flexible.
4) My awareness of the body and its postures during the day has increased.
5) My breathing is deeper, slower and quickly returns to its normal rate after aerobic exercise or exertion.
6) I have noticed that my posture has spontaneously improved (position of my chest and my spine) and it is independent of whatever activity I am doing at the time.
7) When I go on with various daily activities I have noticed

that I am more aware of my breath and I am consciously trying to regulate my breathing activity, also my body is more relaxed.

Below is the typical, favorite daily routine of Suryanamaskar which I follow:

1) 10 rounds slowly with the speed about two rounds per minute (1 round 30 seconds).
2) 10 rounds faster with the speed of 1 round per 20 seconds.
3) 20 rounds very fast with the speed of 1 round per 12 seconds.
4) 10 rounds slower at the speed of 1 round per 20 seconds.
5) 10 rounds slowly at the speed of 1 round per 30 seconds.
6) 10 rounds very slowly at the speed of 1 round per 90 seconds; in addition after each and every *asana* I do one extra deep breath.

All together it takes about 35 minutes. After that, I do as a standing posture *tadasana* for about 2-3 minutes and full relaxation in s*havasana;* so the total time takes 45 minutes. When I get more time in the morning (for example on holidays) I like to do, at the end, an extra dozen of very, very slow Suryanamaskars, where each round takes about 2 and a half minutes. At that time I perform 2 extra deep breaths after each and every *asana* in the Suryanamaskar sequence.

I end the whole morning practice with a shower after which I get dressed and then wake up my young children for school.

## KRYSTYNA BIALOWOLSKA (57), INSTRUCTOR OF SHIVANANDA YOGA, WARSAW, POLAND

I have been practicing yoga for over 16 years. The first 12 years it was B.K.S. Iyengar Yoga. At that time I did not practice Suryanamaskar very regularly. Also, the number of Suryanamaskar rounds I completed was much lower than today. On average we would do from 12 to 24 rounds once a week in our class and perhaps 108 Suryanamaskar rounds 3-4 times a year. However, once I learned about the Shivananda Yoga I have changed my practice to this new yoga style. In this method, each yoga class begins with Suryanamaskars.

The number of Suryanamaskar rounds in my weekly practice is now much higher. I usually perform 24 Suryanamaskar rounds before *asanas* so it gives a total of about 100-160 rounds per week. During these years of practicing Suryanamaskar, I discovered some advantages of doing it regularly. These are my conclusions:

1) I do Suryanamaskar at the start of each of my yoga classes not because I was told to do this, but because I feel that Suryanamaskar distributes energy over all my body, and moves all my muscles, joints and tendons. And after that I feel that my body is prepared to work smoothly with all its parts during my *asana* practice. Therefore I feel it is an excellent yogic warm-up.

2) Also I do Suryanamaskar when I'm distracted, a little frantic or feel stressed. I clearly experience the Suryanamaskar practice 'brushes' or cleans my aura.

After that I'm quite collected and composed. However, to get such results, I have to increase the number of Suryanamaskar rounds to about 108.

3) I do Suryanamaskar also when I feel that I may be getting a cold. And when I complete 108 Suryanamaskars, the cold symptoms disappear. I'm usually much sweatier in this case as the practice is more intense.

4) Also I have noticed that when I do Suryanamaskar before meditation or *pranayama* practice, I can sit comfortably for a much longer time, my mind focuses more easily, and the state of my concentration is much deeper and is reached effortlessly.

5) My Suryanamaskar practice is not always the same, but I always co-ordinate the movements with the breath. Often I start slowly, though when the energy starts circulating I will gradually increase the speed. I may reach quite a fast speed, according to my needs and conditions on that particular day, and I maintain that speed throughout the remaining practice. At the end I start slowing down, bringing the energy of the practice down. Of course, if, on a given day, I feel more nervousness and agitation from the start, then I go with a faster tempo, and at the end, when my emotions subside, I gradually slow down. So in short, I tune my practice to my emotional state.

I think that is not easy to separate the benefits of Suryanamaskar from the benefits of the other yoga practices. Everything is integrated and interconnected. But in the future I would like to increase the number of Suryanamaskar in my daily practice, especially because it 'brushes' my aura, makes me peaceful and brings my mind clarity.

## RADOSLAW RYCHLIK (30), ASHTANGA YOGA INSTRUCTOR, WARSAW, POLAND

I have been doing Suryanamaskar for 12 years in the tradition of Sri K.P. Jois of Mysore (Ashtanga Yoga). In this tradition, 10 Suryanamaskar are done at the beginning of the practice of *asanas* and afterwards one Suryanamaskar or a part of it is being done between every *asana* as a linking movement, so during an entire 90 minute practice, Suryanamaskar is done about 50 times.

Before starting this practice I was suffering from back pain and gastric disorders, my physical condition was very low. Now I am an example of health and well-being with high strength, flexibility and stamina.

Below are some typical experiences from a few students from the OmGurudev Secondary and Higher Secondary Gurukul, Kokamthan who participated in a 3 month long Dynamic Suryanamaskar experiment. Perhaps school authorities should take a closer look at these reports and introduce this form of the practice to all the remaining *gurukula* students. The experiment could accommodate only 100 students out of the three thousand attending classes at the *gurukula*.

## WADEKAR AKSHAY MADUKHAR (18), MUMBAI, INDIA

I have observed the following positive changes:

1) My resistance, power, and flexibility have increased. Also my grasping power how to do other sports is better.
2) Now after starting regular Suryanamaskar practice I feel fresh and calm throughout the day. Before I felt sleepy and tired and had difficulty to attend all the classes. However, now, after Suryanamaskar, I feel alert at every class. I do not feel sleepy or lazy anymore.
3) Also I feel that my thinking is better, I can concentrate more clearly.
4) While sitting long hours in the classroom frequently I was feeling back pain but after starting the Suryanamaskar training this problem is completely gone.
5) By the end of the Suryanamaskar experiment, I was able to perform 300 rounds but my mind and heart tells me that I can do more and more.
6) I feel that this Suryanamaskar training helps me in my other favorite sports like volleyball and basketball.

## AMIT UTTAM GANGUDRE (16), MANMAD, INDIA

I have done Suryanamaskar regularly and it has benefited me as follows:

1) It has enhanced my back flexibility. Before I could not

touch the ground without bending my knees, but now after only three months of training I can touch the floor, and without bending my knees!

2) I can run faster, my running capacity is better.

3) In the beginning I completed only 15 rounds and it caused pain in my body. Now I can complete about 680 rounds without any pain in my body.

4) The practice has enhanced my memory. Also my concentration is better and I can study well.

5) Now I am more disciplined; before I started Suryanamaskar I was a lazy person but now I feel enthusiastic.

6) I was experiencing a back problem having pain especially after long sitting on a classroom bench but now I got rid of this problem. Likewise I felt pain in my chest and hands, and now all is gone.

7) I have taught Suryanamaskar to my parents. They experienced problems with their knees. After starting the Suryanamaskar practice, they got relief from their paining knees.

## DIWATE TUSHAR OMKAR (17), AKOLA, INDIA

I have been practicing sports and especially *kushti* (Indian wrestling) for several years and I am doing now regularly Suryanamaskar rounds. I feel the following effects on my body:

1) My weight has increased and I feel more healthy.

2) My body has become more flexible and this is very useful in my wrestling. Also my stamina has gone up.

3) I feel that it benefited me not only physically but also mentally and intellectually. I can concentrate better on my studies and I can recognize the progress in my studies.

4) Prior to undertaking Suryanamaskar training I had eyes problem in the early mornings, now that problem has cleared, I do not have any more problem with my eyes.

5) But most importantly I have attained power over my will power and my ambition has increased.

6) At the end of the three months long Suryanamaskar training at our *Gurukula,* I was able to complete over 500 rounds of Suryanamaskar in one session(!)

## MANESH RUPE RAMCHANDRA (18), NAVI MUMBAI, INDIA

Here are a few benefits:

1) The practice of Suryanamaskar has created interest for regular exercise.

2) I was always sleeping longer but now I habitually rise early.

3) I feel that because of Suryanamaskar I am more healthy.

4) Now I understand better how to concentrate.

5) Because of Suryanamaskar practice I am confident.

6) I have increased my strength, power and flexibility.

7) I feel that my body height has increased because of this regular exercise.

8) Also my food intake is increased; I have more of an appetite.

16

# BENEFITS OF SURYANAMASKAR PRACTICE

The most important benefit of yoga is considered spiritual well-being, yet to accomplish that we start at the physical and mental level. By keeping the body clean, flexible, strong and well hydrated, the mind calm, and the emotions well balanced, we can significantly reduce the catabolic process of cell deterioration. This means that the ageing process, which is, to a significant degree, an artificial condition, caused mainly by wrong life-style, resulting in auto-intoxication or self-poisoning, can be slowed down by practicing yoga and adhering to its associated life-style guidance. Modern science indeed, in the form of increasing amounts of evidence from the realms of physiology and medicine, is also able to support the conclusions drawn by yogis, over at least the last one thousand years, from their personal experience.

It is said that to get the maximum benefits from yoga one should combine the practices of *asanas, pranayama* and meditation.

The sequence of Suryanamaskar combines all these elements in one easy and simple 'package'. This set can be practiced in a number of ways thus focusing on one or other aspect of the human psychosomatic organism. Perhaps the fastest and most profound changes take place when the rigor and intensity of the Suryanamaskar practice is the highest. Hence the fourth level of Dynamic Suryanamaskar could be considered to be the fastest means of reaching and maintaining the optimal level of psychosomatic performance.

Yoga and Suryanamaskar act not only as a preventive measure but they also work well as an alternative and complementary therapy. A large body of scientific evidence shows that **regular** practice of *asanas*, *pranayama* and meditation can help treat such diverse ailments as diabetes, high blood pressure, digestive disorders, arthritis, arteriosclerosis, chronic fatigue, asthma, varicose veins, and heart conditions, among many others. According to yoga therapists, physiologists, and medical scientists, yoga as a therapy is successful because of the balance created in the endocrine and nervous systems, which directly influence all the other systems and organs of the body.

In that respect this type of beneficial impact will also apply to the practice of Suryanamaskar as it exercises the whole body in a very complete way. Since Suryanamaskar is such a complete exercise, it is difficult to speak about the specific areas that it impacts more or less, i.e. that one system of the body is influenced in a more special way than another. What is important is that it is done in an integrated and holistic manner. Nonetheless, for the sake of clarity a few most important points are discussed below.

I wish to emphasize that these benefits can be enhanced if Suryanamaskar practice is combined with a proper, natural diet, as discussed earlier.

## Physical Fitness Benefits

**Physical Fitness.** This is the ability to carry out daily tasks with vigor and alertness, without undue fatigue and with ample energy to engage in leisure pursuits and to meet emergency situations (Clarke, 1979). It consists of five components as listed below:

**Strength**. One of the important features of yoga and also of Suryanamaskar practice is that your own body weight is used as the tool to train your strength. Numerous tests show that maximum strength increases considerably. However, to develop this specific characteristic one would select a Suryanamaskar sequence rather different from the *Rishikesh Series*. Perhaps the *Ashtanga Yoga* Suryanamaskar sequence would be more challenging. However, the Suryanamaskar set in any variation will improve muscle tone.

**Strength Endurance**. The findings of various tests show that this component can increase considerably with Suryanamaskar practice, especially when a higher number of rounds are completed.

**Cardiovascular Endurance**. This is one of the characteristics that improve considerably in most of the scientific findings. For someone who does practice the Rishikesh style at the fourth level, as suggested in this book, it is impossible not to improve this parameter when practice is regular. Anyone doing hundreds of rounds at the fourth level will have this fitness parameter at the high level of professional sportsmen. The result is a combination of lower heart rate, lower breathing rate, and overall improved oxygenation of all tissues.

**Flexibility**. This component is probably the most frequently investigated and nowadays, yoga is almost synonymous with flexibility. Suryanamaskar with its constant flexing of the spine back and forth can increase your flexibility in a very speedy way. And this flexibility, which is developed with Suryanamaskar, is the most important one, meaning it is the flexibility of the spine. There is a plethora of scientific evidence supporting this view that joint range of motion improves significantly.

**Body Mass Index (BMI)**. It is a calculated value obtained by dividing the weight of the subject body expressed in kilograms by its height in square meters and is expressed as $kg/m^2$. In simple terms it is a way of measuring the fat content of the body and of checking whether a person is obese, overweight, or underweight. Suryanamaskar practice has a beneficial effect in all these cases, tending to bring body weight closer to the mean.

## Physiological Benefits

**Internal Organs**. The Suryanamaskar set is a yogic practice, which massages in a unique rhythmical way all the internal organs, facilitating the exchange of unoxygenated blood for oxygenated, and thus improving the ability of the body to prevent disease. Additionally, with experience, a *sadhaka* becomes better attuned to the body and better able to recognize the first signs of something being wrong, thus allowing a faster response to any potential health problem.

**Blood Pressure**. A regular Suryanamaskar practice decreases blood pressure. Better circulation and oxygenation of the body produce a very efficient de-toxification.

**Pulse Rate**. The fourth level especially of Suryanamaskar is a superb training tool for exercising the heart muscle, and the pulmonary and vasculatory systems. The heart gradually needs to beat less and less frequently in order to supply all the required nutrients and oxygen. Circulation is more efficient, and that is observed in a lower pulse rate, which indicates that the heart is strong enough to pump more blood with fewer beats.

**Red Blood Cells (RBC)**. Suryanamaskar has been shown to increase the level of red blood cells in the body. Most correctly performed endurance exercise programs bring about this beneficial response, since red blood cells are the means whereby oxygen is carried through the blood. Too few RBC can result in anemia and low energy.

**Respiration**. Just as with the circulatory system, a lower respiratory rate indicates that the lungs are working more efficiently. The lower rate indicates a better fitness level. The regular use of the *vinyasa* technique (*ujjayi pranayama*) during Suryanamaskar practice can assist with reducing the respiratory rate.

**Gastrointestinal System.** Gastrointestinal functions improve greatly due to Suryanamaskar. The combination of increased and decreased abdominal pressures associated with the backward and forward stretches has an amazingly stimulating effect even on the so-called 'sluggish colon'. Also, due to such stimulation the digestive power increases and normalizes. Consistent Suryanamaskar practice helps find the balance in maintaining proper body weight and controlling hunger and creates a more efficient metabolism. Proper metabolism and increased circulation lower the cholesterol level.

**Autonomic Nervous System**. Suryanamaskar stimulates both parts of the system. As you stretch backwards the sympathetic part is stimulated and as you stretch forwards the parasympathetic part.

**Immunity**. By applying better dietary principles we free our immunological system from 'false alarms', and do not waste its protective potential, thus saving strength for dealing with real sickness. Suryanamaskar practice has frequently been correlated with a stronger immune system; it includes some postures that work specifically on immunity by stimulating the functioning of the lymphatic system.

**Vertebral Column**. Through the very nature of yogic postures

Suryanamaskar teaches the practitioner to hold and control the body in a proper way. Suryanamaskar is a wonderful system of corrective exercises for the spine. After regular practice your posture will improve so that you look more healthy and confident.

**Energy and Vitality**. It was mentioned earlier that Suryanamaskar acts as a *pranic* generator. Regular Suryanamaskar practice will provide abundant energy and enthusiasm. In fact, when you reach the fourth level of the practice, you will feel so much energized that it will be almost impossible for you to get tired. This energy can later be used for spiritual growth.

**Aging**. At the beginning of the book it was mentioned that Suryanamaskar was considered a very potent *kriya* (purification process) used for the detoxification of the body. Many scientific experiments have shown that toxins and oxidative processes are some of the main culprits behind the aging process. It is nothing unusual or extraordinary, therefore, that detoxification produces a delay in aging, among many other health benefits. Detoxification is also accomplished by the balanced workout of all the major muscle groups, so there is no area untouched by the practice of Suryanamaskar. In addition, skin gains a youthful look and feel, and hair loss and greying are prevented. Any unpleasant odors of the body are checked.

## Mental and Emotional Benefits

**Stress and Anxiety Reduction**. Several scientific findings show the capacity of Suryanamaskar to help with stress management. Among other things, the concentration required during yoga practice tends to focus your attention on the matter at hand, thereby reducing the emphasis on other aspects of your life problems. Again the intensity and strenuousness of the fourth level of Suryanamaskar are useful because the required concentration does not leave any capacity for defocusing from the practice.

**Mood**. Suryanamaskar improves overall well-being. It creates a strong mind-body connection, thus creating a healthy human being. The extra energy created by the practice generates great enthusiasm. A positive outlook on life comes naturally. Negative feelings are much less frequent and at much lower level; consequently there is a reduction of feeling of depression.

**Concentration**. Suryanamaskar teaches both focusing of the mind and *pranayama* techniques. Researchers have shown that even a few weeks of regular Suryanamaskar practice can improve memory, concentration and attention. In yogic science the direct connection between breathing, *prana* and mind has been known for a long time. This connection is exploited to the advantage of the *sadhaka*.

**Peace and Calmness**. Suryanamaskar requires much concentration, especially in its high intensity form, and that has the effect of bringing a feeling of calmness. Watching how you breathe, focusing your mind on various *chakras*, and disengaging from your thoughts, all help to pacify the mind.

**Well-being**: Almost all other forms of vigorous physical exercise involve stimulation of the cortex, whereas yoga is associated with the sub-cortical areas of the brain. Postural patterns, holding a position, and maintaining balance activate the cerebellum rather than cortex. Suryanamaskar consists of 7 to 8 *asanas* (depending on the style) connected in a natural sequence, with the result that it is the sub-cortex that is stimulated.

**Depth Perception**. Suryanamaskar gives an unusually rich perception of the body's movements in space. Maintaining for a prolonged period full focus on and awareness of the body's positions and its rhythmic movements, leads to increased depth perception.

## Potential Disease Prophylaxis

**Heart Disease**. Suryanamaskar reduces stress and anxiety, lowers blood pressure, maintains a healthy weight, keeps lungs healthy, and improves cardiovascular fitness, all of which lead to reducing the risk of heart disease.

**Back Pain**. Suryanamaskar is one of the most effective methods of fighting common back pain. Statistics show that back pain is the most common reason for seeking medical attention. This simple and easy set of *asanas* can be used to cure and prevent back pain by enhancing the strength and flexibility of the vertebral column as well as of all the core muscles. Both

| Human Parameters | |
|---|---|
| **Healthy** | **Unhealthy** |
| **Consciousness**: continuous sublime and blissful state, good mood, lack of strong emotions, lack of stubborn thoughts and feeling of exhaustion, access to universal knowledge. | **Consciousness**: continuous feeling of stress, frequent strong emotions, persisting and stubborn thoughts, continuous feeling of exhaustion and aversion to life, constant bad mood. |
| **Breathing**: 5 - 7 cycles per minute (inspiration, expiration, and a clear stoppage in-between). The fewer breaths per minute and the more equal the flow of air between the nostrils, the healthier the person is. | **Breathing**: 16 or more cycles per minute (only inspiration and expiration, without any stoppage). The more breaths per minute and the more unequal the flow of air between the nostrils, the unhealthier person is. |
| **Alimentation**: hunger satisfied by a small amount of natural foods, permanent feeling of light hunger, one large defecation in the morning or light stool after each meal that lasts only a few seconds. | **Alimentation**: eating large amounts of thermally processed unnatural foods, never feeling hungry, difficulty in evacuation after a meal, very rare stools, less then one every 24 hours and they take long time. |
| **Skin**: clean, attractive, without eczema, pimples, wrinkles or unpleasant smell, perfectly regulating heat exchange (small amount of subcutaneous fat). | **Skin**: oily with eczema, pimples, blackheads and wrinkles, unpleasant smell, too much or not enough subcutaneous fat. |
| **Immunological system**: lack of any disease, fast healing in case of skin burns, cuts, or wounds; without much pus, etc. | **Immunological system**: frequent chronic sickness, vulnerable to infectious diseases, slow healing in case of skin burns, cuts, or wounds, with much pus, etc. |

| | |
|---|---|
| **Muscles**: elastic, resilient, flexible, moderately strong, proportionally developed throughout the body, good elasticity of joints, ligaments and tendons, muscles practically never become exhausted (super-endurance). | **Muscles**: weak, stiff, inflexible, not proportionally developed, drooping, poor elasticity of joints, ligaments and tendons, muscles quickly become fatigued. |

**TABLE 11:** Characteristics of the healthy and unhealthy human being.

acute and long-term stress can lead to muscle tension and exacerbate back problems. There are a number of integrated components in Suryanamaskar, which help to ease back pain: (1) seven or eight specially selected *asanas*, which help through gentle stretching to increase flexibility and correct bad posture; (2) the breathing pattern, which increases flexibility of the ribs and the whole chest, and is at the same time relaxing; (3) the concentration required in Suryanamaskar and, later, the relaxation obtained in *shavasana*, which help to remove both tension on the physical level and stress on the mental and emotional.

**Arteriosclerosis**. It was found that Suryanamaskar practice lowers the levels of cholesterol and of triglycerides; this is brought about through increased blood circulation and the burning of fat (improved metabolism). Triglycerides are the chemical form of fat in the blood, and their increased level can indicate a risk of heart disease and high blood pressure.

**Type II Diabetes**. Suryanamaskar demonstrates glucose reducing capabilities. It reduces stress and gives an extremely good massage to the pancreas (as well as to all the other internal organs). In addition, it is an excellent physical exercise and therefore a superb preventative for type II diabetes.

**Alzheimer's Disease**. A recent study indicates that yoga can help elevate brain levels of gamma-amino-butyric acid (GABA). Low GABA levels are associated with the onset of Alzheimer's. Cultivation of a state of mental peace and yogic meditation alike have also demonstrated the potential to slow the progression of Alzheimer's.

A partial list of further diseases or conditions beneficially affected by Suryanamaskar practice follows: asthma, arthritis, multiple sclerosis, cancer, muscular dystrophy, scoliosis, chronic bronchitis, emphysema, epilepsy, sciatica, osteoporosis, insomnia, chronic fatigue, and varicose veins, among many others.

# APPENDICES

# Sun Salutation

## *Surya Namaskar*

Yoga has a complete message for humanity.
It has a message for the human body.
It has a message for the human mind,
and it also has a message for the human soul.
*Swami Kuvalayananda (1883 – 1966)*

1 - EXHALE
*Pranamasana*
Prayer Pose

2 - INHALE
*Hasta Uttanasana*
Raised Arms Pose

3 - EXHALE
*Padahastasana*
Hand to Foot Pose

4 - INHALE
*Ashwa Sanchalanasana*
Equestrian Pose
(right leg forward 1st time)

*(Traditional naming convention)*

# Sun Salutation

*Surya Namaskar*

Yoga has a complete message for humanity.
It has a message for the human body.
It has a message for the human mind,
and is also has a message for the human soul.
*Swami Kuvalayananda (1883 – 1966)*

1 - EXHALE
*Tadasana*
Mountain Pose

2 - INHALE
*Urdhva Namaskar*
Upward Salute

3 - EXHALE
*Uttanasana*
Intensive Stretch

4 - INHALE
*Ashwa Sanchalanasana*
Equestrian or runner pose
(right leg forward 1st time)

*(Krishnamacharya naming convention)*

# Sun Salutations / *Surya Namaskar*

*(Suggested modifications of the practice for people with physical impairments. The description applies primarily to those sitting. Those lying down should adopt a supine or prone position as appropriate.)*

To begin Sun Salutation when sitting on a chair or lying on the floor, first relax the body by taking the following steps:

- **In a chair:** sit about half way between the back of the chair and the front edge in such a way that you do not use the back of the chair to support your spine; keep the spine straight with the body weight evenly distributed on the buttocks.
- **Straight spine:** extend the spine comfortably upwards as much as possible, as if someone were pulling you up by the hair on the crown of your head.
- **On the ground:** lie flat on your back in the Shavasana pose.
- **Eyes closed, yogic breathing:** a few comfortable repetitions of simple inhalation and exhalation, if possible through the nose, with no holding of the breath, and building up gradually and comfortably to the exhalation being twice as long as the inhalation.
- **Omkara mantra recitation:** three repetitions of "OM / AUM".

1 **Pranamasana** (hands together in prayer): Om Mitraya Namaha. First breathe a little deeper than normal and when you are ready to start the routine - *exhale*.

2 **Hasta Uttanasana** (hands up above the head): Om Ravaye Namaha. Upwards and in the later phase, where possible, backward stretch with straight arms - *inhale*.

3 **Padahastasana** (hands to feet): Om Suryaya Namaha. Bend forward from the waist, allow the hands to touch the ground outside the feet, or, when lying down, sit up if possible and do a seated partial forward bend - *exhale*.

4 **Ashwa Sanchalanasana** (equestrian pose): Om Bhanave Namaha. Lift left arm above the head and lift up left leg as much as comfortably possible - *inhale.*

5 **Parvatasana** (mountain pose): Om Khagaya Namaha. Complete forward stretch, chest resting on thighs, hands to feet - *exhale.*

6 **Ashtanga Namaskara** (salute with eight parts); Om Pushne Namaha. Lean forward, forearms on thighs, spine extended - *if possible hold your breath (out) after previous exhalation.*

7 **Bhujangasana** (cobra): Om Hiranyagarbhaya Namaha. Chest upward, chin and face rise as much as possible - *inhale.*

8 **Parvatasana** (mountain pose): Om Marichaye Namaha. Complete forward stretch, chest resting on thighs, hands to feet - *exhale.*

9 **Ashwa Sanchalanasana** (equestrian pose): Om Adityaya Namaha. Lift left arm above the head and lift up left leg as much as comfortably possible - *inhale.*

10 **Padahastasana** (hands to feet): Om Savitre Namaha. Bend forward from the waist, allow the hands to touch the ground outside the feet, or, when lying down, sit up if possible and do a seated partial forward bend - *exhale.*

11 **Hasta Uttanasana** (hands up above the head): Om Arkaya Namaha. Upwards and in the later phase, where possible, backward stretch with straight arms - *inhale.*

12 **Pranamasana** (hands together in prayer): Om Mitraya Namaha. First breathe a little deeper than normal and when you are ready to start the routine again - *exhale.*

* The second round Equestrian pose (steps 4 and 9) should be performed by lifting the right arm and leg instead of the left.

** The description of Surya Namaskar on this page is based on the methods used by Dr. Dilip Sarkar MD, FACS, CAP, Associate Professor of Surgery (Retired), Eastern Virginia Medical School, Norfolk, VA, Executive Director, School of Integrative Medicine, Taksha University, Hampton, VA, Chairman of the Board, Life in Yoga Institute.

Further information: http://www.dilipsarkar.com.

# Table of Asanas, Mantras and Chakras in Suryanamaskar Rishikesh Series

| Asana (traditional naming convention) | Translation | Asana (Krishnamacharya convention) | Solar Mantra | Bija Mantra | Chakra |
|---|---|---|---|---|---|
| Pranamasana | Prayer pose | Tadasana | Om Mitraya Namaha | Om Hrām | Anahata |
| Hasta Uttanasana | Raised arms pose | Urdhva Namaskar | Om Ravaye Namaha | Om Hrīm | Vishuddha |
| Padahastasana | Hand to foot pose | Uttanasana | Om Suryaya Namaha | Om Hrūm | Svadhisthana |
| Ashwa Sanchalanasana | Equestrian pose | Ashwa Sanchalanasana | Om Bhanave Namaha | Om Hraim | Ajna |
| Parvatasana | Mountain pose | Adho Mukha Svanasana | Om Khagaya Namaha | Om Hrāum | Vishuddha |

| Ashtanga Namaskara | Salute with eight parts | Ashtangasana | Om Pushne Namaha | Om Hrah | Manipura |
|---|---|---|---|---|---|
| Bhujangasana | Cobra pose | Bhujangasana | Om Hiranyagarbhaya Namaha | Om Hrām | Svadhisthana |
| Parvatasana | Mountain pose | Adho Mukha Svanasana | Om Marichaye Namaha | Om Hrīm | Vishuddha |
| Ashwa Sanchalanasana | Equestrian pose | Ashwa Sanchalanasana | Om Adityaya Namaha | Om Hrūm | Ajna |
| Padahastasana | Hand to foot pose | Uttanasana | Om Savitre Namaha | Om Hraim | Svadhisthana |
| Hasta Uttanasana | Raised arms pose | Urdhva Namaskar | Om Arkaya Namaha | Om Hrāum | Vishuddha |
| Pranamasana | Prayer pose | Tadasana | Om Bhaskaraya Namaha | Om Hrah | Anahata |

# *Purna-Suryanamaskar*: intensive practice using the *Mahayoga* method

## (*Suryanamaskar* Practice for Advanced Students)

The practice of yoga has been a part of my life for as long as I can remember, in fact for more than 50 years. Even as a five year-old child I used to sit spontaneously in the lotus posture and become immersed in the experience of listening to *nada*, the internal sound, heard in the *chidakasha* (space located in the center of the head). Many years later I learnt that this type of meditation was called *nada-anusandhana* and was ideal for practicing *Suryanamaskar*. I also learnt that the experience of hearing *nada* was considered possible after deep cleansing of the body and the long-term nurturing of pure thoughts and feelings.

At first I practiced spontaneously when I felt the need. Then, at the age of nine, I began a regular yoga practice, performing asana sequences in silence twice a day, in the morning and the evening, for two hours on each occasion. I used to hold each posture for a few minutes, except in the case of the headstand (*shirshasana*), which I would hold for about 12 minutes. Later on I extended the duration of the headstand to 20 and sometimes even up to 45 minutes. While holding each asana I repeated the mantra *Om*, following and immersing myself in the internal sound of *nada* and experiencing a sensation of the infinite (*ananta*) expansiveness of time and space.

I received an introduction to yoga from Tomek Nowakowski, later a senior colleague, who also taught me the Japanese martial art of judo. In 1982, he founded the International School of Tai Chi, which has opened branches in many European countries.

By means of constant practice as a boy I had reached a high level of physical fitness and endurance. As a result my parents enrolled me in sport acrobatics, which I subsequently practiced for many years, as a participant in the vault and floor forms of the exercise. During my high school years I also practiced karate, and took part in mountain climbing and sailing. When in college I practiced judo and zazen, and later, capoeira (a Brazilian mixture of martial art and dance), boxing, and yiquan (a Chinese martial art), while continuing my running and mountain climbing.

I traveled to India many times, sometimes once or twice a year for several months. I had the opportunity to meet amazing yogis in the Himalayas of India and Nepal, in Tibet, Varanasi, and in Maharashtra and Kerala, where I received initiation into the various practices of *Mahayoga, Suryavijnana* (the solar science) and *Tantra*.

I have also studied Indian philosophy with, among others, Dr. Tomasz Rucinski (especially for the philosophy of Yoga and Kashmir Shaivism), and Professor Andrzej Poltawski (for phenomenology, the philosophy of consciousness, and epistemology).

After graduation I worked for 11 years as an author of encyclopedia entries and, eventually, as the editor of the Great Universal Encyclopedia published by PWN (State Scientific Publishers in Poland). I worked closely with Professor Tadeusz Gadacz and many other distinguished philosophers and theologians in Poland. This collaborative work had an impact on my own understanding of reality.

Amongst my scientific work, family and social life, and intensive sports training, including extreme sports, yoga has always been my mainstay and the background to any other activity. Yogis call it *upaya-yoga*, or yoga found in everyday life and in all our daily activities.

I started teaching yoga after more than 20 years of intense practice and learning. The latter took place through an in-depth study of the philosophy of yoga, including the analysis of texts, and through comments, thoughts and discussions with people on various issues and aspects of yoga practice and teaching, and also from my own developing understanding of life itself and the world. I tried to understand where I was, how I had got there, and where I was going. I had experienced how a personal quest for truth could offer a kind of protection from the vicissitudes of life and provide a way of breaking through a countless number of false beliefs and convictions. I was aware that contact with nature, especially in the high mountains, always had a healing effect on me.

I felt that the degree of cleansing of my body, the state of my mind, and my perception of reality were all affected by diet, and that these three components in turn affected my practice of yoga and my physical fitness. Each transition from a more gross to a more subtle diet not only increased my efficiency, endurance and strength, but also improved my insight into and trust in myself, and increased in me a crystal and joyous lightness of heart and mind.

Even as a child I did a few days' fasts on water alone, while at the same time practicing very intensively. For many years since 1998 I have experimented by every few months going onto a different diet. For example, after five months on a vegan diet I spent the next six months just drinking freshly squeezed orange juice. On another occasion I spent seven months on a diet of fruit, followed by half a year on salads and a raw food vegan diet, and then four months on honey, the juice of apples and pears, and drinking tea. If, sometimes while travelling, I had eaten a vegetarian meal, then, after returning home or reaching my destination, I would for the next two months go onto water alone, and then one month without food and without water altogether, and then go back to the juice diet.

During these periods I observed positive changes in my state of mind and mood, with glowing eyes, clearer skin condition, and improved physical strength. For example, when drinking just a good quality, fresh-pressed orange juice (about 4 liters per day), I did not feel any fatigue during the day, which included heavy physical practice for up to 5 or 7 hours without rest, plus many hours of intensively intellectual work, such as writing and editing articles. I did not need more than 1 to 2 hours of sleep to regenerate. On this diet I could work much better and without fatigue for several months. However, eating even a single vegan meal during this phase would result in deterioration in the sense of well-being that had pertained when my digestive system had been almost completely empty.

I realized that nutrition was a key principle in nature, opening the way for a very intense, advanced practice of *Pūrna-Suryanamaskar* with the minimum of effort. If occasionally my body went through a period of overexertion and, in consequence, lost the ability to regulate and regenerate itself in the normal way, and the heart no longer felt the deep joy of the practice of *Mahayoga*, then during those periods I could not stand the intense, prolonged mode of practising the exercises, with the very slow breathing and long periods without breathing at all. In general, however, my experience was otherwise. The methodology of a progressive and comprehensive training in *Mahayoga* allowed me to develop an uncommon ability to function, even under difficult and extremely unfavorable circumstances.

*Mahayoga*, as a dynamic method of integrating and coordinating the structural and systemic aspects of a human being, is, simply expressed, a *sadhana* of *sushumna*. It is a practice related to the spinal cord and the primary flow of breath. It is a practice aimed at healing by cleaning up the energy channels (*nadis*), by removing discomfort from the body by undoing blocks and tension in the fascia, muscles and organs, and by opening and strengthening the joints and skeletal system. This is achieved by especially composed set of practices, consisting of *vyanga* (dynamic exercises), *asanas* (postures), *vinyasa krama* (fluid and timed combinations of sequenced *asanas* and of breath), *pranayama* (breathing practices to extend and stabilize the life force) and *pratyahara* (detachment from the senses, which can lead to a state of inner balance and insight).

The dynamic aspects of *Mahayoga*, referred to as *vyayama krama*, are divided into *vyanga* and *vinyasa*:

A) *Vyanga krama* - the practice exercises and sequences of movements - slow, fast, circulatory, rotary, centrifugal and centripetal movement, rocking, dangling, shaking, in passive, active, and passive-active styles - are divided into six classes:

1) *Shakti vikasakas* - excitation and distribution of energy.
2) *Shakti vardhakas* - reviving, nourishing and regenerating energy.
3) *Shakti shuddhis* - cleansing, allowing natural freedom and lightness.

4) *Shakti gatis* - developing and gathering strength and reinforcing joints.
5) *Shakti urdanas* - developing coordination and regulating the flow of *prana*.
6) *Shakti pushtis* - integrating, rejuvenating and calming.

B) *Vinyasa krama* - the dynamic practice of 11 basic *asana* sequences carried out in harmony with the breath, of which the version known as *Suryanamaskar C* corresponds most closely to the sequence described in the book Dynamic Suryanamaskar by Krzysztof Stec:

1) *Usha pranam A* ('reverence for predawn A').
2) *Usha pranam B* ('reverence for predawn B').
3) *Surya pranam* ('reverence for the Sun').
4) *Chandra pranam* ('reverence for the Moon').
5) *Indra pranam* ('reverence for Indra').
6) *Suryanamaskar A* ('Sun salutation A').
7) *Suryanamaskar B* ('Sun salutation B').
8) *Suryanamaskar C* ('Sun salutation C').
9) *Chandra namaskar A* ('Moon salutation A').
10) *Chandra namaskar B* ('Moon salutation B').
11) *Matre vandanam* ('tribute to Mother Earth').
    and further exercises for developing inner strength:
    *Shakti Sanchar* ('collecting inner healing Power').

Against the background of the practice of the dynamic exercise *vyayama krama, Pūrna- Suryanamaskar* occupies a special place. It is particularly associated with multiple repetitions of *Suryanamaskar A*, consisting of 10 positions in the system sequence (*krama*) asanas, performed in a way that regulates and integrates body, breath and mind (*tristhana*). By balancing and gradually building power (*Maha-Shakti*) at all levels of operation, it is possible to open the heart and to enable the emergence of subtle feelings, allowing entry into a deep level of the unity of Reality, where everything is equal and sacred.

*Suryanamaskar* meditation and *pranayama* are performed in *Mahayoga* with silent repetition of the mantra *So'ham*:

- during the in-breath one is merged with the sound *So* (from *Sah* - which means 'That', 'The Supreme Reality', 'God as the Divine Mother, who takes us into her arms', or 'infinite space and power, which is saturated with energy, gives life and embraces our entire body').
- during the out-breath one is merged with the sound *Ham* (from *Aham* - which means 'I', 'Self', 'Myself and a sense of expansion of embracing the whole Reality with the feeling of unconditional love').
- during the pronunciation of the words '*Sah*' and '*Aham*', where there is contact between these two, a phenomenon occurs called *sandhi*, which results in the following sound: *So'ham*.
- during periods of voluntary cessation of breathing (apnea) one may experience an internal sound, in yoga called '*nada*', which can lead to the state of meditation called '*nadaanusandhana*', in which, in this case, the sound is experienced in the heart.

In the internal area of the body one experiences the infinity of Microcosm, which is one with the infinite universe as Macrocosm.

*Suryanamaskar* should be practiced with a sense of joy, lightness and brightness. This type of practice combines *mantra-yoga, hatha-yoga, laya-yoga* and *raja-yoga*.

*Suryanamaskar A*, which I used to practice as *Pūrna-Suryanamaskar*, is a sequence of the following asanas:

1) *Samasthitihi.*
2) *Urdhva mukha vrikshasana.*
3) *Uttanasana A.*
4) *Uttanasana B.*
5) *Chaturanga dandasana.*
6) *Urdhva mukha svanasana.*

7) *Adho mukha svanasana.*

8) *Uttanasana B.*

9) *Uttanasana A.*

10) *Urdhva mukha vrikshasana.*

and then

1) *Samasthitihi* (as the end and the beginning of a new round).

There are 3 stages in the practice, basic, intermediate and advanced. Each stage has 3 steps, weak, moderate and strong. The number of rounds is gradually increased to 108 in each step. When there is no breath holding, the inhalation and exhalation phases merge seamlessly into one another.

(N.B. In order to engage in this type of exercise, it is highly advisable to be in a state of excellent health and to have already allowed the body to adjust to a raw food diet. Any discomfort or pain should prompt the immediate discontinuance of the practice, and the allowing of sufficient time for the body to recover its well-being, if necessary by adopting a more strict raw diet or even a vegan diet.)

1.A. Step Basic-Weak. 108 rounds of the *Suryanamaskar A* sequence. The performance of each asana takes as long as the relevant breath. Inhalation (*puraka*) and exhalation (*rechaka*) should take place in a ratio of 1:1, at a tempo of 5 seconds each, going into one asana breathing in and going into the next asana breathing out, without stopping in the asana and so remaining in constant motion. To the rhythm of six breaths per minute, performing one sequence of *Suryanamaskar A* takes 50 seconds and performing 108 repetitions (rounds) takes 1 hour and 30 minutes.

1.B. Step Basic-Moderate. 108 rounds with inhalation and exhalation in the ratio of 1:1, at 10 seconds each. There are thus three breaths per minute, and one round takes 1 minute and 40 seconds, and 108 repetitions take 3 hours.

1.C. Step Basic-Strong. 108 rounds with inhalation and exhalation in the ratio of 1:1, at 15 seconds each. There are thus two breaths per minute, and one round takes 2 minutes and 30 seconds, and 108 repetitions take 4 hours and 30 minutes.

In the Intermediate-Weak and Intermediate-Moderate steps, exhalation should last twice as long as inhalation. Transition from inhalation to exhalation and vice versa should be smooth and uninterrupted, and there should be no holding of position in the asanas.

In the Intermediate-Strong step two phases of breath holding are introduced. One occurs after the inhalation (internal breath holding or *antar kumbhaka*) and the other after the exhalation (external breath holding or *bahya kumbhaka*, or *shunyata*). All four phases of a single breath have the same duration. The phases where the breath is stopped are also the periods when the asana is held, i.e. without any movement. For this level of practice (Intermediate-High), a diet is recommended that consists of liquids (juices) only, i.e. with no solid food intake.

(N.B. In order to engage in this type of exercise, it is highly advisable to be in a state of excellent health and to have already allowed the body to adjust to a raw food diet. Any discomfort or pain should prompt the immediate discontinuance of the practice, and the allowing of sufficient time for the body to recover its well-being, if necessary by adopting a more strict raw diet or even a vegan diet.)

2.A. Step Intermediate-Weak. 108 rounds of the *Suryanamaskar A* sequence with inhalation and exhalation in the ratio of 1:2, with 5 seconds inhalation and 10 seconds exhalation. At four breaths per minute, one sequence takes 1 minute and 15 seconds and 108 repetitions take 2 hours and 15 minutes.

2.B. Step Intermediate-Moderate. 108 rounds with inhalation and exhalation in the ratio of 1:2, with 10 seconds inhalation and 20 seconds exhalation. At two breaths per minute, one sequence takes 2 minutes and 30 seconds and 108 repetitions take 4 hours and 30 minutes.

2.C. Step Intermediate-Strong. 108 rounds with breathing performed in the ratio of 1:1:1:1, i.e. with 10 seconds inhalation, 10 seconds holding the breath in, 10 seconds exhalation, and 10 seconds holding the breath out. This procedure creates a rhythm of three breaths every 2 minutes. One sequence takes 3 minutes and 20 seconds and 108 repetitions take 6 hours.

In the advanced stage of the practice of *Suryanamaskar A* the asanas are performed solely during periods of breath holding.

In the Advanced-Weak step the sequence of asanas is performed during the phase of breath holding after inhalation (internal breath holding). The phases of original inhalation, additional inhalation (see below), exhalation, and breath holding after exhalation (external breath holding), are performed in a stationary, standing position called *samasthitihi*.

In the Advanced-Moderate step the sequence of asanas is performed once during the phase of breath holding after inhalation and a second time during the phase of breath holding after exhalation. The inhaling and exhaling phases are performed in a stationary, standing position called *samasthitihi*.

In the Advanced-Strong step (so-called 'pyramid') the number of rounds performed of *Suryanamaskar A* during breath holding is gradually increased and then gradually decreased.

(N.B. In order to engage in this type of exercise, it is highly advisable to be in a state of excellent health and to have already allowed the body to adjust to a raw food diet based primarily on fruits, liquids and so on. Any discomfort or pain should prompt the immediate discontinuance of the practice, and the allowing of sufficient time for the body to recover its well-being, if necessary by adopting a more strict raw diet or even a vegan diet.)

3.A. Step Advanced-Weak. 108 rounds with breathing performed in the ratio of 1:4:½:2:1, with 10 seconds inhalation, 40 seconds of holding the breath in (during which one round of the *Suryanamaskar* sequence is performed), then for 5 seconds take a small further in-breath, then exhale for 20 seconds, and then hold the breath out for 10 seconds. Thus one breath lasts 1 minute and 25 seconds, but the performance of the *Suryanamaskar* sequence takes place only in the phase in which the breath is held in (40 seconds). On this basis, 108 repetitions take 2 hours and 33 minutes.

3.B. Step Advanced-Moderate. 108 rounds with breathing performed in the ratio of 1:3:½:2:3, with 10 seconds inhalation, 30 seconds of holding the breath in (during which one round of the *Suryanamaskar* sequence is performed), then for 5 seconds take a small further in-breath, then exhale for 20 seconds, and then hold the breath out for 30 seconds (during which one round of the *Suryanamaskar* sequence is performed). Thus one breath lasts 1 minute and 35 seconds. During that time two rounds of *Suryanamaskar* are performed, one round during the phase of holding the breath in and one round while holding the breath out. On this basis, 108 repetitions take 1 hour, 25 minutes and 30 seconds.

3.C. Step Advanced-Strong. *Suryanamaskar A* is performed in the phases of breath holding in the form of a so-called 'pyramid', i.e. increasing and then decreasing the number of rounds performed during each phase of breath holding. The breathing ratios specified in steps 3A and 3B are used, 3A for the so-called 'weak' rhythm practice, and 3B for the 'strong'.

In the rhythm called 'weak', during each phase (round) of internal breath holding, the number of rounds performed of *Suryanamaskar A* is first increased and then decreased by one, starting with 1 in the first round, then going to 2 in the second, 3 in the third, and 4 in the fourth, and then decreasing, to 3 in the fifth, 2 in the sixth, and 1 in the seventh round. This makes a total of 16 rounds of *Suryanamaskar A* performed during 7 rounds of breath holding. The 'weak' rhythm is sometimes described as the '1:2:3:4:3:2:1' practice.

In the rhythm called 'strong' the procedure is identical to that described under the 'weak' rhythm practice, except that the *Suryanamaskar A* rounds are performed during the phases of external breath holding as well as internal. This makes a total of 32 rounds of *Suryanamaskar A* performed during 7 rounds of breath holding. The 'strong' rhythm is sometimes described as the '1:1:2:2:3:3:4:4:3:3:2:2:1:1' practice.

The practice of the 'pyramid' begins at an initial level of 2 rounds ('1:2:1'), building up when ready to 3 rounds ('1:2:3:2:1'), and then to 4 ('1:2:3:4:3:2:1'). When well established in the 'weak' rhythm, practice of the 'strong' is commenced, starting again with 2 rounds and gradually increasing the number of rounds as capacity develops.

*Purna-Suryanamaskar* is for me a daily practice, but once or twice a year, at the time of the spring and/or autumn equinox, I do long hours of additional intense practice, when I perform 1008 rounds of *Suryanamaskar A*.

It is important to remember for the practice as a whole that duration, tempo and rhythm change according to the increase in capacity. The individual's capacity is dependent on diet, lifestyle and the nature of the practitioner. Capacity increases gradually when starting on a vegan diet, especially after the exclusion of cooked food. It continues to increase slowly when moving to ever more subtle diets, such as raw vegan, fruitarian, liquidarian, and finally, after what is certain to have been many years, if not decades, of strenuous self-discipline, to breatharian, that is, up to full self-regulation of the organism. In diet, as in other aspects of the practice, it is essential to proceed step by step, in a measured way, preferably under guidance. There is nothing to be gained by trying to rush to the destination. The journey itself is the greatest teacher.

**Wlodek Lagodzki**
*Mahayoga* teacher, Dzierzoniow, Poland

# Exceptional Human Adaptation

**Wieslaw Pilis**[1], **Krzysztof Stec**
Institute of Health Prophylaxis in Czestochowa, Poland
Jan Dlugosz University in Czestochowa, Poland

## Introduction

Life has taught me that outstanding people are everywhere, but that very often only a highly perceptive observer can notice them. I trained for several years two to three times a week on the weightlifting platform in one of the leading sports clubs in Poland, and I was not aware that a training colleague on the same barbell, Mr. Jerzy Kukuczka[2], was already also an outstanding mountaineer and rock climber, and in the process of becoming one of the leading mountaineers in the world.

At the same time, that is in the 1970s, I met Mr. Krzysztof Stec, a student at the University School of Physical Education in Katowice; a subtle, well-behaved and mature young man, quiet in demeanor and showing a strong resemblance in personality to my friend, Mr. Kukuczka. I knew that he had practiced yoga for some time because photographs of him had been used in a book about yoga written by Professor Wieslaw Romanowski and published in 1975. Mr. Krzysztof Stec, however, subsequently disappeared from my life for many years. Some time about 2010, when visiting someone in Warsaw, I came across a familiar face and, after a short while, I realized that the person was Mr. Krzysztof Stec, by now a mature human being with extensive experience in life, having a professional

1 Professor Wieslaw Pilis, former President (Rector in Poland) of the University School of Physical Education in Katowice in Poland, a specialist in sport and exercise physiology, weightlifting champions coach, and author of over 200 original research papers.

2 Jerzy Kukuczka (24 March 1948 – 24 October 1989), born in Katowice, Poland, was a Polish alpine and high-altitude climber. He is widely considered among the climbing community to be one of the best high-altitude climbers in history. He ascended all fourteen mountains, which exceed eight thousand meters in height in just over eight years, a shorter time than any climber before ('Jerzy Kukuczka', Wikipedia).

career, being a 'globe-trotter' and a person who had 'fallen in love' with yoga.

His strong determination to study yoga had become the guiding force in his life. With lots of enthusiasm he talked about his yogic experiences, about his stay in various ashrams in India, about current trends in yoga, about great Hindu yogis, and about the sacrifices some people make on the path to perfection. His accounts from visits to many places around the world, where practices leading to perfection of mind and body were cultivated, revealed to me that yoga was a broad field and an indivisible whole, containing within it proper relaxation, appropriate diet, a strong resolve to perform asanas frequently, practices of pranayama (special yogic breathing techniques different from regular deep breathing), positive thinking, and meditation. As a professor of human physiology and applied physiology, I began to experience an increasing state of shock as I realized that Krzysztof's life brought into question the scientifically recognized norms of human physiology that I considered to be 'sacred' and unbreakable.

Listening to Krzysztof's account of his own nutrition, I at first thought it highly inappropriate for a human being, in fact just laughable, when compared to the recognized standards for the consumption of proteins, fats, carbohydrates, and so on. To my expostulations Krzysztof responded with a somewhat wry smile, and insisted that I should just stop counting calories and comparing everything with those recognized standards. He stated that he was well aware that his diet did not meet the standard of nutrition specified by physiological science, but that he was nonetheless in great physical and mental condition. He was living proof, by his daily yogic training, consisting, among other practices, of a few hundred cycles of the ancient practice called Suryanamaskar or Sun Salutation, in the version called by him Dynamic Suryanamaskar, that the conventional view of human nutritional needs was not unquestionable. At the same time he pointed out that the practicing of yoga on a regular basis had a comprehensive influence on the development of the human body (Stec, 2013), and also had therapeutic effects (Kuvalayananda & Vinekar, 1966).

In the end, out of scientific curiosity, I decided to review all of my own assumptions about human physiology, starting with nutrition. It quickly became apparent to me that the vegetarian life-style followed by Krzysztof for 43 years would be feasible for me. I did indeed adopt it and found that it contributed to an improvement in my quality of life. According to Krzysztof, proper eating habits are a decisive factor in maintaining good health and a feeling of well-being; they are a way of achieving a higher level of physical and mental efficiency, of greatly improving quality of life, and of prolonging life expectancy, as they are one of the most potent measures of prophylaxis against disease available to humankind. Krzysztof spoke at length about his previous fasting and how he was even then preparing himself for a long fast in extremely unfavorable climatic conditions in India. He then asked me, if possible, to record beforehand his physiological indices and to determine the efficiency and capacity of his organism. He planned to conduct a long fast, traditionally called Christ's Fasting because of its duration of 40 days. Unfortunately, at that time I had only very limited scientific knowledge and experience of what was conventionally regarded as fasting/starvation. I was, however, familiar with some of the physiological aspects of hunger, and I knew that the longest scientifically registered period of human survival without food was 74 days (Keys et al., 1950). Experiments at the Polish Academy of Science, on dogs given no food for seven days, had demonstrated that the animals were able to sustain the physical effort required on a treadmill for a duration that was the same as or longer than the time achieved when they were on a regular, mixed diet (Nazar et al., 1987). However, the experiments had been quite soon abandoned on ethical grounds. Now I had a perfect opportunity to investigate the issue further, because Krzysztof was about to undertake his long fast. I asked him to observe his body carefully during the fast and to keep daily records of all the physiological variables characterizing the functions of his body that he could possibly observe and measure.

I was well aware that both dietary changes and starvation influence the body's acid-base balance, water and electrolyte balance, and thermo-regulatory capability. It was clear that prolonged fasting combined with not drinking water or any other fluids when in high ambient temperatures, as Krzysztof intended, could create conditions extremely hostile to survival. The data available from the literature indicated that in such conditions there would occur a significant reduction in body weight, increased thirst, decreasing and then increasing hunger, followed by significant changes in somatic, mental, metabolic, hormonal and thermo-regulatory parameters. With significant changes in the amount of water in the organism, the efficiency of different organs gradually deteriorates, eventually causing death (Collins, 1995). The data previously gathered about people forced to work or to try to survive in extreme environmental conditions have confirmed the occurrence of these kinds of drastic changes in the body. The cases of workers constructing the hydroelectric dam in Boulder, Colorado in the USA, when hyperthermia was the factor (Talbot and Michelson, 1933), or on other occasions when extreme physical work was undertaken in very high temperatures (Talbot et al., 1955), or when survivors of maritime disasters suffered starvation and lack of drinking water (Gamble, 1946-1947), all gave a clear picture of the various physical dangers to health in such conditions. Therefore, in order to establish baseline parameters before departing for India, Krzysztof's blood, urine and physical fitness were tested (for results see below). While Krzysztof was away undertaking the fast, I was pondering how the data acquired during it could be compared to the baseline data in such a way as to describe accurately and also explain the reaction of his body during and after the long fast, combined as it was going to be with an absence of fluid ingestion and the presence of persistently high ambient temperatures. There follows the formal analysis.

## Person researched and applied research methods

Before leaving for India, Mr. Krzysztof Stec, aged 58, was subjected in Poland to various medical examinations and physical fitness tests. He was a healthy individual, not taking any drugs or alcohol, not smoking, having been on a vegetarian diet for 43 years, and following an intensive daily yoga practice that included several hundred repetitions of the practice called Dynamic Suryanamaskar. His height was 181 cm (Bh) and body weight 82 kg (Bw). Calculated were the following somatic indicators: Quetelet [Bw (g) / Bh (cm)], BMI [Bw (kg) / $Bh^2$ (m)], and Rohrer [Bw (g) / $Bh^3$ (cm)]. For three days the quality and quantity of all foods and liquids consumed by the subject were recorded. They were then analyzed using the Polish-made computer program 'Diet 2'[3], which allows determination of the daily intake of energy, proteins, carbohydrates, fats, water, vitamins, and many minerals. The subject's diet is compared in the table below to the (mean) nutritional data from the best young Polish athletes (age 23.8 ± 2.39 years) competing in race-walking. A sample of blood was taken from the vein in the subject's elbow on an empty stomach. The following parameters of the blood plasma were tested: concentration of glucose, urea, uric acid, total protein content, endogenous creatinine (in serum), sodium, potassium, calcium, total cholesterol, cholesterol HDL, triglycerides, and the molality of serum. In addition the concentration of cholesterol LDL was calculated. The lactate dehydrogenase (LDH) and phosphokinase (CK) values were also determined. Urine analysis was performed for density, pH and concentration of endogenous creatinine, urea, uric acid, sodium, potassium, calcium and the molality of urine. Further characteristics of renal functioning were assessed by calculating:

- clearance: endogenous creatinine (CCr), urea (CU), uric acid (CUA), sodium (CNa), potassium (CK), calcium (CCa)
- osmotic clearance (Cosmol)
- free water clearance (CH2O).

On a different day the subject was tested for physical fitness on the cycloergometer under a gradually increasing load. Before the test, in resting conditions, body weight, height and blood pressure (BP) were measured. During resting and at each load level the following parameters were recorded: one-minute lung ventilation (VE), one-minute oxygen uptake ($VO_2$), one-minute carbon dioxide elimination ($VCO_2$), respiratory exchange ratio (RER), and heart rate (HR). Based on the analysis of the occurring parameter changes of VE, $VCO_2$ and RER, the anaerobic (ventilation) threshold (AT) was

3 The software "Diet 2" has been developed by The National Food and Nutrition Institute (Instytut Żywienia i Żywności -[www.izz.waw.pl/en/] that has responsibility for establishing proper nutritional standards and norms for Poland.

determined. The cycloergometer test began at the load level of 60 W and it was increased by 30 W at a time until reaching the maximum observable load level of 270 W. At each load level the test lasted for 3 minutes. During the last load, the maximal oxygen uptake ($VO_2max$) was measured.

A few days later, while the subject was performing Dynamic Suryanamaskar for 30 minutes, the following parameters were recorded: VE, $VO_2$, $VCO_2$, RER and HR.

Then, in June and July of 2010, while staying in the state of Maharashtra in India, the subject voluntarily undertook a total fast of 42 days. After the initial 23 days he started taking orally some unadulterated pure water. The subject had undertaken many previous fasts, from short periods of several days to longer ones of a few weeks, and was therefore familiar with the expected changes to body and mind. During the fasting period the humidity level was low for about the first three weeks, before the monsoon, and the subject was spending the day in a room or in a close-by temple. Before the monsoon the temperatures in central India were very high and had consistently reached 45-47°C, even one day at noon reaching 49°C. At 10 p.m. the temperature frequently was still about 40-42°C. At night the subject usually slept on the roof of the building, because of the lower temperatures there, which in the morning decreased to about 25°C. In addition to tracking changes in his body weight, pulse rate and rate of respiration, the subject recorded observations of the amount and color of urine and stool, and also of general body reactions. He gave himself a regular enema (every other day from the 24th day onwards until the end of the fast) and stayed physically very active by practicing Dynamic Suryanamaskar and by swimming for about two hours every day. He observed and recorded his feelings and mental reactions, and for a few hours daily he worked intellectually. He meditated for a while daily. When the fasting was over the subject recorded his body weight, heart rate and blood pressure.

## Test results

Before the fast the subject's body height was 181 cm, body weight was 82 kg, determined body surface: 2,03 $m^2$, Quetelet index - 453.04

g / cm, BMI - 25.03 kg/m$^2$, Rohrer index - 1.38 g/cm$^3$.

After the fast body weight was 59 kg (a reduction of 23 kg or 28.05 %) and the other somatic indices were: body surface - 1.72 m$^2$, Quetelet index - 325.97 g/cm, BMI - 17.99 kg/m$^2$, Rohrer index - 0.99 g/cm$^3$. Body weight returned to its previous level of 82 kg by 3 months after the end of the fast. The indexed blood variables are shown in Table 1.

**Table 1.** Subject's blood variables before fasting.

| No. | Variable | Result | Unit | Min | Max | Notes |
|---|---|---|---|---|---|---|
| 1 | Glucose (ICD-9: L43) | 99 | mg / dl | 70 | 110 | - |
| 2 | Urea (ICD-9: N13) | 38 | mg / dl | 10 | 50 | - |
| 3 | Uric acid (ICD-9: M45) | 4.0 | mg / dl | 3.5 | 7.2 | - |
| 4 | Total Protein (ICD-9: 177) | 6.8 | g / l | 6.1 | 7.9 | - |
| 5 | Serum creatinine (ICD-9: M37) | 0.95 | mg / dl | 0.7 | 1.3 | - |
| 6 | Sodium (ICD-9: O35) | 145 | mmol / l | 135 | 145 | - |
| 7 | Potassium (ICD-9: N45) | 5.70 | mmol / l | 3.5 | 5.10 | H |
| 8 | Total calcium (ICD-9: O77) | 9.84 | mg / dl | 8.4 | 10.20 | - |
| 9 | LDH (ICD-9: K33) | 179 | U / L * | - | 248 | - |
| 10 | Phosphocreatine kinase (ICD-9: M18) | 56 | U / L | 24 | 195 | - |
| 11 | Total cholesterol (ICD-9: --) | 193 | mg / dl | 140 | 200 | - |
| 12 | HDL cholesterol (ICD-9: --) | 50 | mg / dl | 40 | 60 | - |
| 13 | LDL Cholesterol (ICD-9: --) | 125 | mg / dl | - | 135 | - |
| 14 | Triglycerides (ICD-9: --) | 87 | mg / dl | 40 | 140 | - |
| 15 | Molality of serum | 300 | mmol / kg $H_2O$ | 283 | 295 | H |

* - Reference range belongs to the age group,
H - values above the norm.

The test urine was clear, yellow in color, pH 7.5 (normal: 5.0 - 7.0), density 1.020 g/ml (normal: 1.015 - 1.030), did not contain glucose, ketones, bilirubin, protein, nitrite, did contain a few flat epithelia and bacteria, but urobilinogen content was normal, and in the field of view 1-3 leukocytes were encountered. The volume of daily urine excretion was 1400 ml. More precise urine characteristics are shown in Table 2.

**Table 2.** Subject's characteristics of urine and renal functioning before fasting.

| No. | Variable | Result | Unit | Min | Max | Notes |
|---|---|---|---|---|---|---|
| 1 | Creatinine (ICD-9: M37) | 0.95 | g/24h | 1.00 | 2.00 | L |
| 2 | Urea (ICD-9: N13) | 13.30 | g/24h | 15.00 | 34.00 | L |
| 3 | Uric acid (ICD-9: M45) | 0.34 | g/24h | 0.20 | 1.00 | - |
| 4 | Sodium (ICD-9: --) | 220.32 | mmol/24h | 30.00 | 300.00 | - |
| 5 | Potassium (ICD-9: --) | 105.56 | mmol/24h | 30.00 | 300.00 | - |
| 6 | Calcium (ICD-9: Ø77) | 54.88 | mg/24 L | 100.00 | 300.00 | L |
| 7 | Urine molality | 600 | mmol / kg $H_2O$ | 450 | 900 | - |
| 8 | Endogenous creatinine clearance | 59.23 | ml/min/1.73m$^2$ | 80 | 140 | L |
| 9 | Urea clearance | 20.71 | ml/min/1.73m$^2$ | 40 | 90 | L |
| 10 | Uric acid | 5.03 | ml/min/1.73m$^2$ | 4.0 | 9.5 | - |
| 11 | Sodium clearance | 1.26 | ml/min/1.73m$^2$ | 0.3 | 1.0 | H |
| 12 | Potassium clearance | 10.95 | ml/min/1.73m$^2$ | 5.0 | 20 | - |
| 13 | Calcium clearance | 0.33 | ml/min/1.73m$^2$ | 0.5 | 2.0 | L |
| 14 | Osmotic clearance | 1.68 | ml/min/1.73m$^2$ | 1.7 | 2.5 | L |
| 15 | Free water clearance | 0.69 | ml/min/1.73m$^2$ | +0.5 | -0.5 | H |

L-values below the norm, H-values above the norm.

The maximum volume of oxygen consumption ($VO_2max$) was at the load of 270 W and it was 4570 ml/min (55.73 ml/min/kg), with maximal heart rate of 155 beats/min. The determined ventilation threshold in this test appeared at the load of 190 W, which accounted for 70.37% of the $VO_2max$. The size of the $VO_2$ during a 30 minute Dynamic Suryanamaskar practice reached 90% of the $VO_2max$.

The composition of the regular diet followed by the subject is shown in Table 3.

The data presented in table 3 served as the calculation base for determining that the daily energy intake was: from proteins 8.8%, from fats 16.8%, and from carbohydrates 74.4%. The mineral daily consumption was as follows: sodium - 1816.34 mg, potassium - 7275.44 mg, calcium - 636.94 mg, phosphorus - 986.92 mg, magnesium - 450.54 mg, iron - 21.95 mg, zinc - 11.80 mg, copper - 2.54 mg, and manganese - 8.31 mg. The vitamin intake was: A (retinol equivalent) - 10341.58 $\mu$g, D - 1.08 $\mu$g, E (alpha-tocopherol equivalents) - 13.67 mg, B1-1, 59 mg, B2-1.31 mg, B3 - 14.12 mg, B6 - 2.69 mg, B9 - 762.36 $\mu$g, B12 - 1.18 $\mu$g, C -215 mg.

**Table 3.** Characteristics of the subject's diet before fasting compared to the diet of race-walking champions.

| Ingredients | Tested | Race-Walkers | PNN | EAR | RDA |
|---|---|---|---|---|---|
| Protein [g] | 47.60 | 188.95 ± 43.47 | | 37 - 66<br>33 - 58 | 45 - 81a<br>41 - 72b |
| Fats [g] | 40.92 | 146.88 ± 23.39 | 67-152 d<br>64-123 e | | |
| Carbohydrates [g] | 402.24 | 538.20 ± 61.59 | | 100 | 130c |
| Energy Value [kcal] | 2216.71 | 4357.38 ± 286.83 | 3900d<br>2900e | | |
| Protein [g / kg] | 0.58 | 2.66 ± 0.51 | | 0.73 | 0.90 |
| Fats [g / kg] | 0.50 | 2.08 ± 0.31 | | | |

| | | | | | |
|---|---|---|---|---|---|
| Carbohydrates [g / kg] | 4.91 | 7.65 ± 1.20 | | | |
| Energy Value [kcal / kg] | 27.03 | 61.74 ± 4.83 | | | |
| Proteins [kcal] | 195.16 | 774.70 ± 178.23 | | | |
| Fats [kcal] | 372.37 | 1336.61 ± 212.85 | | | |
| Carbohydrates [kcal] | 1649.18 | 2206.62 ± 252.52 | | | |

* PNN (Polish nutrition norm), EAR, RDA - Dietary Norms; a, d - norms for men; b, e - norms for women; c - norms for men and women.

## Description of the body responses during fasting

When the subject came back to Poland several months after the end of the fast, I was able to hear his oral account about the fasting and read his observations written during that time. By deciding to fast without any water intake he assumed that the human organism was capable of adapting itself to the extreme conditions to a much greater extent than conventional medicine claimed was possible. Before starting the fast, he performed a deep colonic enema 3 times: a procedure called in yoga *jala-basti* (the technique is significantly different from the western gravitational enema), each time utilizing about 2 liters of water mixed with two heaping tablespoons of kitchen salt. He performed the colonic cleansing until the expelled water did not contain any visible fecal matter and was completely clean. Just after this procedure he started the fast and stopped consumption of any foods or liquids. He had noticed that bowel movement stopped and that the excreted urine, being initially yellowish, quickly became brighter. Unfortunately, he did not measure the exact amount of urine, but estimated its volume as about 150 ml/ day. Urination did not cause him any problems. After about 3-4 days the sensation of being hungry disappeared, but a slight thirst remained all the time until the 24th day. During that period of time the amount of secreted saliva was visibly lower and he experienced some dryness in his mouth.

After 23 days he decided to force himself to start drinking some water because the thirst sensation was so weak that it did not stimulate him to resume taking fluids. For two days he tried to adapt his body to hydrate itself, however water was just passing through the digestive tract without any noticeable absorption. During that time he performed a deep enema with salty water (*jala-basti*) a number of times. After the first two rinses with water volume of about 2 liters each, the expelled content of bowel deposits was black, sticky like tar and exceptionally malodorous. After four equal procedures the expelled water was finally clear and therefore he decided not to perform additional rinses on that day. During the undertaken fasting the subject performed daily intense yogic practices, such as Dynamic Suryanamaskar, prolonged head standing (shirshasana) and, starting from the 24th day, colon cleansing every second day using the yogic technique of *jala-basti.* In each session of Dynamic Suryanamaskar he usually performed approximately 250 rounds in about 35 minutes. As it was the summer before the monsoon and the temperatures were reaching 45 degrees Celsius, the subject cooled himself down by swimming in a very large and well-like agricultural water reservoir ten meters deep. He used to swim there for about two hours nearly every day, with the exception of the last week of fasting, covering an estimated distance of 4-5 kilometers. On two occasions he even managed to swim an estimated 8 kilometers in that day's session.

The subject discovered that his resting heart rate was slower at that time, down to about 38-42 beats per minute. In comparison his heart rate while on his regular vegetarian diet was about 44 beats per minute. He slept for only for 3-4 hours per night and felt rested during the day.

At the same time he claimed that the body, when it did not have food in the digestive tract, saved the energy normally required for digestion, and therefore was able to slow down the metabolism, which in turn stimulated him to continue fasting. He also had the impression that his body temperature was lowered helping him mentally to pass through the dangerous heat waves persisting at that time. The recorded respiration rate also decreased, reaching 2 to 3 per minute; when on his regular diet it was 4 to 5 per minute. He felt also an increased flexibility in his joints and comfort in his movements, to such an extent that it was more comfortable for him to sit down on the ground with legs crossed or in a kneeling position, than to sit in a chair. The skin was very flexible, quickly returning to normal after being stretched with the fingers, and retained its normal color and texture. The eyes were not congested despite the long daily head-standing practice. The ability of the body to adapt to the demands of the headstand was better than normal, in that he was able to remain in that position for up to 90 minutes, whereas on his regular diet the comfortable maximum ranged from 35 to 45 minutes per day. The senses worked perfectly well; they were subtler and everything was perceived more clearly. No dysfunction in the body was observed. Muscle strength began to decrease at the end of the fourth week and a deterioration in muscle endurance occurred later, in the sixth week. During the first three to four weeks he experienced an *increase* in muscle endurance and probably because of that he was able to swim long distances every day, something that he had never done before. For that reason he was surprised that swimming for so long was so easy.

When the subject started fasting his thoughts were more optimistic, but the thinking process itself was slower, than when he was on his regular vegetarian diet. Then he noticed that the longer the fasting lasted, the slower the time seemed to pass, but his ability to concentrate was better. He had the impression that his body "became more subtle", and he started having specific yogic experiences of the circulation of subtle energies (*prana*). Until the end of the fifth week of fasting he did not have any significant problems, except perhaps observing that certain physiological reactions slowed down. In the sixth week though, his motor activities clearly and quite dramatically slowed down and he started feeling weak, although fainting never occurred. Going up the stairs became a problem, and perception and speech became much slower. When he sat down in one body position he could stay in it for a very long period. At the same time he experienced worsening concentration, but without the feeling of being annoyed or of losing enthusiasm for life. Even then he had no experience of anxiety, depression or suicidal thoughts. He perceived all of these changes as a great spiritual practice and perhaps because of it, he had extremely high motivation to continue the fasting. He remained calm, however, when eventually exhaustion from fasting began to occur, and the organism went into "maximum saving mode". The subject became strongly introverted, a state that was perceived by him as a pleasant "constancy". During the fasting he lived in an ashram, participated in meditation programs and Hindu religious chants called *bhajans*. He talked with others very little, but as he was studying a lot and preparing his doctoral thesis, he spent a great deal of time writing and thinking analytically.

In terms of having spiritual experiences he did not notice any dramatic changes and attributed that to the fact that he was focused on the observation of his own organism and on scientific work, and not on the void. However, he meditated and tried to "be inside himself and with himself".

The longest previous fast undertaken by the subject had been of thirty days. As he progressed beyond that point, he gradually gained confidence that he would be able to maintain control over his body despite physical weakness and mental slowing down. He subsequently stated that he believed that this meant that he had increased his mental capacities regarding the possibility of survival in extremely adverse conditions. He believed then and he continues to believe now that, after passing through this extreme fasting experience, he would be able to survive for much longer than people without such experience, who, in situations such as being trapped in a mine or after a shipwreck at sea, usually die relatively quickly. Such premature demise occurs because, bereft of all hope, they lose the will to survive. He noted at the same time that isolating himself from worldly affairs, including family and material possessions, won him the ability to have mental distance from many other things. The subject claims now that, the more time has elapsed since his extreme fasting experience, the more positive the emotions that occur in his life have become, especially the ones that enrich his spiritual life. However, all the issues related to the physical adaptation experienced during that period, which were so stressful to the body, disappeared soon after he ended the fast and returned to his regular diet. Now they can only serve as a medical case or for analyses of the organism's reactions in conditions of extreme starvation, dehydration or hyperthermia.

Immediately after the fasting was over, some problems appeared and were associated with the inability of the body to digest and absorb food. Such a state of low tolerance for consumed food lasted for about three weeks until a swami from Uttarkashi gave the subject some herbal remedies from the Himalayas. The result of taking the remedies was that after about 24 hours he was able to eat food, digest and absorb it normally again. Until that moment the food consumed had just been passing through his digestive tract undigested and only fermented. Three weeks after the end of the fast body weight had not increased much, and it was about 61-62 kg. The pre-fasting body weight of 82 kg was achieved after 3 months.

## Discussion

The most surprising element in the account of the fasting given by the subject is that he had not consumed any water for the entire period of the first 23 days. The possible physiological explanation for such a feat should be given the most careful consideration, because the limit of survival without eating and drinking water reported in the scientific literature is four to seven days, and the survival time of a dehydrated person in conditions of high temperature can be as little as three days.

Adolph (1947) and Adolph and Dill (1938) reported that the survival time limit without drinking water was 12 days and McCance (1936) mentioned 15 days (see 'Dehydration' at www.survival.infocentrum.com). The case of two students trapped in a cave for 25 days has also been described. They remained alive despite complete starvation for the whole of that time, although it is probable that they were able to consume a certain amount of moisture naturally present in their place of imprisonment. However, an absolute surprise has been caused by the information posted on the website http://phys.org/news192690076.html in an article entitled 'Starving yogi astounds Indian scientists'. The piece reports that "An 82 year old Holy Man claiming that he has spent seven decades (70 years) not eating and not drinking, astonished a team of Hindu doctors who scientifically investigated him for a period of two weeks. Mr. Prahland Jani stayed for 2 weeks in a hospital in the Hindu state of Gujarat under constant supervision of 30 doctors equipped with cameras and CCTV. Throughout the entire period of staying in the hospital he did not consume any food, did not have any drinks and did not use the toilet."

Returning to the subject's account of his fast, under the prevalent conditions of very high ambient temperatures, physical activity, and heavy sweating, it seems logical that there would be a reduction in urine production. However, the volume of about 150 ml/day, as estimated by the subject, is surprisingly low, and does not represent a physiologically recognized norm. The lowest limit of the physiological volume of urine production per 24 hours is given as 400 ml. This is considered to be the minimum amount needed for the elimination of liquid products of metabolism. The color of his urine, described by him as light, is also difficult to understand, because in conditions of dehydration the color of urine is dark. Moreover, until the 23rd day of fasting, combined with no consumption of water, there did not occur any other external signs of dehydration, such as slowing down of vital body functions, increased heart rate, or sagging skin (Kokot, 1996). Absence of these symptoms could have been related to the fact that Krzysztof spent a few hours per day in water, swimming recreationally. The surprising reactions of his organism in conditions of dehydration were likely also to have been related to the fact that the subject's kidneys, because he had been on a long-term and principally raw food vegetarian diet, had exhibited a tendency for lesser concentration of urine than normal for a Western man of his age. This had been indicated by the following lowered values for relative density of urine and its molality. For a 58 year old man these average lowest parameters are density 1.021 g/ml and molality 700 mmol/kg $H_2O$, occurring on a diet with regular protein and sodium content. These values are those recorded after 12 hours of hydropenia, that is restraint from the consumption of both liquids and foods with substantial water content, such as vegetables or fruits (Kokot, 1996). One may suspect that the subject's vegetarian diet

and rigorous lifestyle led to lower clearance values of endogenous creatinine, urea, and osmotic calcium, and higher clearance values of free water and sodium. Under the condition of maintaining such a vegetarian diet, the increased clearance value of free water has the ability to maintain the molality of body fluids at the same level by vasopressin (antidiuretic hormone) (Kokot, 1996).

The subject's diet before the fast was low in calories and characterized by low content of proteins, fats, calcium, vitamin D and vitamin B12, and higher content of carbohydrates, potassium, iron, copper, vitamin A, vitamin B9 and vitamin C. A vegetarian diet is usually alkaline, which in the subject's case could have been the cause of the alkaline pH of his urine. This conclusion is highly possible, especially since the diet's low protein content would tend to reduce the acidic character of the blood and urine, thus contributing to the subject's high capacity for exercise (Greenhaff et al., 1988). The hyperkalemia (elevated potassium level, see table 1 above, item 7) demonstrated in pre-fasting testing seemed to be the result of the long-term vegetarian diet with its high daily intake of potassium, significantly exceeding the amount considered physiologically essential of 1.6-3.2 g per day. The subject's daily intensive practice of Dynamic Suryanamaskar would not be expected to reduce residual potassium much because potassium elimination through intense perspiration is minimal.

It is also well known that the content of potassium in the body decreases with age, through decrease in muscle tissue mass and increase in body fat. The elevated level of this chemical element in the subject's blood plasma suggests that his body has maintained a large muscle mass, caused by daily intensive physical training, and has not yet experienced age related muscle degradation.

In the blood plasma lipid profile no deviations from physiological norms were noticed. This is a convincing argument to support the view that the subject's way of life and diet were appropriate for the maintenance of good health. The uric acid concentration in blood plasma, its excretion through urine, and the clearance value of this metabolite were within the normal physiological limits. This is a well known consequence of following a plant-food based diet.

Low content of protein, fat, calcium, vitamin D and vitamin B12 in the described diet are recognized as being the result of not consuming animal products (Jarosz and Bulhak-Jachymczyk, 2008).

During the prolonged fasting period of 42 days there probably occurred in the subject's body an intense stimulation of the starvation-induced process of ketogenesis (Nazar et al., 1987). This process involves the increased production of ketone bodies by the liver and an increase in their concentration in the blood. It is reasonable to assume that the brain was nourished mainly by ketone bodies and that was the cause of the mind's functioning with exceptional efficiency and very clear thinking until the sixth week of the fast. The subject's mental fitness remained very high and he did not fall into states of gloom or depression. On the contrary, he remained cheerful and full of positive thinking, despite the enormous burden placed on his body by extreme hunger, lack of fluid intake, and hyperthermia (high ambient temperatures). He had decided beforehand not to use any psychological help during the fast, and kept to that decision. Such help is, however, recommended, even in situations that are much easier to handle (Pietrzykowska, Wierusz-Wysocka, 2008).

Earlier studies have shown that the anions of ketone bodies filtered by the kidneys are not reabsorbed despite their increased concentration in the blood. Their augmented presence in renal tubules fluid can lead to an increased concentration of sodium ions in the renal collecting duct and their more vigorous excretion with urine. This implies an increased water loss from the body (Kolanowski, 1977). In addition, a long-term pause in water intake, such as the subject's of 23 days, would result in much reduced urine production. This would lead to increased levels of urea and other water-soluble metabolites and thus increase the osmotic load of the urine, which may be the cause of greater osmotic diuresis and so an additional factor contributing to dehydration (Martin et al., 2005).

These two stated causes could possibly lead to dehydration of the organism and significant reduction of body mass exceeding one quarter of its starting value, in addition to other possible factors present during such a long period of fasting. This way of explaining the described changes that occurred in the subject's body should, however, be treated with some caution, because, as mentioned above, the subject declared that, during the period of absence of water consumption, the excreted urine was bright in color. Such a color, however, does not correspond to increased excretion of urea.

It is interesting that the subject was able to retain a high level of physical fitness during the fast. The level of physical effort achieved during the Dynamic Suryanamaskar practice can be compared to a competing race-walker or someone running the distance of 1 kilometer in 4 minutes, which for a young adult on a balanced diet and following a medium level training regime is a very high level of intensity. Every day the subject performed several hundred cycles of this exercise within about 35 minutes. His heart bradycardia (constant heart rate below 60 beats per minute), acquired through several decades of yoga practice, did not change during the fast, additionally pointing to the high degree of his body's adaptation to the making of physical effort. Therefore, one must agree with the subject's opinion that performing Dynamic Suryanamaskar during the fast was not for him an extreme burden, just a training method. Additionally, swimming long distances with such great ease while on constant starvation, on the one hand confirms his particularly good preparation for performing strenuous physical activity and on the other hand suggests the ability of the body to maintain or even increase stamina in conditions of long-term fasting. A similar effect had been observed in dogs (v. sup. and Nazar et al., 1987). Therefore it is possible to make the suggestion that the reduction in body weight which occurs in conditions of starvation can be helpful in maintaining a high level of physical fitness. Such a high capacity for exercise demonstrated by the subject during the period of self-imposed starvation, water intake deprivation and hyperthermia, indicates a very high level of prior body training. His ability to sustain a high capacity for physical exercise in these difficult conditions is remarkable, because Hargreaves et al. (1996) proved that dehydration can increase muscle glycogen utilization to re-synthesize adenosine triphosphate (ATP) during muscle activity. Such additional muscle glycogen utilization, with its reserves significantly reduced during the period of starvation, could be expected to have a negative effect on the capacity of the body to undertake physical exercise. However, if the values of phosphokinase (CK) and lactate dehydrogenase (LDH) had been maintained in the blood within the normal physiological ranges, that would have shown that the subject's muscular system had remained regenerated and thus able to sustain the intense training performed until the sixth week of fasting. Regrettably this remains only a hypothesis, as the CK and LDH levels were not recorded during the fast.

That the subject possessed a high level of physical performance before the fast was established by measuring his $VO_2max$. It was equal to 55.73 ml/min /kg and the value of this variable measured during a 30 minute session of Dynamic Suryanamaskar reached 90% of the above-mentioned maximum value. It shows that the daily practice of Dynamic Suryanamaskar, conducted by the subject for many years with a very high intensity, had given him a greatly elevated level of physical fitness, still not diminishing markedly with age, and corresponding to the level of the best trained athletes.

At this point it is worth mentioning the data gathered by researchers from the Harvard Fatigue Laboratory in Boston on the famous marathon runner Clarence De Mar. He won the Boston Marathon for the first time at the age of 22 years, and during the next 28 years was also a multiple winner of the race, achieving his best results between the ages of 35 and 40. When he was 49 years old his oxygen limit was 58 ml/min/kg (Horvath, Horvath, 1973). This comparison shows that the subject's physical performance was on a par with such an outstanding competitor as De Mar. Taking into account the subject's age of 58 and the diminishing amount of oxygen uptake by the body as it ages, the subject's equivalent oxygen limit at the age of 49 may well have been higher than 58 ml/min/kg. The high level of physical fitness is also confirmed by the anaerobic threshold level's occurring at a workload of over 70% $VO_2max$. The anaerobic threshold appearing at such relative high values of developed $VO_2max$ is also certified by Astrand and Rodahl (1986) as indicating a high level of physical fitness.

## Conclusions

1. The research subject, on a vegetarian diet for over 43 years with a very low daily calorie intake, and demonstrating a high value for $VO_2max$, was characterized as having deviations from the reference values of potassium in his blood, urinary pH, and daily urinary excretion of: creatinine, urea, and calcium, as well as changes to the clearances of creatinine, urea, sodium, calcium, osmotic water and free water. The deviations did not influence his excellent physical and mental condition.
2. The conditions under which the research subject remained were extremely difficult owing to the long lasting combined factors of starvation, dehydration and hyperthermia. The case of a period of deprivation of water lasting 23 days had not been previously reported in the literature.
3. A high level of motivation, outstanding mental and physical preparation, and previously practiced periods of fasting and water deprivation resulted in the subject's organism adapting smoothly and setting a new standard of adaptability to extremely difficult conditions which would ordinarily threaten physical survival.
4. The research subject also achieved and maintained for a long period extremely high levels of physical activity unprecedented in such drastically adverse conditions.
5. The highest value for the research subject, as the result of his having survived in such extreme conditions, was to have overcome certain mental barriers. He intends this achievement to drive him on to further research on the limits of the human body's ability to adapt to abnormal or adverse circumstances.

## References

1. Adolph E.F. Physiology of man in the desert. John Wiley, New York, 1947.
2. Adolph E. F., Dill D. B. Observation on water metabolism in the desert. Am. J. Physiol. 1938, 123; 369-378.

3. Astrand P.O., Rodahl K. Textbook of work physiology. Physiological bases of exercise. McGraw-Hill Book Company, New York-Toronto, 1986.
4. Collins S. The limit of human adaptation to starvation. Nature Medicine. 1995, 1; 810-814.
5. 'Dehydration' available at http://pl.wikipedia.org/wiki/Odwodnienie (accessed 19 November 2013).
6. 'Dehydration' in 'Outdoor Survival for everybody' available at www.survival.infocentrum.com/s/notatki/odwodnienie.html (accessed 19 November 2013).
7. Gamble J.L. Physiological information gained from studies on the life-raft ration. Harvey Lect. 1946-1947, 42; 247-273.
8. Greenhaff P.F., Gleeson M., Maugham R. J. Diet-induced metabolic acidosis and the performance of high intensity exercise in man. Eur. J. Appl. Physiol. 1988, 57 (5); 583-590.
9. Hargreavers M., Dillo P., Angus D., Febbraio M. Effect of fluid ingestion on muscle metabolism during prolonged exercise. J. Appl. Physiol. 1996, 80, 1; 363-366.
10. Horvath S.M., Horvath E.C. The Harvard Fatigue Laboratory: its history and contributions. Prentice-Hall, Inc., Englewood Cliffs, New Jersey, 1973.
11. Jarosz M., Bułhak-Jachymczyk B.: Normy żywienia człowieka. Podstawy prewencji otyłości i chorób niezakaźnych. PZWL Warszawa 2008 (in Polish).
12. 'Jerzy_Kukuczka' available at www.en.wikipedia.org/wiki/Jerzy_Kukuczka (accessed 19 November 2013).
13. Keys A., Brozek J.A., Henschek A., Michelson O, Taylor H.L. The biology of human starvation. Minneapolis Univ. of Minnesota Press, 1950.
14. Kokot F.: Choroby wewnętrzne, podręcznik dla studentów. PZWL Warszawa 1996 (in Polish).
15. Kolanowski J. On the mechanisms of fasting natriuresis and of carbohydrate-induced sodium retention. Diabete Metab. 1977, 3 (2); 131-143.
16. Kuvalayananda, Swami, & Vinekar, S.L. Yoga Therapy. Yoga Mimamsa Mudranalaya: Lonavla, 1966, s120.

17. Martin W.F., Armstrong L.E., Rodriguez N.R. Dietary protein intake and renal function. Nutr. Metab. (Lond) 2005, 2 (1); 25-33.

18. McCance R. A. Medical problems in mineral metabolism. Lancet, 1936, 876; 825-830.

19. Nazar K., Brzezińska Z., Langfort J., Kruk B., Falęcka-Wieczorek I., Pilis W., Kaciuba-Uściłko H.: Working ability and exercise metabolism in dogs deprived of food for one week. W: International Symposium on Exercise Physiology: [abstracts]. - Baranów Sandomierski, 1987, 49.

20. Pietrzykowska E., Wierusz-Wysocka B. Psychologiczne aspekty nadwagi, otyłości i odchudzania się. Pol. Merk. Lek. 2008, 24; 472-476 (in Polish).

21. Romanowski W., Wiśniewska-Roszkowska K., Grochmal S., Pasek T. Teoria i metodyka ćwiczeń relaksowo-koncentrujących, 2 wyd, PZWL Warszawa 1975 (in Polish).

22. "'Starving yogi' astounds Indian scientists" available at http://phys.org/news192690076.html (accessed 19 November 2013).

23. Stec, K. Dynamic Suryanamaskar - Sun Salutations. India: Swami Vivekananda Yoga Prakashan. 2013, s296.

24. Talbott J.H., Edwards H.T., Dill D. B., and Drastich L. Physiological responses to high environmental temperature. Am. J. Trop. Med. 1955, 13; 381-397.

25. Talbott J.H. and Michelsen J. Heat cramps. A clinical and chemical study. J. Clin. Invest. 1933, 12; 533-549.

26. The National Food and Nutrition Institute (Instytut Żywienia i Żywności) available at www.izz.waw.pl/en/ (accessed 19 November 2013).

# GLOSSARY

## A:

***Abhava:*** Absence/lack of.

***Action:*** Neuro-muscular and/or psycho-neuro-muscular activity.

***Acharya:*** Teacher/professor/guide.

***Adhyatmic:*** To do with the inner Self, spiritual.

***Agama:*** Written or verbal testimony of a trustworthy person, directly transmitted to the mind of the listener; traditional doctrine; sacred knowledge; *shastras*.

***Ahamkara:*** Faculty of ego; awareness of the existence of 'I'; awareness of one's ability and capacity to do or perform an action or task.

***Ahara:*** Food, nourishment of a physical and non-physical nature.

***Ahimsa:*** Non-violence; one of the *yamas*.

***Akhara:*** Traditional school of wrestling, where training in wrestling is imparted by a traditional '*Guru*' (teacher) called '*Wastaad*'. Also a wrestling pit filled with processed red mud mixed with *Ayurvedic* herbs and some traditional equipment for exercise. Sect of *sadhus* and yogis.

***Akshayapatra:*** (*Akshaya* + *Patra*) Inexhaustible vessel (of food)

***Anandamaya Kosha/Sharira:*** Sheath or body comprising of bliss.

***Anga:*** Limb or branch.

***Annamaya Kosha/Sharira:*** Sheath or body developed from food.

***Antarakasha:*** Internal space perceived through proprioception and visceroception.

***Antara Kumbhaka:*** An experience of 'filled condition' of the body cavity.

***Anubhava:*** An experience by an individual.

***Anubhuti:*** An awareness of an experience by an individual.

***Anunasika:*** Nasalized sound.

***Anumanta:*** Inference drawing aspect of the individualized consciousness.

***Apana Vayu:*** Neuro-muscular activity and/or psycho-neuro-muscular actions responsible for the expulsion or giving away of any material from the body cavities, throwing, thought, memory, emotion, feeling etc.

***Artha:*** Literally 'object'; also 'wealth'.

***Asamatva:*** Imbalance, disequilibrium. See also *Vishamatva*.

***Asana:*** Posture or postural pattern, i.e. steady and comfortable position of the body not involving any effort. The third component of Patanjali classical yoga. There are thousands of *asanas*.

***Ashrama:*** Place where a community of people live and practice spiritual life; kind of monastery; stage of life.

***Ashtanga:*** Eight steps, means, or limbs.

***Ashtanga Yoga:*** The eight steps (limbs) of yoga of Patanjali, and considered to be classical yoga. The eight steps or means to attain yoga are: *yama* (restraint), *niyama* (observance), *asana* (posture), *pranayama* (regulation of breath), *pratyahara* (withholding of senses), *dharana* (fixity of mind), *dhyana* (meditation), *samadhi* (perfect concentration). Also a name used for a very challenging system of *hatha* yoga developed by Shri Patabi Joyce of Mysore, India.

***Atma:*** Individual Self.

***Atma Darshana:*** Self perception or perceiving the Self.

***Atma Jnana:*** Pure abiding in the Self, knowledge of the Self (soul).

***Atma Vijnana***: Science of the Self.

***Atyahara:*** Overeating.

***Aum***: Cosmic vibration of the universe; universal and very first mantra, which represents the four states of consciousness: unconscious, subconscious, conscious, and supra-conscious. Another expression of this vibration is the mystic syllable *Om*, or *Omkara*, which is *pranava*, or the designator of God.

***Awareness:*** Consciousness of the Self; contents of consciousness as experienced by the individual.

***Avayava:*** Body organs.

***Avidya:*** Misapprehension or ignorance about the real nature of things; it is the breeding ground or primary cause of other *kleshas*.

## B:

***Baithak:*** Indian squatting exercise.

***Bahyakasha:*** External space (outside the body) perceived through five sensory faculties.

***Bahya Kumbhaka/Shunyata:*** An experience of 'empty condition' of the body cavity.

***Bandha:*** To bind or to lock, a type of a special *mudra* used in *pranayama*. There are four *bandhas, jalandhara, jihva, uddiyana* and *muladhara*. Also, an attitude to perceive internal sensations or events.

***Barchi:*** Small size sword, bigger than knife, used as a martial art weapon.

***Bhala:*** Lance or spear used as a martial art weapon.

***Bhaskara:*** Refulgent Sun.

***Bhokta:*** Enjoying nature/aspect of the individualized consciousness.

***Bija Mantras:*** Seed sounds. They do not refer to any particular external objects.

***Body:*** Neuro-musculo-skeletal system with which we work in everyday life.

***Brahma:*** Mythological figure having four heads perceiving from four directions.

***Brahma Mudra:*** An exercise of rotating the head in all four directions.

***Brahma Sutras:*** Canonical text of *Vedanta*.

***Brahmacharin:*** A celibate; one who moves in consciousness of *Brahman*.

***Brahmacharya:*** Continence, right sexual conduct; student stage of life, when the student stays and studies with the teacher till the age of 25.

***Brahmadvara:*** An opening at the base of the spinal column.

***Brahman:*** The Supreme, the Absolute.

***Brahmarandhra:*** The experience of an opening in the vault of the skull through which the consciousness can travel in the infinite sky above the head (posterior fontanelle).

***Brahmashika:*** Posterior fontanelle.

***Brahmin:*** He who knows Brahma. A person devoted to studies and contemplation.

***Breath:*** Amount of air (material substance) taken in and brought out during breathing.

***Breathing:*** Process by which breath is taken in and given out. It belongs to the self.

***Buddhi:*** Intellect. Deciding aspect of the consciousness. Function of the frontal cortex.

## C:

***Chakra:*** Wheel, circle, vortex or energy center; *pranic* or psychic center of conjugating *nadis* in the subtle body responsible for specific psychic and physiological functions.

***Chandra:*** Moon. Left visual field. Awareness of the left side of the body and the self in a right-handed individual. Awareness of one's feelings and emotions.

***Chandra Nadi:*** Experience of the internal pathway along which *pranic/apanic* activity is experienced through the left visual field.

***Chidakasha:*** Awareness of the skull cavity.

***Chitta:*** Stimulated/activated aspect of the consciousness.

***Chittavritti:*** Behavioral modifications of the consciousness.

## D:

***Dakshina:*** Right lateral, south.

***Dakshina Marga:*** Right lateral pathway (along which some sensation is experienced by the individual).

***Darshan:*** Seeing or beholding.

***Deha Bhava:*** Body awareness.

***Deha Bhava Abhava:*** Absence or lack of body awareness.

***Dharana:*** Fixity of the mind; repeated fixation on a particular point, feeling or thought.
It is the sixth component of Patanjali classical yoga.

***Dharma:*** Duty, right code of conduct, religion (it has a great number of meanings depending on the context).

***Dhatu(s):*** The seven fundamental elements of the body in *Ayurvedic* medicine, *rasa, rakta, mamsa, asthi, majja, sukra and medah.*

***Dhyana:*** Meditation or continuous and uninterrupted flow of similar mental modifications. It is the seventh component of Patanjali classical yoga.

***Dosha(s):*** The three bodily humors in *Ayurvedic* medicine, *vata, pitta, kapha.*

***Drasta:*** Observing/perceiving aspect of the individualized consciousness.

***Duhkha:*** Misery, pain, suffering.

***Dvesha:*** Aversion, hatred.

## G:

***Gayatri:*** Hymn-like; one of the most holy mantras in Hinduism.

***Gheranda Samhita:*** One of the basic treatises of *Hatha Yoga*, written by the sage Gheranda. This text distinguishes seven steps of yoga: *shatkarmas, asanas, mudras, pratyahara, pranayama, dhyana* and *samadhi*. The text consists of 317 *sutras* (aphorisms) and is dated to the late seventeenth century.

***Grihastha:*** Householder.

***Gunas:*** Three basic qualities of the visible world (*sattva, rajas,* *tamas*).

***Guru:*** Teacher/guide/mentor of a student/aspirant. The meaning of the word *'Guru'* in Indian mysticism and philosophy has three levels: (i) enlightened being, (ii) God/ *Ishvara,* (iii) Self manifesting itself as a spiritual light in empirical consciousness. This last is the true *Guru,* while each of the other two is only a form of relative *Guru* in the world of illusion.

***Gurudeva:*** Generic address to a *Guru.*

***Gurukula:*** Residential school, run by a *Guru* for aspirants.

***Guru-Shishya Parampara:*** Living tradition where student becomes the *Guru,* usually after a long apprenticeship.

## H:

***Hanuman:*** Messenger of Lord Rama; monkey God; patron of physical education; also known as Maruthi.

***Hatha (Yoga):*** strenuous, rigorous; *ha-tha - pingala* and *ida* or sun and moon; a discipline which brings *nadi-shuddhi* (purification of *nadis*) through systematic and deliberate practices from *asanas, kriyas, pranayama, bandhas* and *mudras* to *nadanusandhana.*

***Hathapradipika:*** Sometimes called *Hathayogapradipika.* It is the basic treatise on the techniques and philosophy of *Hatha Yoga,* by Svatmarama Suri, and dates somewhere from mid-fourteenth to about the mid-fifteenth century AD. Various manuscripts of this text have been found, often containing very different content, with the number of *sutras* (aphorisms) ranging from 389 to 1553, and the number of chapters varying from 4 to 10. The text lists six steps of yoga: *asanas, pranayama,* *pratyahara, dharana, dhyana* and *samadhi*. In preparing this book on *Suryanamaskar* the version of the text used was that published by the well-known research institute of Kaivalydhama, of Lonavla near Mumbai. Their text consists of 409 *sutras* and five chapters. As with most of the ancient texts on yoga, the *Hathapradipika,* in particular because of its succinctness, has its commentaries. The most important of them is the *Yogaprakashika* by Balakrishna.

***Hathatatvakaumudi:*** *Hatha Yoga* treatise written by Sundaradeva at the end of the seventeenth century AD. It could be argued that it is the first encyclopedia of *Hatha Yoga,* because the text is based on and cites 51 other texts of yoga. It is a very extensive manuscript, divided into 57 chapters and consisting of over 1000 pages.

***Homeostasis:*** A state of internal balance and equilibrium.

## I:

***Ida Nadi:*** One of the three most important channels through which *pranic* currents move, it is associated with the left nostril and brings a cooling effect; experiencing internally aroused sensations in the back along the left side of the spinal column.

***Indriyas:*** Sensory faculties. Functional aspects of various brain centers such as the visual cortex, auditory cortex, olfactory cortex, etc.

***Indriya Vishayas:*** Objects perceived through the sensory faculties and reached through motor actions/activities.

## J:

***Jalandhara Bandha:*** Contraction of the throat.

***Jihva Bandha:*** Tongue lock.

***Jivatma:*** Consciousness identified and attached to the body, senses and objects.

***Jnana:*** Knowledge.

***Jnata:*** Knowing aspect of the individualized consciousness.

***Jnanendriyas:*** Sensory faculties of the individualized consciousness.

## K:

***Kabaddhi:*** Tackling team game between two sides.

***Kama:*** Pleasure, desire.

***Kanda:*** Bulb. Starting point of the network of *nadis*.

***Kapalabhati:*** (*Kapala* + *Bhati*). A *kriya* type of vigorous breathing exercise. Shining/brightening (*bhati*) at the level of the forehead (*kapala*) as perceived by the individual (with closed eyes).

***Kapha:*** Phlegm, mucus; one of the three *doshas* in *Ayurvedic* medicine.

***Karana Sharira***: Causal body.

***Karma:*** Voluntary action.

***Karmendriyas:*** Motor organs of the individualized consciousness.

***Karta:*** 'Doer' aspect of the individualized consciousness.

***Kati (Kathi):*** Small size stick used as a martial arts weapon.

***Kaya:*** Body (neuro-musculo-skeletal system with which we work).

***Kho-Kho:*** A game of tag played between two teams.

***Klesha:*** Affliction, trouble.

***Kriya:*** Purification process/procedure; naturally happening involuntary activity.

***Kshatriya:*** A person of warrior community (caste).

***Kumbhaka:*** A phase of holding the breath after inhalation (*antara kumbakha*) or exhalation (*bahya kumbhaka*), and also a synonym of *pranayama*. There are many types of *kumbhaka*, but the most important are *sahita* (associated with *puraka/rechaka*) and *kevala* (independent of *puraka/rechaka*); an experience of the body cavity/consciousness as in a full or empty condition.

***Kundalini:*** Spiritual energy, capacity, consciousness.

***Kundalini Shakti:*** 'Serpent power' lying dormant at the *muladhara chakra* at the base of the spine in its potential form; when awakened, for example, by spiritual practices, it passes through the *sushumna nadi* to the *sahasrara chakra*.

***Kusti (Kushti):*** Traditional Indian wrestling.

## L:

***Lathi:*** Indian martial art based on fighting with canes (sticks).

***Loma:*** Hair on the skin. An experience of internally aroused sensations (*prana*) during exhalation/*rechaka* (*apanic activity*) moving from the centre (self) towards the periphery (skin).

## M:

***Mahavrata:*** Great vow concerning moral restraints. See *yamas*.

***Mahesh:*** Can refer to Lord Shiva, *Maheshwara*.

***Malkhamb:*** Traditional Indian sport in which a gymnast or team of gymnasts perform various exercises based on the use of a wooden pole or a rope.

***Mamsa Dhatu:*** Muscular tissue. Also called flesh.

***Manas:*** That aspect of the consciousness, which receives information from inside the body and gives rise to feelings and emotions. Functions of limbic brain and associated areas of the brain.

***Mandir:*** Hindu temple.

***Manomaya Kosha/Sharira:*** Sheath or body comprising of feelings and emotions.

***Mantra:*** A single syllable, a word or a sentence, which, when continuously repeated, is capable of guiding the individual towards the Self and/or transcendence.

***Merudanda:*** Vertebral column, spine.

***Mitahara:*** Moderate diet involving qualitative and quantitative aspects of food consumption; the stomach should be filled half with solid food, a quarter with water, and a quarter with air (empty).

***Moksha:*** Emancipation, liberation.

***Mudra:*** Psycho-physical gesture or posture which leads to happiness; *hatha* yogic texts describe many *mudras* of which *bandhas* are a part; an attitude to perceive internal happenings.

***Mulabandha:*** Contraction of perineal and anal muscles.

***Muladhara:*** (*Mula* + *Adhara*) Root/base (*mula*) support (*adhara*) (of/for the spinal column/trunk).

***Muni:*** Sage.

***Murdhanya Dhvani:*** Experience of vibrational sound being produced at the top of the head.

## N:

***Nadanusandhana:*** Developing the inner sound.

***Nadi:*** A channel and/or a pathway along which *pranic* currents move and some happening can be experienced through sensory activity by an individual. Out of seventy-two thousand *nadis* fourteen are considered important, and of these three, *ida, pingala* and *sushumna*, are the most important.

***Nadi Shuddhi:*** Purification of *nadis* which is attained by various purification processes (*kriyas*) and breathing techniques; starting to experience happenings along certain pathways.

***Nadi Shuddhi Pranayama:*** A purification yogic breathing technique, a pre-*pranayama;* extension (*ayama*) of sensory inputs/activity (*prana*) along a particular pathway (*nadi*) after its opening (*shuddhi*).

***Namaskar***: Salutation, salute.

***Nath:*** Important sect, from the state of Maharashtra, from which the *hatha* yogic tradition originated; Matsyendranath was the founder of the sect. *Natha* means lord or master.

***Nirodha:*** *(Ni + Rodha)* Annihilation.

***Niyama(s):*** Observance(s); the second component of Patanjali classical yoga, which lists five *niyamas,* whereas the *hatha* yogic texts list ten.

## O:

***Ojas:*** Sublimated sexual energy; vitality; *kundalini shakti.* Contained in the seven *dhatus*, and, in greatest concentration, in the semen.

***Om or Omkara:*** See *Aum*.

## P:

***Pancha:*** Five.

***Pancha Jnanendriyas:*** Five sensory faculties (auditory, tactile, visual, gustatory, and olfactory).

***Pancha Karmendriyas:*** Five motor abilities (vocal cords for speech, hands for manipulation, legs for locomotion, genitals for procreation, and anus for excretion).

***Pancha Koshas/Sharira:*** Five sheaths or coverings/bodies of the consciousness (*annamaya, pranamaya, manomaya, vijnanamaya, anandamaya*).

***Paramatman:*** Universal or cosmic *atman* (soul); highest state of purified consciousness perceived as the 'Creator'.

***Parampara:*** Living tradition handed down from teacher (*guru*) to student (*shishya*).

***Paschima:*** Posterior or back, west.

***Paschima Marga:*** Posterior pathway (along which some sensation is experienced by the individual).

***Patanjali:*** Compiler of the *Yoga Sutras,* the basic treatise on classical yoga.

***Patta (Danda Patta):*** Weapon having a grip like a sword, but with a long flexible belt made of steel having an edge to both sides.

***Pauranika Jnana:*** Knowledge (diluted) for the common people.

***Pingala Nadi:*** One of the three most important channels through which *pranic* currents move, it is associated with the right nostril and brings a heating effect; experiencing internally aroused sensations in the back along the right side of the spinal column.

***Pitta:*** Bile or gall; one of the three *doshas* in *Ayurvedic* medicine.

***Prakasha:*** Light.

***Prana:*** Subtle energy.

***Pranamaya Kosha/Sharira:*** Functioning sheath or body because of life force (*prana shakti*).

***Pranashakti:*** Sensory inputs (*prana*) perceived and recognized as an energy or force (*shakti*).

***Prana Sparsha:*** Experiencing touch of air movement over the upper lip, inside the air passages and other internal areas of the body due to the activity of *prana/apana vayus* (breathing). Experiencing touch/contact of any material (air, liquids, solids) anywhere inside the body due to the activity of *prana/ apana vayus*.

***Prana Vayu:*** Neuro-muscular activity and/or psycho-neuro-muscular actions responsible for receiving or taking-in of any material inside body cavities, grasping an object, receiving a thought/feeling/emotion.

***Pranayama:*** Regulation of breath; control of the breathing process that involves control of inhalation (*puraka*), exhalation (*rechaka*) and retention (*kumbhaka*). It involves a number of inhalation and exhalation techniques and the retention part is accompanied usually by three locks (*bandhas*). It is different from normal breathing, when inhalation is known as '*shvasa*' and exhalation '*prashvasa*'. It is the fourth component of Patanjali classical yoga.

***Pratyahara:*** Withholding of senses from the sense objects. Since there are five types of senses there are also five types of *pratyahara*; getting knowledge about the 'self' through various sensory faculties. It is the fifth component of Patanjali classical yoga.

***Prayatna Shaithilya:*** Slackening of voluntary effort.

***Puraka:*** Regulated inhalation, which is preliminary to the state of *kumbhaka* during *pranayama*; an experience of the body cavity becoming 'filled' by the individual.

***Purana(s):*** Aged, ancient; a class of eighteen Indian scriptures consisting of mythological narrations and legends, which deal with the creation, re-creation, and genealogies of sages and rulers.

***Purusha:*** Individual person or transcendental Self.

***Purva:*** Anterior or front, east.

***Purva Marga:*** Anterior pathway (along which some activity is experienced by the individual).

***Pushan:*** Sun-God as protector of cattle and crops.

## R:

***Raga:*** Attachment; attachment which follows remembrance of pleasure.

***Rajas:*** Quality of nature and mind (*guna*), which is characterized by dynamism, movement, oscillation, and energy.

***Ramayana:*** Epic on the life of Rama.

***Ravi:*** A name for the Sun-God.

***Rechaka:*** Regulated exhalation after holding the breath in *pranayama*. It is done very slowly and never through the mouth; an experience of the body cavity becoming 'emptied' by the individual.

***Rishi:*** Seer of the truth, sage.

***Rishikesh:*** Town on the banks of the river Ganga, at the foothills of the *Himalaya* mountains. A place of magnetic attraction for yogis, *sannyasis*, *sadhus*, and holy men. Currently there are more than two hundred *ashrams* of a multiplicity of traditions in that location.

***Rta Jnana:*** Directly perceived knowledge without the use of the five sensory faculties.

***Rudra:*** A deity, one of the names of Shiva.

## S:

***Sadguru:*** True teacher.

***Sadhaka:*** A spiritual practitioner or a person who is striving to follow a spiritual path leading to Self-realization (*atma-jnana*); aspirant; student determined to study in order to obtain knowledge and experience.

***Sadhana:*** Achievement, accomplishment, striving, reaching the road or the path of yoga, spiritual practice, spiritual search, literally, 'abiding in the truth'.

***Sadhu:*** One who practices spiritual discipline as a renunciant.

***Sakshi:*** Uninvolved witnessing aspect of the individualized consciousness.

***Samadhi:*** Perfect concentration, when the object alone of meditation shines forth in the mind, as though devoid of the thought of even the self; a balanced, undisturbed (basal/primordial) state of consciousness. It is the eighth and final component of Patanjali classical yoga.

***Samahita Chitta:*** Well-balanced state of consciousness.

***Samana Vayu:*** Neuro-muscular activity and/or psycho-neuro-muscular actions responsible for maintaining balance and equilibrium at the level of the body/mind/ consciousness.

***Samatva:*** Balance, equilibrium.

***Samhita:*** Collection or compendium.

***Samkalpa:*** Volition, resolution; state of positive feelings.

***Samvedana:*** A sensation.

***Samyoga:*** Good connection, yoking, union, joining.

***Sandhya:*** Morning and evening prayers.

***Sannyasin:*** A renunciate, who left worldly pursuits and affairs behind in order to live for the experience of Self-realization.

***Sattva:*** Quality of nature and mind (*guna*) which is pure, harmonious, steady, and illuminating.

***Satya:*** Truthfulness; one of the *yamas*.

***Savita:*** A name of the Sun-God.

***Shanti, Shanti, Shanti:*** Peace, tranquility, harmony.

***Shatkriyas (Shatkarmas):*** Six groups of therapeutic and cleansing processes specified in the *Hatha Yogic* treatises. They consist of: *trataka, kabalabhati, neti, dhauti, uddiyana nauli* and *basti*.

***Shishya:*** A student or aspirant desirous of studying, knowing and experiencing a subject, discipline, tradition, or states of consciousness, etc.

***Shloka:*** Verse, or song.

***Shruta Jnana:*** Heard (also read) knowledge.

***Shrutis:*** The revelations of divine origin in the sacred literature of the *Vedas* and the *Upanishads*.

***Shuddhi:*** Purification, cleansing (of body, mind, *vayus, chitta*).

***Shunyata/Bahya Kumbhaka:*** An experience of 'empty condition' of the body cavity.

***Siddha:*** An adept, an accomplished yogi.

***Smriti(s):*** Memory; that part of the authoritative traditional literature recorded as disciples' remembrance of what has been revealed by the great spiritual masters regarding the truth of inner experience. *Smritis* include the six *Vedangas, Manava Dharma Shastra* (Laws of Manu), *sutras, puranas, itihasas* and *nitishastras.*

***Smruta Jnana:*** Memorized knowledge.

***Spanda:*** An impulse or a wave or a vibration.

***Sthira:*** Stable or steady (as experienced by the individual).

***Sthira-Sukham Asanam:*** Steady and comfortable body position as experienced by an individual. The forty-sixth *shloka* from *Sadhana Pada* (the second chapter on practice) of *Yoga Sutras* by Patanjali.

***Sthula Sharira***: Gross or material body.

***Sukha:*** Comfortable (as experienced by an individual), happiness.

***Sukshma Sharira***: Subtle or astral body.

***Surya:*** Sun. Sun-God as giver of light and warmth. Right visual field. Awareness of the right side of the body and the self in a right-handed individual. Awareness of one's thoughts, decisions and thinking.

***Surya Nadi:*** Experience of the internal pathway along which *pranic/apanic* activity is experienced through the right visual field.

***Surya Namaskara:*** Salutation to the Sun, or Sun adoration, is offered by holding both hands together in front of the chest, an ancient *Vedic* ritual. The term **Suryanamaskar**, when written as a compound, is used to refer specifically to the practicing of a pre-ordained sequence of *asanas,* usually twelve in number.

In India there are more than fifty such sets of *Suryanamaskar*.

***Sushumna Nadi:*** The most important of all the *nadis* situated between *ida* and *pingala nadis*, it is responsible for the flow of *prana* after *kundalini* arousal; experiencing internally aroused sensations along the central line of the spinal column in the back.

***Sutra(s):*** Aphorisms.

***Svatmarama (Suri):*** The author of the most important work on *Hatha Yoga*, entitled *Hathapradipika*, which is believed to have been written in the middle of fifteenth century AD. According to the book *Nathasampradaya*, the order of teachers passing on the tradition of *Hatha Yoga* up to Svatmarama is as follows: Matsyendranath→ Gorakshanath→ Gahininath→ Nivruttinath → Jnaneshwar → Sopan → Svayamprakashanandanatha → Vimalananda → Sadananda → Lalitananda → Sahajananda → Cintamani → Svatmarama.

***Swara Yoga:*** Yoga which deals with *swaras* of breath, or the alternating periods of predominance in the activity of one nostril over the other. Flow of air showing greater permeability of the nostrils is closely connected with the activity of the associated subtle energy channels (*nadis*), *ida* (left nostril) and *pingala* (right nostril). When there is balance in the permeability of the two *nadis*, the *sushumna nadi* is activated. Knowledge of and ability to manage the natural alternation in predominance between the nostrils enables identification of certain conditions of health and consequential self-treatment.

***Swarupa:*** Nature of the self. Self image or form.

## T:

***Talawar:*** Sword.

***Tamas:*** Quality of nature and mind (*guna*) that is characterized by laziness, inertia, procrastination, ignorance, darkness, immobility, etc.

***Tanmatras:*** Receptors sensitive to one kind of disturbance in the external space (e.g. rods and cones for light, auditory cells for sound, olfactory cells for smell, taste buds for taste, and receptors sensitive to touch, temperature and pressure).

***Tapasya:*** Mental and physical discipline, process of removing impurities; austerity, one of the five *niyamas* (observances) and also a part of *kriya* yoga.

***Tejas:*** Glow, to glow.

***Tirtha:*** A preceptor, a *guru*.

***Trataka:*** Gazing at a candle flame until tears flow and then working with the after-images; one of the six yogic *shatkriyas* (six purification processes).

***Trimurti:*** Trinity, *Brahma, Vishnu* and *Rudra*.

## U:

***Uchyate:*** It is said.

***Udana Vayu:*** Neuro-muscular activity and/or psycho-neuro-muscular actions responsible for upward movement of any material and/or body/mind/consciousness.

***Uddiyana:*** One of the six yogic *shatkriyas* (purification processes). An experience of fast moving (*yana*) internally aroused sensations (*prana*) from below upwards (*ud*) in the area of the spinal column in a steady condition of the body (*asana*).

***Uddiyana Bandha:*** A contraction of the abdominal muscles.

***Ujjayi (Pranayama):*** One of the eight *pranayamas* listed in the *Hathapradipika* and *Gheranda Samhita;* the glottis is partially closed and a light sound is produced.

***Upanishads:*** Spiritual and theological scriptures, being part of the *Vedas,* and containing the essence of the Vedas. There are 108 basic *Upanishads,* all containing mystical teachings revealed by *Guru* to *shishya* in the form of brief *sutras,* which are saturated with knowledge of the Self and reality. They represent the accumulated realizations of the saints and sages concerning reality and the nature of individual consciousness.

***Upasana:*** Worship, concentration.

## V:

***Vama:*** Left lateral.

***Vama Marga:*** Left lateral pathway (along which some sensation is experienced by the individual).

***Vanaprasthi:*** Hermit.

***Vandana:*** Prostration.

***Vata:*** Wind, air or gas; one of the three *doshas* in *Ayurvedic* medicine.

***Vayu:*** Neuro-muscular activity and/or psycho-neuro-muscular action. *Vayus* are classified under ten categories in *hatha* yoga.

***Veda(s):*** The holiest books of Hinduism consist of four *Vedas*: *Rig, Sama, Artharva* and *Yajur Veda*. The *Vedas* are the most ancient texts revealed to *rishis* and sages, and are believed to be the repository of all knowledge. They explain and regulate every aspect of life, from supreme reality to the uttermost mundanity. These oldest of Hindu scriptures are divided into four parts: *Samhita, Brahmana, Aranyaka,* and *Upanishads.*

***Vidhi***: Regulative principles.

***Vidya:*** Higher and true knowledge or science about spirituality or any other subject.

***Vijnanamaya Kosha/Sharira:*** Sheath or body comprising of thoughts and decisions.

***Vikalpa:*** Fancy or imagination; conclusion without factual evidence; state of negative feelings.

***Viloma:*** An experience of internally aroused sensations (*prana)* during inhalation/*puraka* (*pranic activity*) moving from the periphery (skin) towards the centre (self).

***Vinyasa:*** To proceed step-by-step; co-ordination between the movement of the body and the breath; cultivation of a deep, regulated, full breathing pattern.

***Vishamatva:*** Maladjustment. See also *Asamatva.*

***Vishnu:*** Sun-God as creator and god of fertility.

***Viyoga:*** Getting disconnected, disjointed, separated, unyoked.

***Vyana Vayu:*** Neuro-muscular activity and/or psycho-neuro-muscular actions responsible for locomotion and movement of the body/mind/consciousness in one direction.

***Vyayama:*** Physical exercise.

***Vyayamshala:*** Exercise school. Apart from wrestling, this school imparts training in traditional ancient weapons like *lathi* (stick), *talwar* (sword), *kathi* (small size stick), *bhala* (lance or spear), *patta* also called *dand patta* (weapon having a grip like a sword but with a long flexible belt made of steel having an edge to both sides), *barchi* (small size sword, bigger than a knife).

***Vyutthita Chitta:*** Disturbed and disintegrated state of consciousness (self).

## Y:

***Yagna (Yajna) Kunda:*** Sacrificial fire.

***Yama(s):*** Restraint(s) or restriction(s), the first component of Patanjali classical yoga, which lists five *yamas* (non-violence, truthfulness, non-stealing, celibacy, non-covetousness), whereas the *hatha* yogic texts list ten.

***Yoga, Yogah:*** Yoking, getting connected, united, joined, union, etc. One of the six systems of orthodox Hindu philosophy that accept the *Vedas* as the supreme revealed scriptures. The six systems are listed in pairs due to the compounds of content and the historical links between each couple: *Samkhya - Yoga, Nyaya – Vaisheshika*, and *Mimamsa - Vedanta.*

***Yoga Anubhava:*** An experience of 'self' and/or of 'transcendence'.

***Yoga Nidra:*** 'Yogic sleep' in which the conscious mind is asleep but awareness remains active, a state of deep relaxation; cosmic sleep between worlds.

***Yoga Sutras:*** 195 aphorisms on Yoga compiled by Patanjali. They are divided into four *padas* (chapters): *Samadi Pada, Sadhana Pada, Vibhuti Pada* and *Kaivalya Pada.*

***Yoga Therapy:*** Self-help based on yogic concepts and techniques available to us today.

***Yuddha:*** War.

***Yudhisthira***: Steady in war; one of the characters in the Indian epic *Mahabharata.*

***Yuktahara:*** Controlled diet.

# BIBLIOGRAPHY

## BOOKS

Alter, J. S. Yoga in Modern India: The Body between Science and Philosophy. Princeton University Press: Princeton, 2004, pp.352.

Armour, J.A. and Ardell, J.L. Neurocardiology. Oxford University Press: Oxford, 1994, pp.454.

Bhavanani, A.B. Surya Namaskar – An expression of gratitude to life. Dhivyananda Creations: Puducherry, 2011. pp.158.

Ballentine, R. Diet and Nutrition: A Holistic Approach. Himalayan Institute Press: Honesdale, Pennsylvania, 2007, pp.634.

Ballentine, R. Radical Healing. Himalayan Institute Press: Honesdale, Pennsylvania, 2011, pp.626.

Bhattacharya, P.B. Surya Namaskara. Sri Aurobindo Ashram Trust: Pondicherry, 2007, pp.9.

Bijlani, R.L., et al. Understanding Medical Physiology. with a special chapter on yoga physiology by Bhole, M.V. Jaypee Bros.: New Delhi, 1995, pp.950.

Butler, G., Fiore, R., et al. Pumping Iron, Cinegate: USA, 1977, 2003.

Campbell, T.C. and Campbell, T.M. The China Study: The Most Comprehensive Study of Nutrition Ever Conducted and the Startling Implications for Diet, Weight Loss and Long-term Health. BenBella Books: Dallas, 2006, pp.417.

Christensen, A. Yoga for Sports. Contemporary Books: Chicago, 2000, pp.250.

Coghill, R. The Healing Energies of Light. Gaia Books: London, 2000, pp.159.

Crisp, T. Yoga and Relaxation. Collins: London, 1970, pp.160.

Davis W. Wheat Belly: Lose the Wheat, Lose the Weight, and Find Your Path Back to Health. Rodale: Emmaus, Pennsylvania, 2011, pp.266.

De Michelis, E. A History of Modern Yoga: Patanjali and Western Esotericism. Continuum: London, 2004, pp.282.

De Michelis, E. A History of Modern Yoga. Continuum: London, 2005, pp.250.

Digambarji, Swami, and Gharote, M.L. Gheranda Samhita. Yoga Mimamsa Mudranalaya: Lonavla, 1978, pp.228.

Douillard, J. Body, Mind and Sport. Crown Trade Paperbacks: New York, 1994, pp.198.

Fuhrman J. Eat to live. The Amazing Nutrient-Rich Program for Fast and Sustained Weight Loss. Little, Brown and Company: Boston, revised edition 2011, pp.327.

Gharote, M.L. and Ganguly, S.K. Teaching Methods for Yogic Practices. Lonavla, Yoga Mimamsa Mudranalaya: Lonavla, 1988, pp.120.

Gharote, M.L., Devnath, P. and Jha, V.K. Hathatatvakaumudi – a Treatise on Hatha-yoga by Sundaradeva. Lonavla Yoga Institute, Lonavla, 2006, pp.800.

Gharote, M.L. Guidelines for Yogic Practices. Lonavla Yoga Institute: Lonavla, 1982, pp.106.

Gharote, M.L. and Gharote, M.M. Swami Kuvalayananda – A Pioneer of Scientific Yoga and Indian Physical Education. Lonavla Yoga Institute: Lonavla, 1999, pp.168.

Gitananda, Swami. Surya Namaskar – A Yoga System of Sun Adoration. Lawspet: Pondicherry, 1975, pp.40.

Gore, M.M. Physiology of Yoga Practice. Yoga Mimamsa Mudranalaya: Lonavla, 1980, pp.200.

Hariharananda Aranya, Swami. Yoga Philosophy of Patanjali. Calcutta University Press: Calcutta, 1981, pp.495.

Johnson, E.L. The History of YMCA Physical Education. YMCA Press: Location unknown, 1979, pp.442.

Jurek S., Friedman S. Eat and Run. Bloomsbury Publishing: London, 2012, pp.273

Kabat-Zinn, J. Full Catastrophe Living: Using the Wisdom of your Body and Mind to Face Stress, Pain, and Ilness. Delta Trades Paperback: New York, 1991, pp.467.

Khalsa, S.B., and Gould, J. Your Brain on Yoga (Harvard Medical School Guides). Kindle edition, RozettaBooks LLC: New York, 2012, pp.76.

Karambelkar, P.V. Patanjala Yoga Sutras. Yoga Mimamsa Mudranalaya: Lonavla, 1996, pp.500.

Kuvalayananda, Swami. Asanas. Yoga Mimamsa Mudranalaya: Lonavla, 1933, pp.188.

Kuvalayananda, Swami. Pranayama. Yoga Mimamsa Mudranalaya: Lonavla, 1931, pp.180.

Kuvalayananda, Swami, and Vinekar, S.L. Yoga Therapy. Yoga Mimamsa Mudranalaya: Lonavla, 1966, pp.120.

Lipton, B. The Biology of Belief – Unleashing the Power of Consciousness, Matter and Miracles. Mountain of Love: Santa Rosa, California, 2005, pp.224.

Mansata B. The Vision of Natural Farming. Earthcare Books: Kolkata, 2010, pp.278.

McArdle, W.D., Katch, F.I. and Katch, V.L. Exercise Physiology – Energy, Nutrition & Human Performance. Lippincott Williams & Wilkins: Baltimore, 2007 (sixth edition), pp.1067.

Modak M., et al. Suryanamaskar – from the Scientific and Medical Point of View. Shri Ramdas Naomi: Pune, 2010, pp.170. [in Marathi]

Mujumdar, Dattatraya Chintaman. Encyclopedia of Indian Physical Culture. Good Companions, 1950.

Muktibodhananda, Swami. Hatha Yoga Pradipika - Light on Hatha Yoga. Yoga Publication Trust: Munger, 2006, pp.642.

Nimbalkar, S.P. Soorya Namaskar - Health-Promoting Exercise and Sun-Worship for All. Yoga Vidya Niketan: Mumbai, 2012, pp.88.

Nocun T. Dieta wegetariańska prosta i zdrowa. [Eng. Vegetarian Diet – Simple and Healthy] Wydawnictwo Vegan (2nd edition): Poland, Lublin, 2012, pp.359.

Nocun T. Głodówka i dieta dla zdrowia. [Eng. Fasting and Diet for Health] Wydawnictwo Natura (2nd edition): Poland, Lublin, 2013, pp.359.

Ornish, D. Dr. Dean Ornish's Programme for Reversing Heart Disease. Ivy Books: New York, 1996, pp.631.

Pattabhi Jois, Sri K. Surya Namaskara. Ashtanga Yoga: New York, 2005, pp.60.

Pattabhi Jois, Sri K. Yoga Mala. 3rd. ed. North Point Press: New York, 2002, pp.127.

Pearce, J.C. The Biology of Transcendence. Park Street Press: Rochester, Vermont, 2002, pp.280.

Pratinidhi Pant, B., the Raja of Aundh. Surya Namaskars (Sun-Adoration) For Health, Efficiency & Longevity. Printed at the Aundh State Press, 1928, pp.102.

Pratinidhi Pant, B., the Raja of Aundh. Surya Namaskars: The Ten Point Way to Health. J.M. Dent and Sons Ltd.: London, (edited and introduction by Louise Morgan), 1938, pp.112.

Pratinidhi Pant, B. and Apa Pant, the Raja of Aundh. Surya Namaskara - an Ancient Indian Exercise. Orient Longman: Hyderabad, 1989, pp.88.

Raghavendra, Swami Sri. Guru Namaskara. Anatha Sevashrama Trust: Malladihalli, 1980, pp.89.

Raghavendra, Swami Sri. SuryaNamaskara - Principle and Practice. Anatha Sevashrama Trust: Malladihalli, 1977, pp.45.

Rajarishi Muni, Swami. Classical HathaYoga. Life Mission Publications: Vadodara, 2011, pp.587.

Romanowski, W., et al. Teoria i metodyka ćwiczeń relaksowo-koncentrujących [trans. *Theory and methods of relaxation and concentration training*]. Wydawnictwo Lekarskie PZWL: Warszawa, 1973, pp.350.

Sandow, E. Body Building or Man in the Making. Gale & Polden: London, no date.

Satyananda Saraswati, Swami. Surya Namaskara - A Technique of Solar Visualization. Munger, Yoga Publication Trust: Munger, 2006, pp.97.

Schmitz, O.A.H. Psychoanalyse und Yoga. O. Reichl: Darmstadt, 1923.

Shrinivasrao B. Surya Namaskars (Sun - Adoration) for Health, Efficiency & Longevity. R.K. Kirloskar: Aundh State Press, 1928, pp.102.

Singh, Hardayal. Science of Sports Training. New Delhi: D.V.S. Publications: New Delhi, 1991, pp.164.

Singleton, M. Yoga Body: The Origins of Modern Posture Practice. OUP: New York, 2010, pp.272.

Stec, K. Z. and Choudhary, R. The effects of dynamic suryanamaskar. Germany: LAMBERT Academic Publishing GmbH & Co. KG., 2011, pp.148.

Stiles, Mukunda. Ayurvedic Yoga Therapy. Lotus Press: Twin Lakes, 2007, pp.253.

Strauss, S. Positioning Yoga: Balancing Acts across Cultures. Berg: New York, 2004, pp.224.

Sundaram, Y. and Iyer, K.V. Yogic Physical Culture or the Secret of Happiness. Publisher unknown: Bangalore, 1928.

Svoboda, Robert. Prakruti - Your Ayurvedic Constitution. Geocom Limited: Albuquerque, 1989, pp.250.

Taylor W.C. A Catalogue Raisonnée of Oriental Manuscripts. Publisher Unknown, 1860, pp.246. Re-issued as: A Catalogue Raisonnée of Oriental Manuscripts in the Library of the (Late) College, Fort St. George, Now in Charge of the Board of Examiners. 2010, pp.758.

Verma, J.P. A Text Book on Sports Statistics. Venus Publication: Gwalior, 2000, pp.368.

Vyas Devji Maharaj, S. Science of the Soul (Atma Vijnana). Yoga Niketan Trust: Rishikesh, 1972, pp.250.

White, D.G. The Alchemical Body: Siddha Traditions in Medieval India. University of Chicago Press: Chicago, 1996, pp.596.

# JOURNALS AND PERIODICALS

Aslan, U.B. and Livanelioglu, A. "Effects of Hatha Yoga training on aerobic power and anaerobic power in healthy young adults". Fizyoterapi Rehabilitasyon April 2002, 13(1): 24-30.

Bhavanani, A. B., K. Udupa, Madanmohan and P.N. Ravindra. "A comparative study of slow and fast suryanamaskar on physiological function". International Journal of Yoga July-December 2011: 4(2):71-76.

Bhutkar et al. "Effect of Suryanamaskar Practice on Cardio-respiratory Fitness Parameters: A Pilot Study". Al Ameen J Med Sci 2008: 1(2): 126-129.

Carroll, J., Blansit, A., Otto, R.M., and Wygand, J.W. "The Metabolic Requirements of Vinyasa Yoga". Medicine & Science in Sports & Exercise May 2003: 35(5): S155.

Chaya M.S., Kurpad, A.V., Nagendra, H.R. and Nagarathna, R. "The effect of long term combined yoga practice on the basal metabolic rate of healthy adults". BMC Complementary and Alternative Medicine August 31, 2006: 6: 28.

Choudhary, R., and Stec, K. "The effects of dynamic suryanamaskar on flexibility of university students". Journal of Advances in Developmental Research 2010: 1(1): 45-48.

Choudhary, R., and Stec, K. "Effect of dynamic suryanamaskar on vital capacity of physical education students" Indian Journal of Physical Education, Sports Medicine and Exercise Science 2008: 8 (2): 11-20.

Choudhary, R., Stec, K. and Kulmatycki, L. "The effects of dynamic suryanamaskar on positive breath holding capacity of physical education students". Indian journal of movement education and exercises sciences (IJMEES) 2011: bi-annual journal 1(1).

Clay C.C., Lloyd, L.K., Walker, J.L., Sharp, K.R., and Pankey, R.B. "The metabolic cost of hatha yoga"; Journal of Strength and Conditioning Research August 2005: 19(3): 604-610.

DiCarlo, L.J., Sparling, P.B., Hinson, B.T., Snow, T.K., and Rosskopf, L.B. "Cardiovascular, metabolic, and perceptual responses to Hatha Yoga standing postures". Medicine, Exercise, Nutrition and Health 1995: 4: 107-112.

Hagins M, Moore, W. and Rundle, A. "Does practicing hatha yoga satisfy recommendations for intensity of physical activity which improves and maintains health and cardiovascular fitness?". BMC Complementary and Alternative Medicine November 30, 2007: 7: 40.

Kouchakoff, P. "The Influence of Food Cooking on the Blood Formula of Man". Proceedings of the First International Congress of Microbiology Paris, 1930.

Joshi, L.N., Joshi, V.D. and Gokhale, L.V. "Effect of short term 'Pranayama' practice on breathing rate and ventilatory functions of lung". Indian Journal of Physiology and Pharmacology 1992: 36: 105-108.

Konar, D., Latha, R. and Bhuvaneswaran, J.S. "Cardiovascular responses to head down-body-up postural exercise (Sarvangasana)". Indian Journal of Physiology and Pharmacology October 2000: 44(4): 392-400.

Makwana K., Khirwadkar, N. and Gupta, H.C. "Effect of short term yoga practice on ventilatory function tests". Indian Journal of Physiology and Pharmacology July 1988: 32(3): 202-208.

Malhotra, V., Singh, S., Singh, K.P., Gupta, P., Sharma, S.B., Madhu, S.V. and Tandon, O.P. "Study of yoga asanas in assessment of pulmonary function in NIDDM patients". Indian Journal of Physiology and Pharmacology July 2002: 46(3): 313-320.

Mercogliano, C. and Debus, K. "An Interview with Joseph Chilton Pearce". Journal of Family Life 1999: Vol. 5 #1.

Raju, P.S., et al. "Effect of yoga on exercise tolerance in normal healthy volunteers". Indian Journal of Physiology and Pharmacology April-June 1986: 30(2): 121-132.

Raub, J.A. "Psychophysiologic effects of hatha yoga on musculoskeletal and cardiopulmonary function: A literature review". Journal of Alternative and Complementary Medicine December 2002: 8(6): 797-812. PMID: 12614533.

Ray, A. Prathak, and Selvamurthy, W. "Energy cost and cardio-respiratory changes during the practice of Suryanamaskar". Indian Journal of Physiology and Pharmacology April 2004: 48(2): 184-190.

Ray, U.S., Mukhopadhyaya, S., Purkayastha, S.S., Asnani, V., Tomer, O.S., Prashad, R., Thakur, L. and Selvamurthy, W. "Effect of yogic exercises on physical and mental health of young fellowship course trainees". Indian Journal of Physiology and Pharmacology January 2001: 45(1): 37-53.

Ray, U.S., Hegde, K.S. and Selvamurthy, W. "Effects of yogic asanas and physical exercise on body flexibility in middle-aged men". The Yoga Review Summer & Autumn 1983: 3(2&3): 75-79.

Ray, U.S., et al. "Aerobic capacity & perceived exertion after practice of Hatha yogic exercises". Indian Journal of Medical Research December 2001: 114: 215-21.

Rzesutko, K.M., et al. "Heart rate and perceived exertion response during power yoga asanas". Medicine & Science in Sports & Exercise - May 2002: 34(5) Supplement: S259.

Savic, K., Pfau, D., Skoric, S., Pfau, J. and Spasojevic, N. "The effect of Hatha yoga on poor posture in children and the psycho-physiologic condition in adults". Medicinski Pregled (Novi Sad) 1990: 43(5-6): 268-272. [Article in Serbo-Croatian]

Stec, K., and Choudhary, R. "Effect of dynamic suryanamaskar on negative breath holding capacity of physical education students". Wellness: Journal of Health, Physical Education and Sports 2009:1 (1): 13-19.

Stec, K., and Choudhary, R. "Effect of dynamic suryanamaskar on physical efficiency index of physical education students". Bangladesh Journal of Sports Science 2009: 9 (1): 62-73.

Stec, K., Choudhary, R. and Kulmatycki, L."Effect of dynamic suryanamaskar on differential chest circumference of physical education students". Human Movement 2010: 11 (2): 179-183.

Stec, K. et al. "Energy Cost and Oxygen Debt During Dynamic Suryanamaskar and Graduated Ergocycle Maximal Intensity Test". National Yoga Week-2015 Conference – Yoga for Middle Aged Ministry of AYUSH: Delhi. February 2015, pp.123-125.

Stec, K., Pilis, K., Pilis, W., and Michalski, C. "Individual Metabolic Differences During Dynamic Suryanamaskar". Polish J Sport Med 2016: 32 (3).

Stec, K., Pilis, K., Pilis, W., Pilis A., Michalski, C., and Zych M."Body Loading During Dynamic Suryanamaskar and Cycle Ergometer Test". (In press).

Stumpf, W. "Vitamin D - Solitrol the heliogenic steroid hormone: Somatotrophic activator and modulator". Histochemistry 1988, 89: 209-219.

Tran, M.D., Holly, R.G., Lashbrook, J. and Amsterdam, E.A. "Effects of Hatha Yoga practice on the health-related aspects of physical fitness". Preventive Cardiology Autumn 2001: 4(4): 165-170. PMID: 11832673.

Vaze, S., Porwal, N.K. and Damodaran, A. "Yoga for women: Effect on weight, waist, hips and chest flexibility". In Nagendra, H.R., Ragarathna, R. and Telles, S. 144: Yoga Research & Applications: Proceedings of the 5th International Conference on Frontiers in Yoga Research and Applications. Vivekananda Kendra Yoga Research Foundation: Bangalore 2000, pp.279-284.

Yadav R.K. and Das, S. "Effect of yogic practice on pulmonary functions in young females". Indian Journal of Physiology and Pharmacology October 2001: 45(4): 493-496.

## UNPUBLISHED LITERATURE

Devnath, P. "Asanayoga – Hathabhasya-paddhati by Kapalakurantaka". 1st International Conference on Revival of Traditional Yoga Lonavla. January 2006, pp.2.

Fondran, K.M. "The Effect of Surya Namaskara Yoga Practice on Resting Heart Rate and Blood Pressure, Flexibility, Upper Body Muscle Endurance, and Perceived Well-Being in Healthy Adults". Master's Degree Thesis. Cleveland State University, 2008, pp.64.

Moses, R. "Effect of yoga on flexibility and respiratory measures of vital capacity and breath holding time". Doctoral dissertation. University of Oregon, 1972.

Rakesh, D, Nagarathna R. and Nagendra, H.R. "A Comparative Study of Surya Namaskar and Physical

Exercise on Flexibility, Attention and Concentration in Adolescents". Vth. International Conference on Advances in Yoga Research, Education and Therapy Kaivalyadhama: Lonavla. December 2006, pp.11.

Rychlik, R. "Fizjologiczna Charakterystyka Sesji Treningowej w Systemie Astanga Joga" [trans. *Physiological Characteristics of a Training Session in the System of Ashtanga Yoga]*. Master Degree Thesis #16292. Jozef Pilsudski University of Physical Education (AWF): Warsaw, 2006, pp.62.

Stec, K. "Enhancing Sports Performance with Advanced Purification Techniques". 2nd. National Seminar on Holistic Approach in Healing L.N.I.P.E.: Gwalior. October 2007, pp.22.

Stec, K. "Suryanamaskar Practice as a tool to manage daily stress". International Conference on Stress Management L.N.I.P.E.: Gwalior. October 2008, pp.17.

Stec, K. "Effect of Dynamic Suryanamaskar on Anthropometric and Physiological Parameters of Physical Education Students". Master of Physical Education thesis. BHU: Varanasi. April 2009, pp.131.

Stec, K. "Effects of the yoga practice of Dynamic Suryanamaskar on the physiological, psychological, physical fitness and anthropometric characteristics of Indian students". Doctoral dissertation #734. Jozef Pilsudski University of Physical Education (AWF): Warsaw, 2014, pp.178.

Sudarshan, P.O. "Effect of Suryanamaskara Practice on Stress Management – A Randomized Waitlisted Control Study". Master of Science in Yoga thesis. SVYASA: Bangalore. January 2009, pp.105.

The sun salutation (Surya Namaskar) is perhaps the most well known and most commonly applied of all yoga asana practices and has a widely recognized reputation as a prototypical representation of yoga. This well-written and engaging text takes us through the entire history, philosophy, physiology, anatomy, scientific research, spirituality and experience of this ancient sequence of asanas in remarkable detail. ... Readers will find a wealth of valuable information in this book including both an exhaustive review of the knowledge on Surya Namaskar as well as detailed practical instructions for this practice.

**Sat Bir Khalsa,** PhD
Assistant Professor of Medicine
Harvard Medical School, USA
April 10, 2012

This book is based on the author's own investigations, both practical and literary. To the best of my knowledge it is pioneering in its field. The writer not only provides guidance on practice, together with scientific detail on the effects of Suryanamaskar, but also gives a great deal of information on the cultural and historical background to the practice.

**Prof. dr hab. Leslaw Kulmatycki**
Department Head, Humanities Sciences and Health Promotion,
University of Physical Education in Wroclaw, Poland
April 14, 2012

Perhaps you have studied and even practiced Suryanamaskar through books, teachers and Gurus and feel quite knowledgeable. This book will prove you wrong. It is a concise, illuminating, extensive treatise on the Sun Salutation asana. The foundation for this practice is duly noted in its scriptural origins and the scientific details will establish the Sun Salutation as an effective practice for adjunctive and yoga therapies for health and wellbeing. ...

His presentation and explanation offer readers, teachers and practitioners a way to implement and elevate this self-empowering asana of consciousness to a level of transformation.

**Padma Vibhushan Gurudev (Yogi Amrit Desai)**
Founder of Kripalu Center and Kripalu Yoga, USA
Founder of Kripalu Yoga Institute, Salt Springs, Florida, USA
(www.amrityoga.org)
January 18, 2013

Having learned traditionally from accomplished teachers, and from the depths of experience derived from his substantial and sustained personal practice, Krzysztof has written this book on an ancient yoga sequence, the sun salutation. ... involving body, mind and spirit in an integrated practice of moving meditation, where "movement rides on the rhythm of the breath." This book beautifully combines theory and practice, traditional teachings and scientific research, and readers will also find essential elements of a holistic lifestyle that are critical for deriving optimal benefit from this profound practice.

**Bidyut K. Bose,** PhD
Founder and Executive Director Niroga Institute
(www.niroga.org)
October 3, 2012

This work is a thorough and exhaustive study of the 'crown jewel' of yoga practices, the Suryanamaskar. It is unique in its ability to provide something of value for everyone, from the lay practitioner to the advanced adept and teacher. ... Every aspect of the practice is discussed, the historical, practical, contemporary, philosophical, tantric, rational, scientific, spiritual, religious, cultural and metaphysical. However, rather than being a dry, scholarly tome, the book has a freshness and a practical clarity to it, not least because the author has himself been a serious practitioner of Suryanamaskar from a young age. In summary, this book deserves to be called the 'Gray's Anatomy' of The Sun Salutation.

**Krishna Kant Shukla,** PhD
Formerly Assistant Professor Physics and Astronomy,
SUNY Buffalo, NY, USA
Internationally Renowned Musician, Scientist,
Environmentalist, and Speaker
"Distinguished Visiting Professor" Hartwick College, Oneonta, NY, USA
(www.krishnakantshukla.com)
April 26, 2012

A very comprehensive and well-researched guide written by an experienced practitioner. Combines historical background information, practice methods from different traditions, a full analysis of the psycho-physiological benefits with scientific research data and survey responses, with a full list of mantra and bija mantras recited and their corresponding relationship with the subtle energy system. An in-depth and very practical manual for all levels with a string of endorsements from the highest level in the Yoga world. Also includes dietary advice, a brief and detailed description of Shavasana for stress relief, full glossary, bibliography and charts. Excellent. All proceeds go towards the charitable activities of VYASA Trust.

**Jane Sill.** Editor
Yoga and Health Magazine, UK
(www.yogaandhealthmag.co.uk)
September 26, 2012

The author's prolific practice of Suryanamaskar has enabled him to produce a guide based on experience. According to the author, daily practice will convert a person firstly from a diseased state to a disease-free state, and then from that to a yogic state based on the union of body, mind, and spirit.

There are no other books like this available. It is the only one on the market that explains the physical, mental, and spiritual components of Suryanamaskar. I strongly recommend all practitioners and teachers of yoga to add this book to their collection.

**Dilip Sarkar,** MD, FACS, CAP
Fellow, American Association of Integrative Medicine (AAIM)
Associate Professor of Surgery (Retired),
Eastern Virginia Medical School, Norfolk, VA
(www.dilipsarkar.com)
October 10, 2012

Mr. Krzysztof Stec is to be congratulated for writing this book, which is designed to be of use for both the inexpert beginner and the already experienced. Almost all the practitioners of yoga and traditional systems of Indian physical culture practice Surya Namaskara at some point of time. ... It is both a practical guide and an exploration of every other aspect of the practice from the literary to the spiritual.

In summary, this book contains an all-round treatment of Surya Namaskar which will be most helpful to all serious-minded practitioners, whether they wish to concentrate solely on the practice or wish to explore further afield.

**Yogacharya Mukund V. Bhole,** MD, PhD
Governing Body Member at Central Council of Research in Yoga and
Naturopathy, Ministry of Health,
Government of India and Moraji National
(www.anubhava.org.uk, www.yoganubhava.com)
January 23, 2013

Of late, more people are realizing that Sun Salutations are not mere physical postures, but that practicing them has an effect on the whole personality as well as the physical body. I am therefore so happy to read the logical presentation and the evidence base given by Krzysztof in his book. He has very minutely analyzed aspects of the practice at various levels, from that of the physical body to those of prana, mind, intellect, and emotions. The result is that the practice of Sun Salutations is presented holistically and based on evidence, in such a way as easily to convince the scientific mind. It is also clear that unless he himself had taken up this practice with a spiritual approach, he could not have written about it in such a way and with such detail.

**N.V. Raghuram**

Founder and Chairman of Yoga Bharati, California, USA
President of Hindu University of America, Florida, USA
(www.yogabharati.org)
November 13, 2012

Surya Namaskar is a holistic technique where breath, body and mind work in perfect coordination and harmony, a characteristic of any yogic technique. Along with mantra chanting and exposure to early morning sun, Surya Namaskar can act as a powerful tonic for body, mind as well as soul. Popularization of Surya Namaskar will go a long way in prevention as well as management of 'modern' disorders such as obesity, diabetes mellitus, hypertension, heart problems and arthritis, apart from improving the overall health of the masses.

**Dr. Madanmohan,** MBBS, MD, MSc, FIAY

Professor and Head, Department of Physiology, and Programme
Director, Advanced Centre for Yoga Therapy,
Education and Research (ACYTER)
Jawaharlal Institute of Postgraduate Medical Education and Research
(JIPMER), Pondicherry
January 28, 2013

The book is extremely well written, with excellent supportive information on the history of Suryanamaskar – covering its effects on various human systems and comparing its spiritual aspects through the viewpoints of the Bible, Quran and Hindu scriptures. It is amazing that a non-Indian goes into such details of the Vedic aspects of this ancient practice.

**Pandit Pravinji**

Vedic Astrologer and Spiritual Counselor, San Francisco, CA
Father of the well-known saint, Shri Anandi Ma, Dhyanyoga Centers,
Antioch, CA
(www.satyacenter.com/pandit-pravinji)
October 2, 2012

This book will fill gaps in knowledge in many aspects of the subject and provides evidence for its conclusions from sources ranging from classical texts to modern research. Clearly visible throughout the book is the author's underlying passion for and mastery of the topic, along with his own personal spirituality and humble dedication to his personal Guru. This makes the book a unique combination of science and spirituality, which is the need of the hour. Seekers can utilize this book if they wish to transform their daily sun salutation 'chore' into a full-bodied worship of the Sun and so connect with the greatest Truth of Self, to be found therein. Teachers can use this book as a teaching guide, and to deepen the impact of their teachings. I will be recommending this book to my students who are training to become Ayurvedic Vaidyas (physicians).

**Acharya Shunya Pratichi Mathur**
Founder and Head of Vedika Global, Inc.
and of Vedika Gurukula College of Ayurveda California, USA
President, California Association of Ayurvedic Medicine (CAAM), USA
(www.vedikaglobal.org)
October 13, 2012

I feel grateful that this book is now available for yogis and yoga teachers, as Surya Namaskar has long since spread into many yoga schools all over the world. The book gives many different insights into what the practice really involves.

Thanks to Krzysztof Stec, traditional teachings can be combined with new aspects never before discussed. It is an honor to be able to recommend his book to contemporary readers.

**Andre Riehl**
Président of the French Fédération des Yoga Traditionnels
(www.nidrayoga.wordpress.com, www.somapa.eu)
October 4, 2012

In his book, Polish writer, yoga practitioner and teacher, Krzysztof Stec, explores the deeper aspects that go together with this ancient practice. ... As a dedicated practitioner of Suryanamaskar, having worked towards practicing 1008 rounds in a two hour period, he definitely has a clear knowledge of what it takes to get to that capability and how one should do so safely in a dedicated way, without any expectations or want for results. ... The book concludes with some research done by a number of different writers on the topic of yoga as well as personal stories of students that Krzysztof has worked with, who have showed how the dedicated use of Suryanamaskar in their daily practice has helped to overcome some ailment or physical problem. It ends off sharing the many physical, physiological, mental and emotional benefits of undertaking this practice.

**Nina Saacks**
Founder of Yoga Awakening Africa
(www.yogaaa.co.za)
October 24, 2012

The book takes us through a journey of Suryanamaskar theory and practice that demonstrates that this time-honoured method can almost be regarded as a path of yoga in its own right, addressing, as it does, the physical, mental and spiritual aspects of our being. Of particular interest to me was the author's explanation of the various ways in which Suryanamaskar can be practised, as I have long held that many contemporary yoga teachers misunderstand the distinctions between asana, vinyasa and kriya.

**Leigh Blashki**
President - Yoga Australia
Council of Advisors - International Association of Yoga Therapists
Director - Australian Institute of Yoga Therapy
(www.yogaaustralia.org.au)
October 17, 2012

Suryanamaskar practice is not only physical but also a part of a system that enables the fulfillment of the eternal human desire to be 'strong, beautiful, healthy and *wise*'. This goal is achieved not only through physical effort but also through the equally important practice of *tapasya*, in short, mental and physical discipline, and physical cleansing.

Such ideas will not necessarily appeal to a large part of today's society, because you cannot buy *tapasya*. However, Krzysztof Stec, through his book, gives us, in ways that have been documented by modern science, the very real chance, just as the ancient yogis had it, of extending our lives in a state of good health and in excellent physical, mental and spiritual condition.

**Professor dr hab. Marek Kruszewski**
Department of Martial Arts and Weightlifting
Jozef Pilsudski University of Physical Education in Warsaw, Poland
June 1, 2013

The book is an excellent lecture on yoga written in India by the author, an accomplished practitioner in his own right, who was born on the banks of the Vistula River in Poland. It all started with the suggestion of his uncle, a Benedictine monk, Ludwik Mycielski O.S.B. Krzysztof's way led him first to meeting and learning from the pioneers of yoga in Poland, then to studying the teachings of the best masters, spending time in leading yoga centers and ashrams in India and in the United States, and having personal contact with some of the great yogis of the world.

**Professor dr hab. Wieslaw Pilis**
Institute of Health Prophylaxis in Czestochowa, Poland
J. Dlugosz University in Czestochowa, Poland
June 2, 2013

# आत्मा गुरुदेव

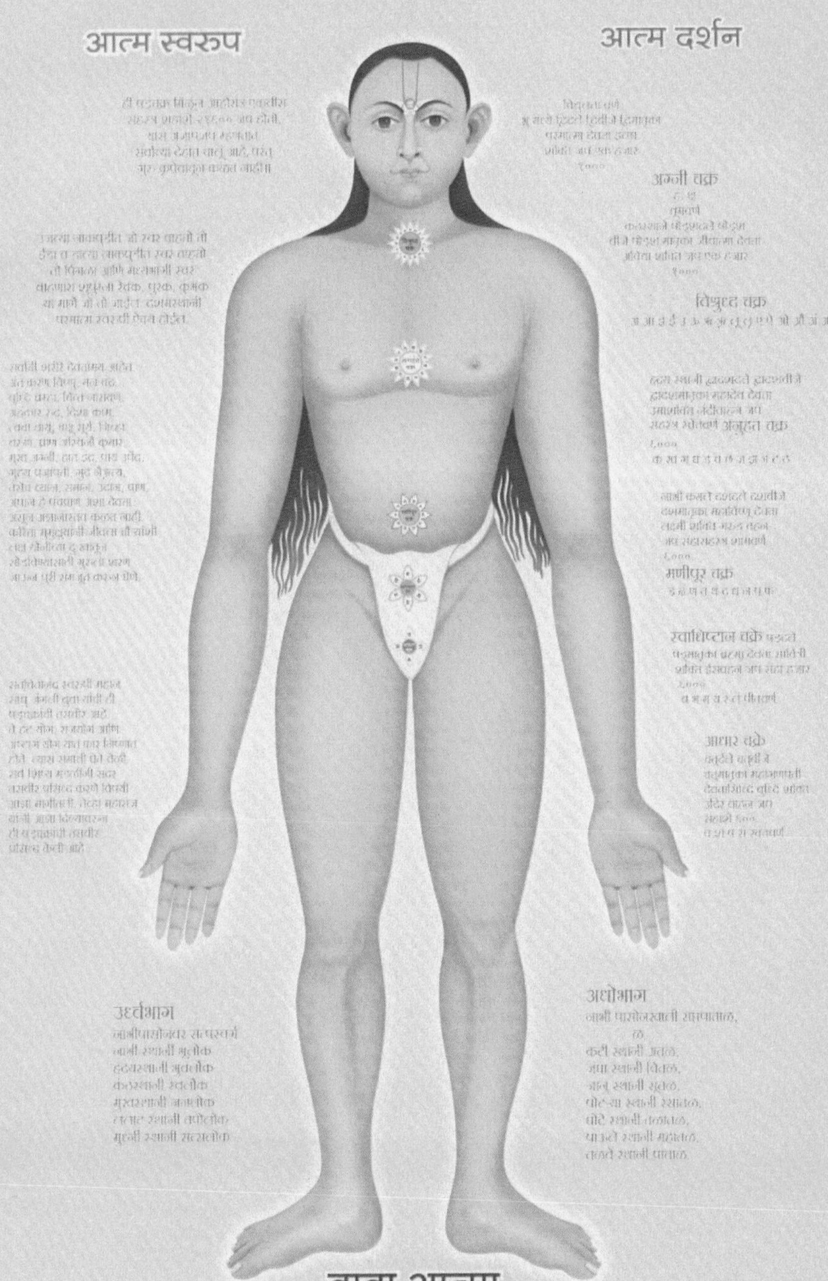


# बाबा आत्मा

# आत्मा गुरुदेव

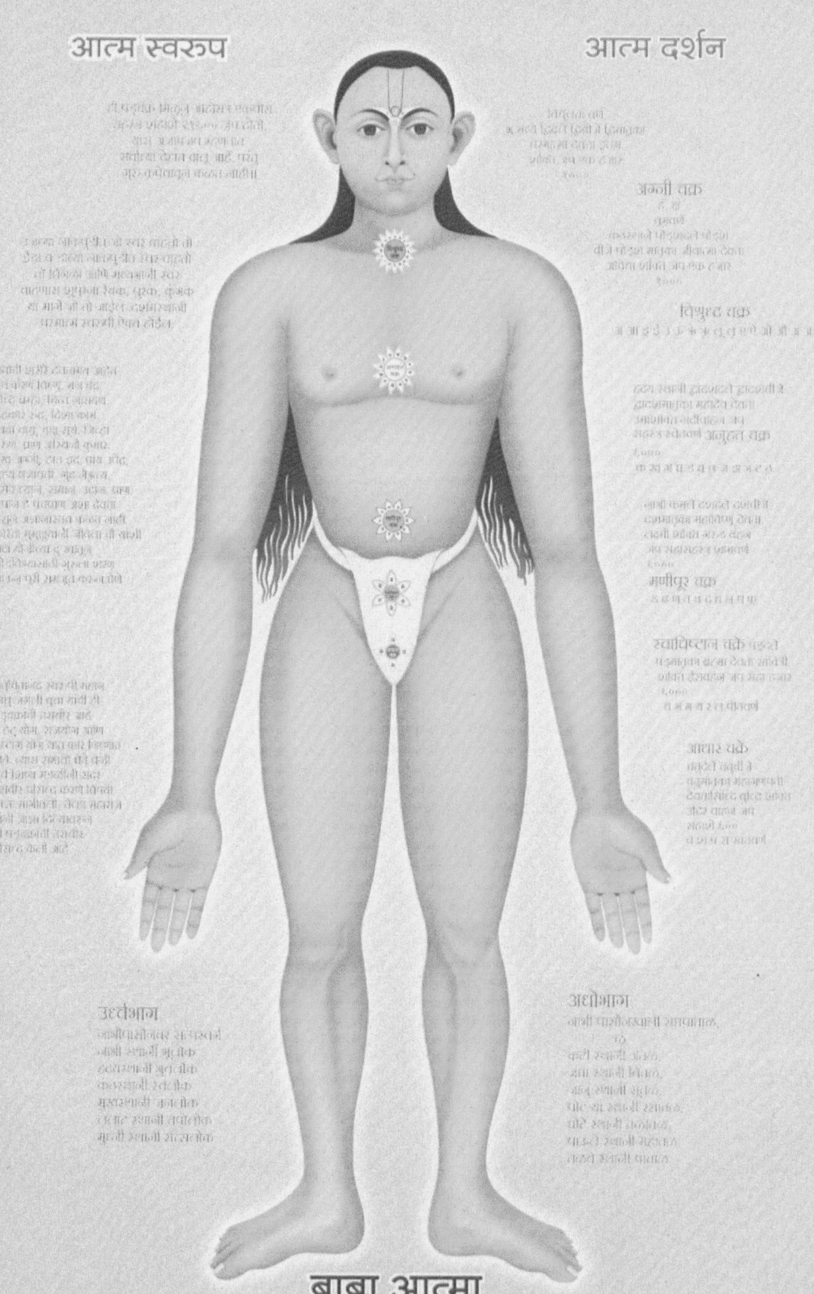
आत्म स्वरुप
आत्म दर्शन
अग्नी चक्र
विशुद्ध चक्र
अनुहत चक्र
मणीपूर चक्र
स्वाधिष्ठान चक्र
आधार चक्र
उर्ध्वभाग
अधोभाग
बाबा आत्मा